AQA
GCSE

Science

Richard Grime, Keith Hirst, Penny Johnson,
Sue Kearsey, Nigel Saunders, Martin Stirrup, Carol Tear

with Brian Turner and Rob Wensley

www.pearsonschoolsandfe.co.uk

✓ Free online support
✓ Useful weblinks
✓ 24 hour online ordering

0845 630 33 33

Series editor
Nigel English

Longman
Part of Pearson

Longman is an imprint of Pearson Education Limited, Edinburgh Gate, Harlow, Essex, CM20 2JE.

www.pearsonschoolsandfecolleges.co.uk

Text © Pearson Education Limited 2011
Edited by Stephen Nicholls
Typeset by Tech-Set Ltd, Gateshead
Original illustrations © Pearson Education Ltd 2011
Illustrated by Tech-Set Ltd, Geoff Ward, Tek-Art
Cover design by Wooden Ark
Cover photo: A bone from someone with osteoporosis, seen through an electron microscope. © Wellcome Images: Professor Alan Boyde

The rights of Richard Grime, Keith Hirst, Penny Johnson, Sue Kearsey, Nigel Saunders, Martin Stirrup and Carol Tear to be identified as authors of this work have been asserted by them in accordance with the Copyright, Designs and Patents Act 1988.

First published 2011

15 14 13 12 11
10 9 8 7 6 5 4 3 2 1

British Library Cataloguing in Publication Data
A catalogue record for this book is available from the British Library

ISBN 978 1 408253 85 4

Acknowledgements
The authors and publisher would like to thank the following individuals and organisations for permission to reproduce photographs:

2–3 Science Photo Library Ltd: Nancy Kedersha / UCLA. 5 Shutterstock: Herbert Kratky (t); Ingrid W. (b). 8 iStockphoto: gladiolus. 9 Science Photo Library Ltd: Hybrid Medical Animation (t); Dr Linda Stannard, UCT (c); Kent Wood (b). 10 Press Association Images: AP. 12 Corbis: Image 100 (l). Science Photo Library Ltd: CNRI (r). 14 Press Association Images: Kirsty Wigglesworth / PA Wire (b). Rex Features: (t). 18 Science Photo Library Ltd: Steve Percival (b). Shutterstock: Brasiliao (t). 20 Shutterstock: Stephen Mcsweeny (l, r). 22 Shutterstock: Lowe Llaguno. 28 Alamy Images: Nigel Cattlin (t). DK Images: (b). 30 Alamy Images: Country Calm / Den Reader (r). Science Photo Library Ltd: Nigel Cattlin (l). 31 DK Images: Dave King. 35 Science Photo Library Ltd: Larry Dunstan. 36 Press Association Images: Steve Parsons / PA Wire. 37 Photolibrary.com. 38 Shutterstock: ostill. 40 Alamy Images: Interfoto. 41 Shutterstock: dundanim (t); Jiri Miklo (b). 48–49 Alamy Images: ArteSub. 50 Brand X Pictures: Photo 24 (l). Susan Kearsey: (c). 51 Shutterstock: LouLouPhotos (r). Susan Kearsey: (l). 52 Corbis: (b). Creatas: (t). 53 Creatas: (cr). Digital Stock: (br). Getty Images: David Tipling (tl). 54 Digital Vision: (tl). Pearson Education Ltd: Tudor Photography (bl). Susan Kearsey: (cr). 55 Digital Vision. 56 Science Photo Library Ltd: Dr Ken Macdonald (b). Shutterstock: Qing Ding (t). 57 Pearson Education Ltd: Richard Smith (r). Science Photo Library Ltd: Thierry Berrod, Mona Lisa Production (l). 59 PhotoDisc: Photolink / J. Link (b). Shutterstock: Ainars Aunins (t); Tom Curtis (c). 60 Shutterstock: svic (r). Susan Kearsey: (l). 61 iStockphoto: Nancy Nehring (l). Science Photo Library Ltd: Martin Shields (r). Shutterstock: Knorre (c). 64 Shutterstock: Matthijs Wetterauw. 65 Corbis: Vienna Report Agency/Sygma (l). Shutterstock: ArnoldW (r). 66 Alamy: Realimage (br). Science Photo Library Ltd: Robert Brook (bl). 67 Shutterstock: jeff gynane. 69 iStockphoto: Gordon Dixon. 70 PhotoDisc. 72 Warren Photographic. 73 Photos.com. 74 Creatas: (c). Photoshot Holdings Limited: NHPA (b). 75 Science Photo Library Ltd: Brian Bowes. 76 Science Photo Library Ltd: Sinclair Stammers. 78 Science Photo Library Ltd: Eye of Science. 79 Photolibrary.com: BSIP Medical (r). Shutterstock: Jaroslav74 (b). 80 Alamy Images: Nigel Cattlin. 81 Rex Features: Philippe Hays (b). Science Photo Library Ltd: Bill Barksdale / AGSTOCKUSA (t). 84 PhotoDisc. 85 PhotoDisc: C Squared Studios. 86 Alamy Images: Interfoto. 90 Corbis: Anthony Bannister; Gallo Images. 91 Digital Vision: (bl). Shutterstock: Gail Johnson (t). 98–99 Corbis: Peter Ginter / Science Faction. 100 Pearson Education Ltd: Trevor Clifford (cl, cr, bl, br). Shutterstock: Vibrant Image Studio (r). 101 Pearson Education Ltd: Trevor Clifford (tl, tr, bl, br). 106 Peter Gould: (l,r). 107 Getty Images: Time & Life Pictures (t). Pearson Education Ltd: Naki Kouyioumtzis (b). 108 Digital Vision: (br). Shutterstock: Andrei Nekrassov (tl). 109 Corbis: Jason Hawkes. 110 Pearson Education Ltd: Trevor Clifford (tr). Peter Gould. (bl). Shutterstock: Buquet Christophe (tl). 111 Getty Images: Eco Images / Universal Images Group (b). Martin Stirrup: (t). Pearson Education Ltd: Trevor Clifford (cr). Jiri Vaclavek (cl). 112 Martin Stirrup: (tl, cl, bl). Photolibrary.com: Aflo Foto Agency (r). 113 DK Images: Tim Ridley (b). Shutterstock: Niels Quist (t). 114 PhotoDisc: Glen Allison (tr). Rex Features: Alex Segre (l). Shutterstock: Vicente Barcelo Varona (tl). 115 Construction Photography: Grant Smith (b). Martin Stirrup: (t). 116 Shutterstock: Jens Mayer (c); Denis Selivanov (r); Lee Prince (l). 117 Shutterstock: jennyt. 118 Photos.com: (l). Shutterstock: Audrey Snider-Bell (r). 119 Alamy Images: Leslie Garland Picture Library. 120 PhotoDisc: Photolink (l). Shutterstock: Roy Palmer (r). 121 Peter Gould. 122 Corbis: Joel Stettenheim (b). PhotoDisc: StockTrek (t). 124 Shutterstock: Olaf Speier (r); holligan78 (l). 125 Science Photo Library Ltd: (b). Shutterstock: MC_PP (t); PJF (c). 126 Pearson Education Ltd: Naki Kouyioumtzis (l). Photodisc: (r). www.imagesource.com: (c). 127 Construction Photography: David Stewart-Smith (t). Martin Stirrup: (b). 130 Peter Gould. 134 Photos.com: Jupiterimages. 139 Shutterstock: Zoran Karapancev. 146–147 Getty Images: G. Brad Lewis. 149 Science Photo Library Ltd: Andrew Lambert Photography. 152 B&H Colour Change: (r). Shutterstock: Andresr (l). 153 iStockphoto: bojan fatur (b). Science Photo Library Ltd: AJ Photo (t). 154 iStockphoto: Aleksandar Jaksic (tr); Michael Utech (b). PhotoDisc: Photolink / Tracy Montana (tl). 156 Peter Gould: (br). Science Photo Library Ltd: Roger Job / Reporters (t). Shutterstock: Chris Hill (bl). 158 Pearson Education Ltd: Richard Smith. 159 Science Photo Library Ltd: Martin Bond. 161 Pearson Education Ltd: Trevor Clifford (l, r).

162 Science Photo Library Ltd: Martyn F. Chillmaid (r). Shutterstock: Dusan Zidar (l). 163 Pearson Education Ltd: Jules Selmes. 164 Digital Vision: Getty Images (b). Shutterstock: Daniel Rajszczak (t). 173 iStockphoto: Lars Nilsson. 175 Shutterstock: Monica Johansen. 176 Shutterstock: iofoto (t); Bronskov (b). 188–189 Science Photo Library Ltd: NASA. 190 iStockphoto: Antony Veale (r). Shutterstock: Morgan Lane Photography (b); Matthew Cole (t). 191 Pearson Education Ltd: Gareth Boden (t). Shutterstock: Bill McKelvie (b). 193 Shutterstock: Falk Kienas. 194 PhotoDisc: Cole Publishing Group / Michael Lamotte. 195 iStockphoto: zoomstudio (cr1); Izabela Habur (cr2). Pearson Education Ltd: Guillaume Dargaud (br). Photos.com: (tr). Science Photo Library Ltd: NREL / US Department of Energy (l). 197 Shutterstock: yampi. 198 Shutterstock: JackF. 199 Shutterstock: JG Photo (t); Christian Musat (b). 202 Pearson Education Ltd: Trevor Clifford. 204 Alamy Images: Stock Image / Pixland (l); Shenval (r). 205 Alamy Images: Image Source. 212 Pearson Education Ltd: Rob Judges (cl). Shutterstock: Chad McDermott (r); Jackiso (l); Monkey Business Images (cl). 214 Pearson Education Ltd: Trevor Clifford. 215 Peter Gould: (t). Shutterstock: LeahKat (b). 216 Food Features: (tr). Sally Farndon: (tl). Shutterstock: Stephen Coburn (b). 217 Pearson Education Ltd: David Sanderson (r). www.imagesource.com: Nick White (l). 218 Photos.com: Jupiterimages. 220 Shutterstock: Ivars Linards Zolnerovics. 221 Science Photo Library Ltd: Ria Novosti. 222 iStockphoto: TT (b). Nature Picture Library: Laurie Campbell (t). 223 Shutterstock: I. Quintanilla. 224 Shutterstock: Zoia Kostina (t); RazvanZinica (bl); Terry Davis (br). 227 Pearson Education Ltd: Ikat Design / Ann Cromack (t). Shutterstock: Brendan Howard (b). 229 iStockphoto: Alexey Dudoladov. 230 Elena Wright: (l, r). 236–237. PhotoDisc: StockTrek. 238 PhotoDisc: Photolink. 239 iStockphoto: jamesbenet. 246 Philip Parkhouse. 247 PhotoDisc: Russell Illig. 248 PhotoDisc: (cr). Photos.com: Jupiterimages (tl). www.imagesource.com: Nigel Riches (bl). 251 Shutterstock: foray. 252 iStockphoto: kshishtof (b). Shutterstock: Sean Prior (t). 253 Alamy Images: Bobo (cr). PhotoDisc: (cl). Science Photo Library Ltd: Ted Kinsman (t). 254 Alamy Images: (t). Peter Gould: (b). 255 Shutterstock: roseburn3Dstudio. 258 Shutterstock: Ashley Pickering. 260 PhotoDisc: StockTrek. 262 Corbis: Roger Ressmeyer (t). Science Photo Library Ltd: NASA / WMAP Science Team (b).

All other images © Pearson Education

The authors and publisher would like to thank the following individuals and organisations for permission to reproduce copyright material. Every effort has been made to contact copyright holders of material reproduced in this book. Any omissions will be rectified in subsequent printings if notice is given to the publishers.

8 Figure 3: British Heart Foundation. 15 Figure 3: Deaths: Office for National Statistics. Crown Copyright click use licence C2008002221. 17 Figure 3 California data: Reprinted with permission from Elsevier (The Lancet 1999; 354: 949–50) and California Department of Developmental Services. Yokohama data: Journal of Psychology and Psychiatry 2005 published by John Wiley & Sons Ltd. 38 Figure 1: Reprinted with permission from Elsevier (The Lancet 2007; 369: 1047–1053). 43 Figure 2, Figure 3: © 2005 by the Association for Professionals in Infection Control and Epidemiology, Inc. 53 Figure 1: Blackburn T, Hawkins B, Bergmann's rule and the mammal fauna of North America, Ecography 27(6) John Wiley & Sons Ltd. 58 Figure 2: © Crown copyright 2009, the Met Office. 60 Figure 1: DEFRA UK Emissions of Air Pollutants: 2008 Additional Results. Crown copyright 2008 click use licence C2008002221. 66 Figure 1: With kind permission from WRAP. Source: Household food and drink waste in the UK (Nov 2009) 71 Figure 4: Eaton MA, Balmer DE, Conway GJ, Gillings S, Grice PV, Hall C, Hearn RD, Musgrove AJ, Risely K and Wotton S. 2009. The state of the UK's birds 2008. RSPB, BTO, WWT, CCW, NIEA, JNCC, NE and SNH, Sandy, Bedfordshire. 87 Figure 3: Data used with permission of Peter and Rosemary Grant. 165 Table 2: Anne CM Thiebaut et al. Dietary Fatty Acids and Pancreatic Cancer in the NIH-AARP Diet and Health Study, Journal of the National Cancer Institute, by permission of Oxford University Press. 166 Table 1: DEFRA e-Digest Statistics about: Waste and Recycling. Crown copyright 2009 Click-use licence C2008002221. 250–251 Health Protection Agency.

Introduction

This student book has been written by experienced examiners and teachers, who have focused on making learning science interesting and challenging. It has been written to incorporate higher-order thinking skills to motivate high achievers and to give you the level of knowledge and exam practice you will need to help you get the highest grade possible.

This book follows the AQA 2011 GCSE Science A specification, the first examinations for which are in November 2011. It is divided into three units – B1, C1 and P1 – covering biology, chemistry and physics. Within each unit there are two sections, each with its own section opener page. Each section is divided into chapters, which follow the organisation of the AQA specification.

There are lots of opportunities to test your knowledge and skills throughout the book: there are questions on each double-page spread, ISA-style questions, questions to assess your progress and exam-style questions. There is also plenty of practice in the new style of exam question that requires longer answers.

There are several different types of page to help you learn and understand the skills and knowledge you will need for your exam:

- Section openers with learning objectives and a check of prior learning.
- 'Content' pages with lots of challenging questions, Examiner feedback, Science skills, Route to A*, Science in action and Taking it further boxes.
- 'GradeStudio' pages with examiner commentary to help you understand how to move up the grade scale to achieve an A*.
- 'ISA practice' pages to give you practice with the types of questions you will be asked in your controlled investigative skills assessment.
- Assess yourself question pages to help you check what you have learnt.
- Examination-style questions to provide thorough exam preparation.

This book is supported by other resources produced by Longman:

- an ActiveTeach (electronic copy of the book) with BBC video clips, games, animations, and interactive activities
- an Active Learn online student package for independent study, which takes students through exam practice tutorials focusing on the new exam questions requiring longer answers, difficult science concepts and questions requiring some maths to answer them.

In addition there are Teacher Books, Teacher and Technician Packs and Activity Packs, containing activity sheets, skills sheets and checklists.

The next two pages explain the special features that we have included in this book to help you learn and understand the science and to do the very best in your exams. At the back of the book you will also find an index and a glossary.

Contents

B1

How organisms work   2

Environment and evolution   48

C1

The Earth provides   98

How to use this book

These two pages illustrate the main types of pages in the student book and the special features in each of them. (Not shown are the end-of-topic Assess yourself question pages and the Examination-style question pages.)

Section opener pages – an introduction to each section

An introductory paragraph to help put what you will be learning into context. There are two section openers for each unit.

Test yourself on what you should have learned previously that will help with your understanding of this section.

A list of the learning objectives you will have achieved by the end of the section.

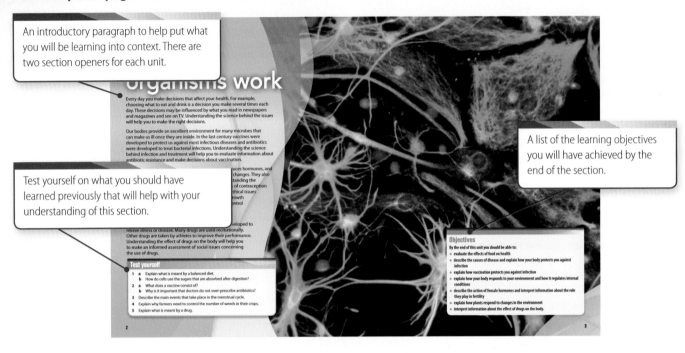

Content pages – covering the AQA specification

A list of objectives for the spread; you can use these to check your progress.

Clear, detailed artwork helps to explain the science.

Keywords are in bold and are listed with their meanings in the glossary at the back of the book to help with revision.

Examiner feedback helps you do better in your exams.

These boxes will help you with your controlled assessment and focus on investigative skills.

Lots of questions at the end of each spread in order of increasing difficulty. The last question on each spread requires a longer answer and is worth six marks.

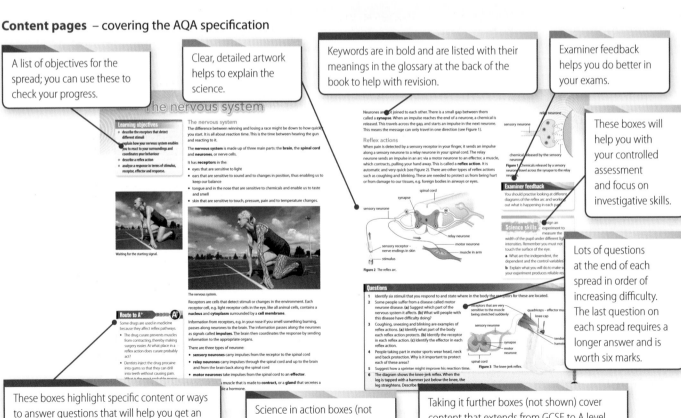

These boxes highlight specific content or ways to answer questions that will help you get an A* grade.

Science in action boxes (not shown) highlight new, exciting applications of science.

Taking it further boxes (not shown) cover content that extends from GCSE to A level. You will not be examined on this content but it will provide helpful background.

ISA practice pages – to help you with your controlled assessment

The questions are similar to the ones you will be asked in your controlled assessment papers.

Section 1 deals with planning, prediction and risk assessment.

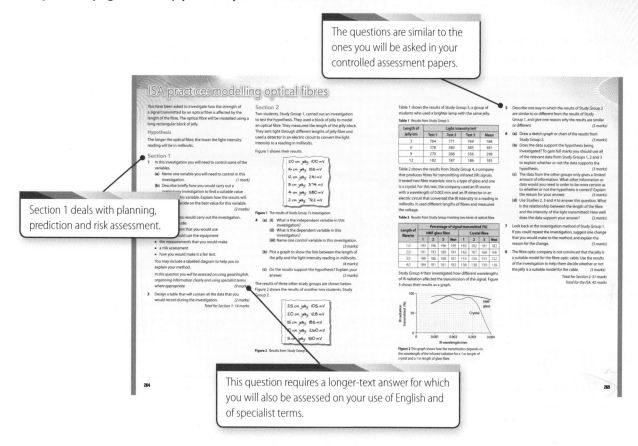

This question requires a longer-text answer for which you will also be assessed on your use of English and of specialist terms.

GradeStudio pages – helping you achieve an A*

'GradeStudio' questions focus on the new exam questions, which require a longer answer.

Three student answers are given at three different grades, B, A and A*, so you can see how they improve.

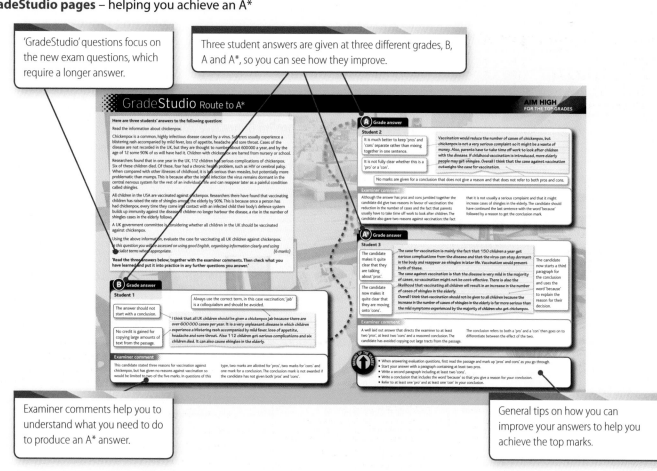

Examiner comments help you to understand what you need to do to produce an A* answer.

General tips on how you can improve your answers to help you achieve the top marks.

Researching, planning and carrying out an investigation

Learning objectives

- research and analyse scientific problems and develop hypotheses about these problems
- research and describe practical ways to investigate hypotheses fairly
- explain the risks present in an experimental procedure and how to minimise them
- describe different types of variables and how to measure them.

Hypothesis: reducing speed saves lives.

Examiner feedback

You should find two different methods to use from your research. Be able to describe both and state which one you plan to use and why.

When writing a plan for an investigation, make sure you write the plan in a logical order, so someone else can follow your instructions. You need to say how you will change the independent variable, what the range of it will be, how you will measure the dependent variable, and how you will make sure other variables are kept constant.

Scientific understanding

Science is all about understanding how things work, and making decisions on that basis. This understanding must be based on evidence, and ideas or explanations must relate to that evidence. Scientists also consider the quality of the evidence, and whether other possible explanations might fit it. They ask: What might make my explanation wrong?

Case study: speed cameras

Every year around 2500 people die in road accidents, and ten times this number are seriously injured. Speed cameras are one method that has been used to try and reduce the numbers killed or injured. Doctors and the police noticed that injuries were less severe, and there were fewer deaths, when pedestrians were hit by slow-moving cars than in high-speed collisions. They used their **observations** to make a **hypothesis**: a good idea that explains the observations. The hypothesis was: 'The faster a car moves, the greater the force when it collides with a pedestrian. The greater the force, the more damage is caused to the pedestrian's body, and too much damage causes death'.

They then made a **prediction** about the speed needed to kill someone. Predictions provide a way to test a hypothesis – if the prediction is wrong, the hypothesis must be false. After several investigations in which the prediction is proved to be right, then the hypothesis may become a **theory**, which can be used to make predictions about other similar events.

In carrying out an investigation you should first research what other scientists have already done. This is helpful as the research can suggest possible methods for your own investigation, and also suggest methods that you shouldn't use as they are too time-consuming or not relevant to the investigation you are planning. Your research may help you to identify the variable that could affect the results. Here are some of the variables in this case:

- speed of car
- mass of car
- make of car
- height of person hit by car.

In this investigation the **independent variable**, the one you change or select to examine, is the speed of the car.

The **dependent variable**, the one that changes as you change the speed of the car, and which you measure, is the amount of damage to the person. The other variables are **control variables** and need to be kept the same if the test is to be fair.

Variables

The speed of the car is measured as a number, and variables that are numerical are **continuous variables**. When recording continuous variables a line graph should be used, with a best-fit curve or line drawn to show the trend. If you were investigating the make of the car, this would be a **categoric variable**. Each categoric value is separate from the other. Categoric variables should be recorded on a bar chart, as there is no trend.

All scientific investigations have **hazards**, things that can go wrong with the experiment and cause injury to people or objects. The biggest hazard in this investigation is the death of someone taking part. The history of science is full of scientists who died as a result of their own experiments. To minimise the risk, or the chance of this happening, **control measures** are used. A control measure is something that reduces the hazard to a level of risk that is acceptable. The control measure in this case would be to replace a living person with a dummy, and then

In road safety tests, dummies are often used to assess the damage caused to pedestrians in a collision.

to assess the amount of damage to the dummy. Alternatively, the investigator could research data from real accidents to find out how speed affects pedestrians hit by cars.

Making measurements

However you carry out your investigation, you need to make some measurements or collect data.

You need to decide on the **range** of your independent variable – the slowest and fastest speeds you plan to investigate. Within this range values should be evenly spaced, using at least six different values if possible, and widely enough separated to ensure that any trend can be identified. You should be able to do this experimentally.

Your measurements should be **repeatable**. This means that when you repeat the measurement you get nearly the same value each time. If you ask someone else to do the same method and they get the same results, then the results are **reproducible**. They are also reproducible if you or someone else gets the same pattern of results using a different method.

Questions

1 Explain the difference between a hypothesis and a prediction.

2 List six more variables that could affect an investigation into speed and road fatalities. State whether each one is a continuous or a categoric variable.

3 Describe the difference between a hazard, a risk, and a control measure.

4 Explain how a pathologist could use a dummy as a model for a real person in a road accident to decide if the speed of the car would kill someone.

5 Describe the differences between repeatable results and reproducible results.

6 Plan an investigation using accident records into the hypothesis: 'the greater the mass of the vehicle, the slower the speed needed to kill a pedestrian'. Remember to list the information you need to make sure control variables can be controlled.

A*

Presenting, analysing and evaluating results

Learning objectives

- describe how to report and process your experimental data
- evaluate the data collected, identifying errors
- understand the terms reproducible, resolution and calibration
- analyse the evidence
- use research to confirm whether the findings are valid.

Recording and displaying results

In the previous spread you read about how to design an investigation. How should you record your results?

It is best to collect your results in a table that you have already prepared. Table 1 shows how you could record the percentage of damage done to a crash-test dummy by a car travelling at different speeds. The independent variable, that is, the one you change, is usually recorded in the left-hand column. In this case the independent variable is the speed. The right-hand columns are for the dependent variable. Both columns should have the units in the heading.

Table 1 Example table for recording results of an investigation.

Speed of car/mph	Percentage damage to the body of the dummy (%)				
	Trial 1	Trial 2	Trial 3	Trial 4	Mean
10					
20					
30					
40					
50					
60					

Reproducibility

To check that your results are reproducible you should repeat each measurement several times. Table 1 has space for four trials. You should get nearly identical results. If not, you may have errors in your measuring methods.

If the results are numerical you can then calculate the mean for each set of measurements. This will give you a more reliable value closer to the true value.

If a result is anomalous (doesn't fit) it should be discarded. So, for instance, if the results at 30 mph were 12%, 16%, 27% and 14%, you would discard 27% as it is not close to the rest, then calculate the mean as $\frac{(12 + 16 + 14)}{3} = 14\%$

Sometimes you can spot a trend or pattern in a set of results from the table, but it is more likely that you will need to see them as a bar chart, if the independent variable is categoric, or as a line graph for continuous variables, as in Figure 1.

Identifying errors in results

Every scientist has errors in their results. The different types of errors are:

- **anomalous** results – ones that don't fit the pattern at a value of the independent variable, sometimes called 'outliers'. The example above shows the outlier being excluded from the mean.

- **random errors** – these make the results spread around the true value. Scientists calculate the mean to try to reduce the effect. The more values used to calculate the mean, the nearer it should be to the true value, provided there is no systematic error (see below).

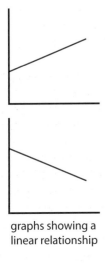

graphs showing a linear relationship

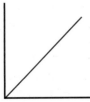

graph showing directly proportional relationship

Figure 1 Examples of line graphs.

- **systematic errors** – these occur when something is causing the readings to be spread about another value, rather than the true value. It may be the way the reading is recorded, the instrument being used or something about the environment. Repeating the measurement cannot correct the problem; a change of equipment or method is needed to get fresh results to allow for a comparison.

- **zero error** – this is a systematic error in which the instrument used for measurement is not set at zero and either adds or subtracts a set amount whenever a reading is taken. For example, bathroom scales always need to be set to zero before you weigh yourself if you are to get the true weight.

If you get an anomalous result, think about it – was it an error in measurement, or do you need to amend your hypothesis or your experimental technique?

If there are errors in the data, it may be that the measuring instruments are not correctly calibrated. **Calibration** is carried out by taking a relevant fixed point, such as the freezing point of water to calibrate a thermometer, marking it on the instrument, and then marking a second fixed point, in this case the boiling point of water. A scale can then be produced.

All measuring equipment has limitations to its accuracy. Thermometers are often described as being accurate to within 1°C, which is often referred to as the level of confidence.

How good are the results?
To be able to draw a conclusion from a set of results, your data must be **repeatable**. This means that if you repeated the investigation you would get the same or similar results.

If you change the method or use different equipment, or if someone else does the investigation and the results are still similar, then we say that the results are **reproducible**.

Analysing the evidence
Your conclusion must relate to the investigation. The graph of the results in Figure 2 shows that as the speed increases, the amount of damage to the crash-test dummy increases. The data collected give no information about the amount of damage needed to cause death, so you can draw no conclusion about this.

It is important not to go any further than the evidence you have. At the lower end of the graph it looks as though doubling the speed will double the damage, but this relationship cannot be correct at higher speeds. For example, at 45 mph the damage is over 50%, but doubling the speed to 90 mph could not make the damage greater than 100%.

Using research to establish validity
It is important that you check the **validity** of your investigation: has it actually investigated the hypothesis and the prediction you made? If not, then the findings are not valid. You can check whether the findings are valid by looking for similar evidence. This may be present in the research you have already found in textbooks, classmates' data, and other scientists on the internet.

Examiner feedback
When calculating a mean, make sure you discard anomalous results, and record the mean calculated to the same number of decimal places as the original readings.

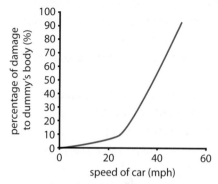

Figure 2 Line graph showing damage to dummy at different speeds.

Questions
1 Explain the difference between an anomalous result and a random error.
2 Why is a zero error a type of systematic error and how could you deal with a zero error?
3 What evidence does Figure 2 provide in support of a speed limit of 30 mph in built-up areas?
4 One council has stopped using speed cameras. A spokesman for the council said: *'Since the introduction of speed cameras there has been no reduction in road injuries and fatalities in the borough.'* However, a neighbouring council is increasing the number of speed cameras. Their spokesman said: *'There has been a significant reduction in accidents at speed camera sites since they were introduced.'* Explain why both spokesmen could be right.
5 Suggest a hypothesis to explain the findings in question 4.
6 Plan an investigation to prove your hypothesis.

B1 How organisms work

Every day you make decisions that affect your health. For example, choosing what to eat and drink is a decision you make several times each day. These decisions may be influenced by what you read in newspapers and magazines and see on TV. Understanding the science behind the issues will help you to make the right decisions.

Our bodies provide an excellent environment for many microbes that can make us ill once they are inside. In the last century vaccines were developed to protect us against most infectious diseases and antibiotics were developed to treat bacterial infections. Understanding the science behind infection and treatment will help you to evaluate information about antibiotic resistance and make decisions about vaccination.

Two body systems – the endocrine system, which produces hormones, and the nervous system – enable us to respond to external changes. They also help us to control conditions inside our bodies. Understanding the science underlying the use of hormones in some forms of contraception and in fertility treatments will enable you to consider ethical issues concerned with these treatments. Hormones control growth in plants. Understanding the science underlying this control will help you to assess the use of plant hormones in agriculture and horticulture.

Drugs affect our body chemistry. Medical drugs are developed to relieve illness or disease. Many drugs are used recreationally. Other drugs are taken by athletes to improve their performance. Understanding the effect of drugs on the body will help you to make an informed assessment of social issues concerning the use of drugs.

Test yourself

1 a Explain what is meant by a balanced diet.
  b How do cells use the sugars that are absorbed after digestion?

2 a What does a vaccine consist of?
  b Why is it important that doctors do not over-prescribe antibiotics?

3 Describe the main events that take place in the menstrual cycle.

4 Explain why farmers need to control the number of weeds in their crops.

5 Explain what is meant by a drug.

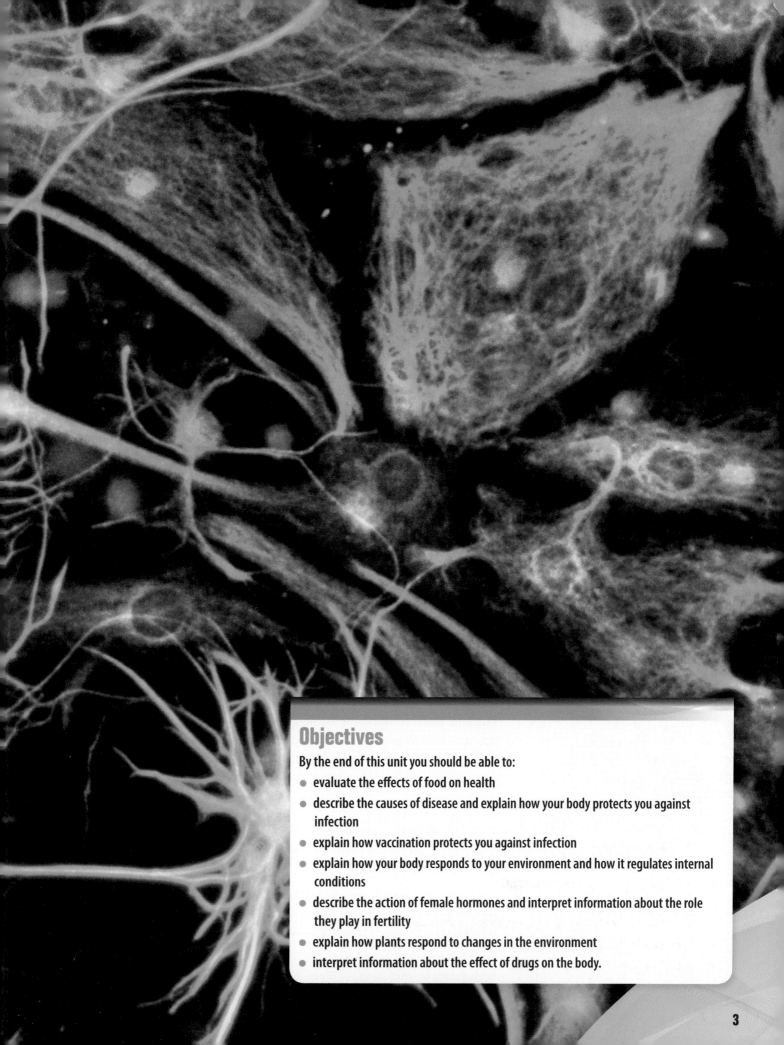

Objectives

By the end of this unit you should be able to:

- evaluate the effects of food on health
- describe the causes of disease and explain how your body protects you against infection
- explain how vaccination protects you against infection
- explain how your body responds to your environment and how it regulates internal conditions
- describe the action of female hormones and interpret information about the role they play in fertility
- explain how plants respond to changes in the environment
- interpret information about the effect of drugs on the body.

Diet and exercise

Taking it further

Insulin controls the amount of glucose in the blood. In one form of **diabetes**, type 2 diabetes, the body still makes insulin, but needs more than it produces, or cannot use insulin properly. Type 2 diabetes is much more common than type 1 diabetes (in which no insulin is produced). It usually develops in people over the age of 40. The risk of developing diabetes increases with body mass; it is three times more common in people who are 10 kg overweight. However, type 2 diabetes is now being reported in children, all of whom so far have been overweight.

Figure 2 These are the proportions of different foods that make up a balanced diet. Does this match the food that you eat?

Changing lifestyles

The newspaper article in Figure 1 shows how medical experts are worried about the effects of poor diet and lack of exercise on young people. Experts are warning that many children are overweight or obese and therefore have more chance of developing serious health problems in later life.

Science skills

BRITISH CHILDREN TOP LEAGUE FOR UNHEALTHY LIVING

From our health correspondent.

The largest study of youth health reveals that British children live on sugary snacks and almost no fruit and vegetables.

The World Health Organisation report, based on surveys of more than 160 000 children in 35 countries, found that the dietary habits of Britain's young were among the worst.

Doctors recommend at least five portions of vegetables daily for a healthy diet. More than two-thirds of children aged 11–15 admitted that they did not eat even a single portion of vegetables a day. A third of 11-year-olds drank at least one sugary drink a day, as well as eating sweets and chocolate every day. Snacks and sugary drinks are high-energy foods.

Poor diet and increasingly inactive lifestyles are blamed for a massive increase in the number of people who are overweight.

Figure 1
Unhealthy children.

a Use information from the newspaper article to explain why poor diet and inactive lifestyles are blamed for the increase in obesity.

You are what you eat

The amount and type of food that you eat has a major effect on your health. **Carbohydrates** and **fats** in your food provide the energy you need to stay alive and be active. Food also provides the **proteins**, **vitamins** and **minerals** your body uses to grow and to replace damaged cells and tissues. By eating a varied diet you are more likely to get everything you need to keep your body healthy.

Malnutrition happens when you eat the wrong amount of each type of **nutrient**; either too much or too little. **Deficiency diseases** can occur when the body doesn't get enough of a certain vitamin or mineral. These diseases are avoided by eating the right kinds of food. Figure 2 shows the types and proportions of different foods that make up a healthy **balanced diet**.

Metabolism

The more exercise you do, the more energy you need. Many chemical reactions take place in your body. These reactions release the energy from food. Your **metabolic rate** is the speed at which your body uses that energy.

Even when you are resting, you need energy to keep your heart beating and for breathing and digestion. The rate at which you use energy when you are resting is called your resting or basal metabolic rate.

The higher your metabolic rate, the more energy you use. As you exercise your body builds up muscle tissue. Regular exercise also increases your metabolic rate.

Your body uses some of its fat stores to replace the energy that it uses. Exercise increases the proportion of muscle to fat in the body, which in turn increases metabolic rate.

Everybody has a different metabolic rate. It depends on many factors including inheritance and how you live your life. Your metabolic rate decreases with age.

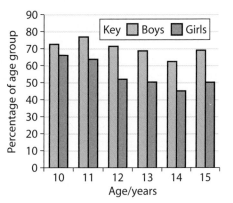

Science skills

b Medical experts recommend that young people carry out at least 60 minutes of moderate exercise every day. What percentage of 15-year-old boys achieve this recommendation?

c Suggest a reason for the change in activity levels among girls as they get older.

Figure 3 Percentage of young people taking part in at least 60 minutes of physical activity a day.

Does your work affect your metabolic rate?

Blood cholesterol level

Cholesterol is a fatty substance transported by the blood. We all need some cholesterol to keep our body cells functioning normally. Blood cholesterol level depends on the amount of fat in the diet. It is also affected by inheritance. People with high blood cholesterol levels are at increased risk of developing diseases of the heart and blood vessels.

Examiner feedback

Examination questions are likely to provide data that you will be asked to comment upon or evaluate.

Practical

You can compare the energy values of different foods by burning them under a beaker of water as shown in Figure 4. The rise in the temperature of the water is measured for each food. The greater the temperature rise, the greater the energy content of the food.

d Give two variables that should be controlled in this experiment.

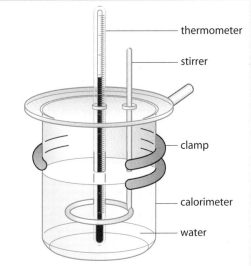

Figure 4 Comparing the energy values of foods using a calorimeter.

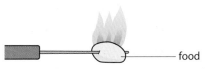

Questions

1 Give the function in the diet of:
   (a) fat **(b)** minerals.

2 What is meant by deficiency disease?

3 Give two factors that affect blood cholesterol level.

4 What is meant by metabolic rate?

5 List the factors that affect metabolic rate.

6 Explain the relationship between diet, metabolic rate and body mass.

Slimming plans

New Slimcredible contains 100% natural ingredients that amazingly:
- burn fat
- block hunger pangs from reaching your brain
- boost your concentration
- speed up your metabolism.

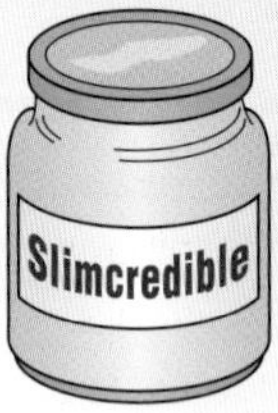

Slimcredible

Using Slimcredible, you can lose up to one dress size in just two weeks!

Our unique formula contains a blend of guarana, lemongrass, green tea, *Garcinia cambogiam*, L-carnitine and the Acai berry.

Years of scientific studies have shown that this combination of organic ingredients, amino acids and the renowned Brazilian superfood the Acai berry massively boost your weight loss power.

Figure 1 Can you trust all adverts?

Do you believe what you read?

People in the UK spend around £2 billion a year on products that claim to help them lose weight.

Currently, manufacturers are not compelled by law to prove that their products work and can make claims that are unsupported by evidence.

The advert in Figure 1 shows how a fictitious company tries to get people to buy their slimming product as a way of losing mass. The advert tries to convince you that this product works. Many companies use adverts like this. The claims made in the adverts are rarely based on scientific evidence but rather on hearsay. Having an understanding of how evidence is used to provide **reliable** results enables you to question what you read and to make informed decisions.

Medical experts say that there is only one way to lose weight, which is to eat healthy foods and keep energy intake below energy use. Exercise increases the amount of energy used by the body.

Science skills

Adverts showing photographs of a person before and after losing weight by using a slimming product used to be common. This type of advertising has now been banned.

a Suggest reasons why the evidence in this kind of advert should be regarded as unreliable.

Slimming drugs warning

Trading standards officials investigated a variety of slimming products offered for sale over the Internet. They found that three-quarters of the products tested made false claims. Most companies could not provide reliable evidence to back up their weight-loss claims. These are some of the claims that companies make about their products:

- tablets that enable the body to burn fat before food is digested
- pills that allow people to lose weight without dieting or exercising
- a product that burns fat while people are asleep.

Health experts warn that if a product or a diet programme sounds too good to be true, it probably isn't good for you and isn't true.

Science skills

Diet Trials was a study organised by the BBC and a group of scientists. The study compared four popular commercial weight-loss programmes with a control group. The diets were:

- the Slim-Fast plan: a meal replacement approach
- Weight Watchers' Pure Points programme: an energy-controlled diet with weekly group meetings
- Dr Atkins' New Diet: a self-monitored low-carbohydrate eating plan
- Rosemary Conley's Eat Yourself Slim diet and fitness plan: a low-fat diet and a weekly group exercise class.

300 overweight people matched for age, sex and mass were randomly divided into the five groups for the study.

Figure 2 shows some of the data from the study.

b Which variables were controlled in the study?

c What feature of the study made it a 'fair test' between the weight-loss programmes?

d Which was the most effective programme in the first two months?

e How did the four programmes compare over the six months?

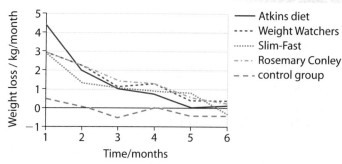

Figure 2 Results from the diet trial.

Science in action

Only one slimming pill, orlistat, has been approved by the NHS.

Orlistat works by inhibiting enzymes that digest fat. Nearly a third of the fat that you eat is not digested if you take orlistat. The undigested fat is passed out with your faeces. Studies have shown that orlistat, plus a mass-reducing diet and exercise, causes more mass loss than a mass-reducing diet and exercise alone. Some people lose 10% or more of their body mass within six months with the help of orlistat. In others, it is less effective.

Examiner feedback

Examination questions will be based upon the evaluation of data against the claims made for various products. Remember to look at the data carefully and not jump to conclusions based on what you think you know.

Questions

1 Explain as fully as you can how a slimming programme such as the Rosemary Conley plan might help a person to lose mass.

2 Look at the four diets in Figure 3.
(a) Compare the ways in which the four diets are intended to make you lose mass. **(b)** Which diet do you think is likely to be most effective? Give reasons. **(c)** Which diet seems to be least credible? Give the reason(s) for your answer.

Atkins Diet

1st stage
• You only eat proteins (meat, fish, poultry, eggs) and fats (oils, butter, etc.).
• You are only allowed 20 g of carbohydrate each day.
• You don't eat any fruit, vegetables or bread. This tricks your body into thinking it is starving and your body uses up its glycogen store.
• Your body loses a lot of water at first.
• If your body is starving it might begin to break down muscle tissue
• It might also damage your kidneys.
Second stage (after a couple of weeks)
• You start to eat more carbohydrate until you stop losing weight.
• This gives you your maximum carbohydrate limit.
• You must stay under that limit to carry on losing weight.

Weight Watchers

• Uses a points-based system.
• Each food is given points based on the amount of fat, fibre and energy it contains.
• Each person is set a points target for the day.
• You can eat anything as long as you do not go over the target.
• You can meet once a week with other 'weight watchers' to measure and discuss progress.

Slim-Fast Diet

• Slim-Fast is a meal-replacement diet.
• You can eat as often as six times a day to avoid highs and lows.
• You take two Slim-Fast shakes for breakfast and for lunch.
• You have a normal dinner.
• Each Slim-Fast meal replacement is around 240 calories and with the meal you should not go over 1200 calories.
• Slim-Fast shakes contain added vitamins and minerals, essential fatty acids and proteins.

Cabbage Soup Diet

• Take a large white cabbage and slice it up. Put it in a pan and cover it with water. Boil it until it becomes a soft pulp. Season to taste.
• You can eat as much cabbage soup as you like.
• It is low in fat but high in fibre.
• You can combine the soup with any fruit or vegetable you like (except for corn, beans, peas and bananas).
• You only stick to this diet for 7 days then move onto a longer term dieting plan.

Figure 3 There are many approaches to dieting.

Pathogens

Learning objectives

- explain what causes infectious disease and how diseases are spread
- explain how pathogens cause disease
- describe the contribution made by Semmelweiss to controlling infection in hospitals today.

Transmitting infections

Up to 5000 people die each year from infections picked up in hospitals in England. The problem actually affects 100 000 people and costs the NHS a thousand million pounds. It is thought that deadly infections are spread because **hygiene** rules are broken. For example doctors and nurses do not always wash their hands or use hand gel between treating patients.

A senior nursing officer said: 'Levels of cleanliness have deteriorated in recent years. I have seen dust under beds, cotton wool buds on the floor and dirty needles dumped in discarded meal trays. There are guidelines about changing the curtains around beds, cleaning floors and cleaning bathrooms but these are often ignored.'

Potentially fatal infections are carried in dust mites and a study has shown that improving ward cleanliness can reduce infections. Hospitals now employ infection control specialists to reduce the number of infections.

Ignaz Semmelweiss

Microorganisms are the tiny living things that can only be seen using a microscope. They are everywhere, including in the food you eat and inside you. Microorganisms that cause illness or disease are types of **pathogens**.

Ignaz Semmelweiss was a doctor in the mid-1800s. He wondered why so many women died of 'childbed fever' soon after giving birth. He also noticed that student doctors carrying out work on dead bodies did not wash their hands

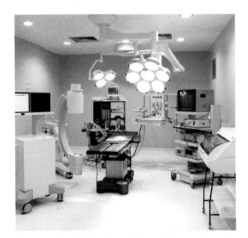

The standard of hygiene in hospitals needs to be high to avoid infections spreading. Think about ways hygiene can be improved in hospitals.

Science skills

a What was Semmelweiss' observation?

b What was his hypothesis?

The table shows Semmelweiss' original data.

c Why did Semmelweiss calculate the percentage of deaths on each ward rather than relying on the number of deaths?

d What conclusions can be drawn from this data?

Year span	Hospital ward	Number of deaths	Number of patients	Deaths (%)
1833–1838 (same number of doctors and midwives in each ward)	Ward 1	1505	23 509	6.4
	Ward 2	731	13 097	5.81
1839–1847 (medical students and doctors in ward 1; midwives in ward 2)	Ward 1	1989	20 204	9.84
	Ward 2	691	17 791	2.18
1848–1859 (chlorinated hand wash used)	Ward 1	1712	47 938	3.57
	Ward 2	1248	40 770	3.06

Figure 1 Semmelweiss's original data.

Taking it further

Bacterial cells do not have a nucleus like animal and plant cells. Instead, the genes are found in a looped chromosome and in **plasmids**, small seperate rings of genetic material. Plasmids are used by genetic engineers to transfer genes into both animal and plant cells.

before delivering a baby. When he got them to wash their hands in a **chlorinated** hand wash before delivering babies, fewer women died. He concluded that something was carried by the doctors from the dead bodies to the women.

The discovery of pathogens

Louis Pasteur and Joseph Lister studied 'objects' that became known as 'microorganisms'. Pasteur proved that there were **'germs'** in the air and that they carried infection and disease. Lister developed a special soap called carbolic soap. He insisted that all medical instruments, dressings and even surgeons should be cleaned with it before any operation. More of Lister's patients stayed healthy than those of other surgeons.

Chemicals that are used to clean wounds or get rid of sores, such as nappy rash, are called **antiseptics**. Chemicals that are used to clean work surfaces and other places where pathogens might be found are called **disinfectants**.

Semmelweiss showed that keeping things clean helps to stop the spread of pathogens. We call this hygiene. Hygiene is about keeping things clean to reduce the risk of disease. Washing removes the dirt and grease that pathogens stick to and use as a source of energy to multiply.

Microorganisms

Pathogens are the 'germs' identified by Semmelweiss, Pasteur and Lister. Two of the main types are:

- **bacteria** – cause cholera, boils, MRSA, typhoid, tuberculosis
- **viruses** – cause warts, herpes, polio, flu, mumps, measles, smallpox.

Spreading disease

Bacteria and viruses can pass from one person to another. This is how some diseases spread and affect many people. You can become infected by pathogens in the air you breathe, the food you eat, the liquids you drink, and by touching someone. By making sure that your environment is clean, you lessen the chance that you will become infected.

Passing on pathogens.

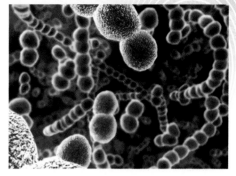

These spherical bacteria are the type that cause sore throats.

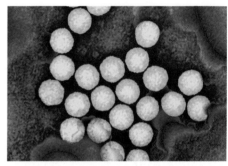

Polioviruses cause the disease polio. They are one thirtieth the diameter of the bacteria above.

Examiner feedback

Do not use the term 'germ' in answers. The general term to use is pathogen. If you use the terms 'bacteria' or 'virus', make sure that they correctly apply to the disease in the question.

Questions

1 What is a pathogen?
2 Name two types of pathogen.
3 Give two ways in which pathogens pass from one person to another.
4 Explain the difference between an antiseptic and a disinfectant.
5 Explain fully why it is important to wash your hands after visiting the toilet.
6 Write a hygiene memo with 10 bullet points for hospital staff. Base your memo on the scientific principles that Semmelweiss applied to his work.

A*

Defence against disease

Immunity

This boy has a condition known as SCID, also called 'bubble boy' disease. He would not survive outside of his 'bubble' because he has no natural defence against pathogens; he is not **immune** to them.

A boy in a bubble.

Bacteria and viruses make you ill by releasing poisonous chemicals called **toxins** or by preventing your cells from working properly. You might get **symptoms** such as a headache, fever or feeling sick.

Once bacteria are inside you, they can multiply rapidly, doubling in number about every 20 minutes. Viruses multiply by entering the cells in your body. They use the chemicals inside the cell to make copies of themselves. The new viruses burst out of the cell ready to invade other body cells. This damages or even destroys the cell.

Cells to fight pathogens

Your body has different ways of protecting itself against pathogens. **White blood cells** are specialised cells that defend your body against pathogens. There are several different types of white blood cell. Some **ingest**, that is, take into the cell, any pathogens that they come across in your body. Once the pathogen is inside the cell, the white blood cell releases **enzymes** to **digest** and destroy it.

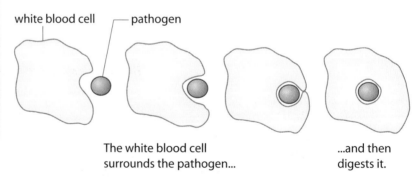

white blood cell — pathogen

The white blood cell surrounds the pathogen...

...and then digests it.

Figure 1 Some white blood cells ingest and destroy pathogens.

Other white blood cells release chemicals called **antibodies**, which destroy pathogens. A particular antibody can only destroy a particular bacterium or virus, so white blood cells learn to make many different types of antibody. For example, when a flu virus enters the body, antibodies are made that destroy the flu virus. After the virus has been destroyed, flu antibodies remain in the blood and act quickly if the same pathogen enters in the future. White blood cells also produce **antitoxins**. These are chemicals that prevent the toxins made by pathogens from poisoning your body.

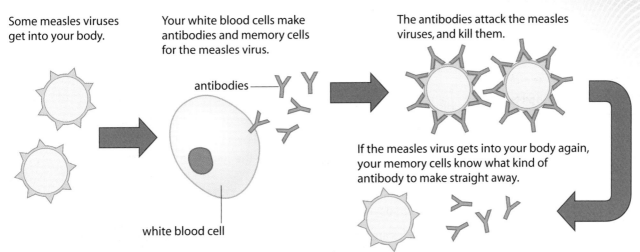

Some measles viruses get into your body.

Your white blood cells make antibodies and memory cells for the measles virus.

antibodies

white blood cell

The antibodies attack the measles viruses, and kill them.

If the measles virus gets into your body again, your memory cells know what kind of antibody to make straight away.

Figure 2 Some white blood cells release antibodies, which destroy pathogens.

Life-long protection

Once your white blood cells have destroyed a type of pathogen, you are unlikely to develop the same disease again. This is because your white blood cells will recognise the pathogen the next time it invades your body and produce the right antibodies very quickly to kill the pathogen before it can affect you. This makes you immune to the disease.

Science skills

Figure 3 shows what happens when someone is infected by a particular pathogen. The graph also shows what happens when the person is infected a second time by the same pathogen.

a How long did it take to start producing antibodies:
  i after the first infection **ii** after the second infection?

b Explain why antibodies were produced more quickly after the second infection.

c Suggest why the person did not become ill after the second infection.

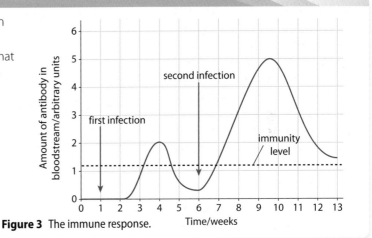

Figure 3 The immune response.

Questions

1 **(a)** Classify the following as B, caused by bacteria, or V, caused by viruses: chicken pox, measles, tuberculosis, mumps, rubella, dysentery, smallpox, cholera, polio, influenza. **(b)** Which of these have you had? **(c)** Which of these have you had only once? **(d)** Which have you had more than once? **(e)** Which are you not immune to?

2 What is meant by immunity?

3 What is meant by a symptom?

4 Explain the difference between antibody and antitoxin.

5 Describe the ways in which pathogens make us feel ill.

6 Describe the ways in which white blood cells protect us against pathogens.

7 Write a paragraph to explain fully why you do not usually suffer from a particular infectious disease more than once.

Science in action

Antibodies are not all useful. Some antibodies produced by a pregnant woman can cause problems for her unborn baby. These antibodies destroy the baby's red blood cells. In severe cases the baby is given a blood transfusion before birth. All pregnant mothers are screened for production of these antibodies so that the problem can be anticipated and dealt with.

Treating and preventing disease

Feeling ill

If you have a sore throat you might take throat lozenges to reduce the pain. The sore throat is a symptom caused by a pathogen that has infected your body. This **medicine** helps to relieve the symptom but it will not kill the pathogen.

Killing bacteria

Antibiotics are medicines that help to cure diseases caused by bacteria. You take antibiotics to kill bacteria that get inside your body. Doctors use many different antibiotics to treat people. **Penicillin** was the first antibiotic to be discovered.

Antibiotics can't kill viruses. Because viruses live and reproduce inside body cells, it is difficult to develop medicines that kill viruses without damaging body cells and tissues.

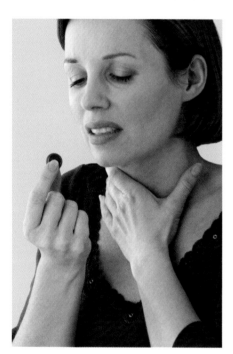

How will this throat lozenge help?

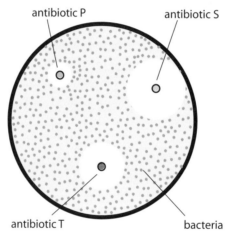

antibiotic P   antibiotic S

antibiotic T   bacteria

Figure 1 Finding out which antibiotic works best.

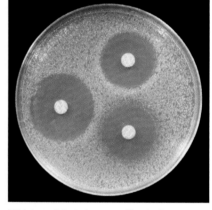

Which antibiotic is most effective?

The effect of different antibiotics on bacteria can be measured in the laboratory. This is done by using small discs of paper containing antibiotics. The discs are placed in a dish containing bacteria growing on a **gel**. The photograph shows the effect of three antibiotics. The clear zone that forms around each disc is where bacteria have been killed. Figure 1 shows the results of testing three other antibiotics. Gel tests are useful, but the body is more complicated than a gel. The results in the body may be different.

A quick jab

Immunity to a disease can be gained without ever having had the disease. A newborn baby receives antibodies from its mother in the first few days that it feeds on her milk. When you were a young child you were probably **immunised** to protect you from very harmful diseases, such as whooping cough, measles and polio. **Immunisation** (**vaccination**) usually involves injecting or swallowing a **vaccine** containing small amounts of a dead or weak form of the pathogen.

Because the pathogen is weak or inactive, the vaccine does not make you ill, but your white blood cells still produce antibodies to destroy the pathogen. This makes you immune to future infection by the pathogen. Your white blood cells will recognise the pathogen if it gets into your body and respond by quickly producing antibodies. The pathogen does not get a chance to reproduce enough to make you ill.

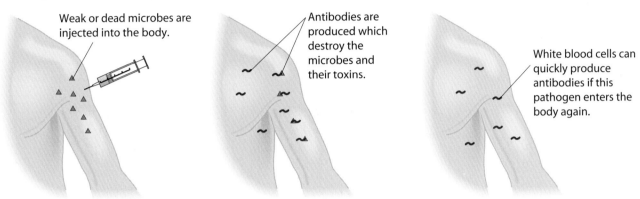

Weak or dead microbes are injected into the body.

Antibodies are produced which destroy the microbes and their toxins.

White blood cells can quickly produce antibodies if this pathogen enters the body again.

Figure 2 How vaccination works.

Science skills

The level of antibody in the blood after some vaccinations does not get high enough to give protection. In this case, a second, or booster, injection of vaccine a few weeks or months later is needed. The graph shows the level of antibodies in a person's blood following a first and second injection of a vaccine.

a What was the difference in arbitrary units in the level of antibody between the first and second injection?

b Explain why the person became immune after the second injection but not the first.

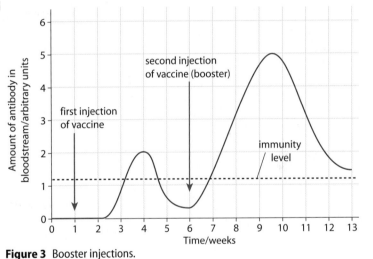

Figure 3 Booster injections.

Questions

1. What symptoms might you have if you catch a cold?
2. What is the most common type of medicine *that is not on these two pages* that is used to treat the symptoms of an infectious disease?
3. Which antibiotic in Figure 1 – P, S or T – works best against this bacterium?
4. Explain why antibiotics can be used to treat bacterial infections but not viral infections.
5. Rubella is a pathogen that can pass across the placenta. Why is it important that girls are vaccinated against rubella?
6. Explain how vaccination protects you against a disease, but does not cause you to develop the disease.

A*

Controlling infection

Learning objectives

- explain how strains of bacteria can develop resistance to antibiotics
- explain the consequences of the overuse of antibiotics and of mutations of bacteria and viruses
- describe how epidemics and pandemics occur.

Taking it further

Bacteria may develop antibiotic resistance in several ways. These include mutating to:

- deactivate the antibiotic before it reaches the inside of the bacterial cell
- pump antibiotic out of the bacterial cell
- alter the protein on the bacterial cell so that the antibiotic cannot recognise the cell
- produce enzymes to destroy the antibiotic.

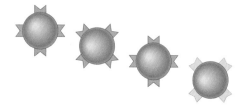

Figure 2 A mutation sometimes occurs when bacteria reproduce.

Dr Semmelweiss's recommendations (lesson B1 1.3) two centuries on.

Antibiotic resistance

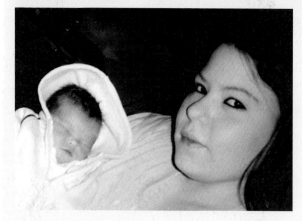

HOSPITAL SUPERBUG KILLS BABY

A one-day-old baby boy was killed by the hospital superbug MRSA.
Baby Luke was only 36 hours old when he died.
Luke was born showing no signs of bad health, but within a day he became ill.

Figure 1 Newspaper article about a hospital 'superbug'.

Bacteria grow and divide every 20 minutes. Each new bacterium is exactly the same as the one it came from. Sometimes a bacterium is produced that is slightly different to the others. This is called a **mutation**.

The mutation might result in the bacteria being **resistant** to existing antibiotics, so that the bacteria are no longer killed by antibiotics. When an antibiotic is used, the non-resistant bacteria are killed but a small number of resistant bacteria remain. The resistant bacteria survive and reproduce. Continued use of the antibiotic causes the number of resistant bacteria to increase. This is an example of **natural selection** (see lesson B1 7.2).

You should always complete a course of antibiotics, even if you start to feel better. If you do not complete a course of antibiotics, it is likely that some bacteria will survive. You could become ill again and need a second treatment course. There would be more chance of resistant bacteria developing.

Scientists are continually developing new antibiotics to replace those that are no longer effective.

Superbugs

Methicillin-resistant *Staphylococcus aureus* (**MRSA**) is a variety of *S. aureus* that is resistant to methicillin and most of the other antibiotics that are usually used to treat bacterial infections. MRSA is responsible for hundreds of deaths of hospital patients every year in the UK.

Patients who die with MRSA are usually patients who were already very ill. It is often their existing illness, rather than MRSA, that is given as the cause of death on the death certificate. In these cases, MRSA is only 'mentioned' on the death certificate.

All UK hospitals now have campaigns to prevent the spread of MRSA.

a Describe the trend in the number of deaths from MRSA.

b Suggest an explanation for the large increase in the number of death certificates where MRSA was 'mentioned'.

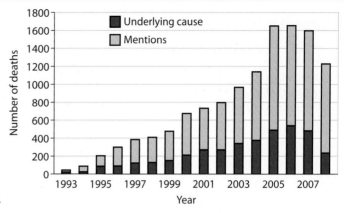

Figure 3 Deaths from MRSA in the UK.

Preventing more superbugs

To prevent more and more types of bacteria becoming resistant, it is important to avoid overusing antibiotics. This is why antibiotics are not used to treat non-serious infections like a sore throat. Doctors should only prescribe an antibiotic to treat a serious disease. By avoiding overusing antibiotics, you increase the likelihood that they will work when you really do need them.

Changing viruses

Flu, or influenza, is a viral disease that affects many people every year. Most people recover within one to two weeks, but flu can cause serious illness and death, especially in very young children and old people. Flu viruses are always mutating, producing new strains. Because the new strain is so different, people will have no immunity to it. This allows the new strain to cause more serious illness and to spread quickly from person to person.

When an outbreak of flu affects thousands of people in a country it is called a flu **epidemic**. Sometimes flu spreads very rapidly around the world, affecting people in many countries. This is called **pandemic** flu. In 2009 a pandemic flu called 'swine flu' developed. The UK government organised vaccination for all vulnerable people and stockpiled millions of doses of Tamiflu, an **antiviral** drug.

Figure 4 An old NHS advert.

Questions

1 What is MRSA?
2 Name the process that produces antibiotic-resistant strains of pathogens.
3 Explain why patients are advised to always complete a course of antibiotics.
4 Explain why antibiotics are not used to cure viral infections.
5 Suggest why antiviral drugs are only used to treat the most dangerous infections.
6 Explain why the 'swine flu' virus spread rapidly around the world.
7 Explain in terms of natural selection why doctors should not over-prescribe antibiotics.

Vaccination programmes

Learning objectives

- evaluate the advantages and disadvantages of being vaccinated against a particular disease.

Route to A*

About 85% of UK children have been vaccinated against measles. The World Health Organisation has set a vaccination target of 95%. Explain why it is important to reach the World Health Organisation target.

Examiner feedback

Many examinations give data about the number of cases of disease and percentage vaccination.

The data will often have two different y-axis scales. Take time before you answer the questions to familiarise yourself with the key to the two sets of data and the different y-axis scales.

Remember to give arguments both for and against if you are asked to evaluate such data. Conclude your answer with a reasoned conclusion. It is not sufficient to write 'I think the pros outweigh the cons'.

Immunisation programmes

Immunisation provides protection against several diseases that used to be very common in children. An example is the **MMR** vaccine, a combined vaccine that makes your body develop immunity to measles, mumps and rubella. Each of these diseases is caused by a virus that is easily spread from someone with the disease to someone who is not immune.

Vaccines such as MMR have saved millions of children from illness and even death. Before a measles vaccine was available, an average of approximately 250 000 children developed measles and 85 children died every year, and many others suffered severe symptoms.

If enough people in a community are immunised against certain diseases, then it is more difficult for that disease to get passed between those who aren't immunised. This is because most people who come into contact with the carrier are immunised, so the disease is less prevalent in the population, and therefore even those who are not immunised are less likely to get it. Medical experts recommend that at least 90% of the population should be vaccinated to prevent epidemics of a disease.

Science skills

a What was the maximum number of cases of measles in any one year before a vaccine against the disease was introduced?

b What was the maximum number of cases of measles in any one year after the introduction of the measles vaccine?

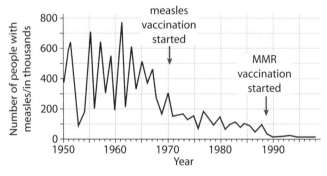

Figure 1 The graph shows the effectiveness of the immunisation programme against measles.

Concern about vaccines

Children who are not vaccinated are much more likely to develop serious illnesses. Whooping cough is a disease that can cause long bouts of coughing and choking, making it hard to breathe. The disease can be very serious and can kill babies under one year old. More than half the babies under one year old with whooping cough need to be admitted to hospital and many need intensive care.

In the 1970s, parents were concerned about possible **side effects** of the whooping cough vaccine and fewer children were vaccinated against whooping cough. As a result, major outbreaks of whooping cough occurred, with thousands of children being taken into hospital.

c Explain why two major outbreaks of whooping cough occurred in 1982 and 1986.

d Describe the relationship between the percentage of children being vaccinated and the number of whooping cough cases since 1990.

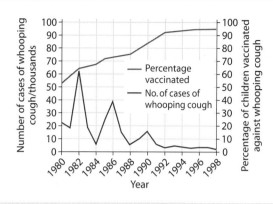

Figure 2 What caused whooping cough epidemics in the 1980s?

The MMR controversy

In 1998, many parents panicked and vaccination rates dropped rapidly after a doctor claimed that the MMR vaccine might trigger **autism**. However, the claim was based on a study of only 12 children. Soon the vaccine was being blamed for the apparent rise in autism in California. In some parts of the UK, the proportion of children receiving the MMR vaccine had dropped to 60% by 2005. This led to a rise in measles outbreaks and fears of an epidemic. Since then, other studies have failed to show any link between autism and MMR. By 2010 the percentage receiving the MMR vaccine had risen to 98%.

Society needs people to be immunised but individual parents can easily be scared off by the risk that their child might react negatively to the vaccine. Balancing risk factors is made more complicated because parents are thinking only of their child, whereas governments are looking at society as a whole.

Examiner feedback

In examination questions asking you to evaluate, make sure that you give your view and that it is supported by the evidence in the article(s).

Questions

1 What is contained in the MMR vaccine?
2 What does MMR stand for?
3 Why is it important to be vaccinated against the three diseases?
4 Why have some parents stopped their children having the MMR vaccine?
5 How would you advise these parents? Explain your answer.

Is there a link between MMR and autism?

The California data in Figure 3 was used by opponents of the MMR vaccine. At first glance it appears to show that an increase in autism is linked to the MMR vaccine. In fact it shows all people registered as having autism in a single year, 1991, plotted by year of birth. The data also do not take into account increases in population in California, nor improved diagnostic measures.

The Yokohama graph shows the number of cases of autism before and after the MMR vaccine was withdrawn.

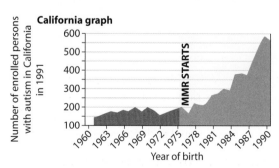

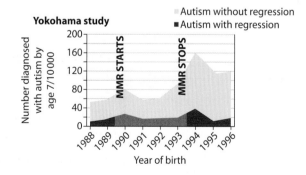

Figure 3 The graphs show data from two studies.

e Do the data in the two graphs indicate a link between the MMR vaccine and autism? Give the reasons for your answer.

Keeping things sterile

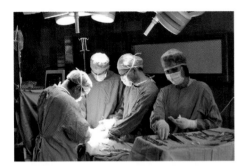

Kitted out to avoid infection.

Growing bacteria

Like all living organisms, bacteria and fungi need nutrients to grow and reproduce. In the laboratory, nutrients are often supplied to the microorganisms, also known as microbes, in a gel called **agar**. Agar is called a growth medium or **culture medium.** It melts at 98 °C and, as a liquid, it can be poured into plastic or glass **Petri dishes**. It solidifies at about 44 °C. Microbes cannot digest agar, so it is not used up as they grow.

Besides nutrients, many microbes need a temperature between 25 °C and 45 °C to grow. In school laboratories, the Petri dishes are put into a cabinet, or an **incubator,** set at a maximum temperature of 25 °C. Pathogens could accidentally be present in the culture dishes, so keeping the temperature at a maximum of 25 °C minimises health risks from them, as they will grow much less well at lower temperatures.

Why do we need to keep things sterile?

The air, the surfaces around you, your skin and clothes all have microorganisms on them. If you culture microorganisms in the laboratory, it involves growing very large numbers of bacterial cells. If safety procedures are not followed, you may accidentally introduce a harmful microbe into a harmless **strain** that you are growing. This would multiply rapidly, just as the harmless microbes do, and would be a greater health risk than if it were a single cell. Sterile or aseptic techniques must therefore be used to prepare uncontaminated cultures.

Glassware and culture media are **sterilised** in an **autoclave** using pressurised steam at a temperature of 121 °C for 15 minutes.

The type of autoclave used in most schools.

The high temperature needed to kill microbes melts plastic, so Petri dishes and disposable instruments are sterilised by **ultraviolet** or **ionising radiation**. This is done commercially. Petri dishes remain sterile inside until the lid is opened.

Safety first

You must wash your hands before and after working with microorganisms. A clean, cleared working surface is also essential. Hair should be tied back, broken skin covered with a plaster and hand-to-face contact avoided while culturing microbes. Work is carried out near the upward draught from a lighted Bunsen burner. The upward movement of air around the burner minimises the risk of airborne microbes falling onto **culture plates**.

Inoculation

Inoculation is the process of transferring microbes to the culture medium. For solid agar, a wire **inoculating loop** is used. It is first sterilised by holding it in a Bunsen burner flame. After cooling the loop for ten seconds, near the Bunsen burner, the microbes can be picked up from the **pure culture** and transferred to the sterile agar by gently sweeping the loop back and forth over the surface.

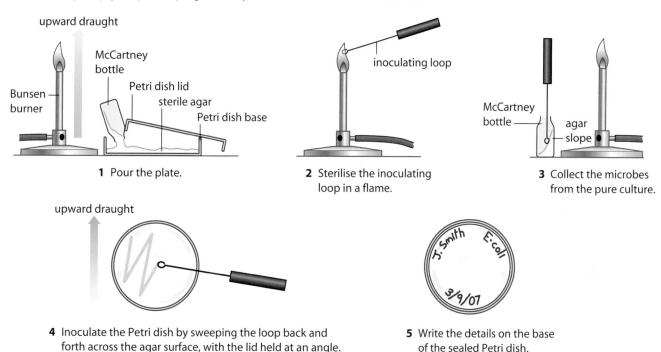

1 Pour the plate.

2 Sterilise the inoculating loop in a flame.

3 Collect the microbes from the pure culture.

4 Inoculate the Petri dish by sweeping the loop back and forth across the agar surface, with the lid held at an angle.

5 Write the details on the base of the sealed Petri dish.

Figure 1 The process of inoculation.

Before **incubation** the Petri dishes are sealed with adhesive tape to prevent contamination from airborne bacteria. After 24–72 hours, when the results have been noted, the cultures are autoclaved by a technician before disposal.

Questions

1 Give three ways in which microbiological equipment and media can be sterilised.

2 What is meant by 'aseptic'?

3 Give three personal safety precautions that should be taken when experimenting with microorganisms.

4 Describe what would happen if a single cell of a pathogen entered a culture dish.

5 Explain why the wire loop needs to be cooled before picking up the microbes.

6 Suggest why the lid of the Petri dish is not removed completely when introducing the microorganisms.

7 Describe what you should do with your successful culture after an experiment.

8 Explain why agar is suitable as a culture medium for growing bacteria.

The nervous system

The nervous system

The difference between winning and losing a race might be down to how quickly you start. It is all about reaction time. This is the time between hearing the gun and reacting to it.

The **nervous system** is made up of three main parts: the **brain**, the **spinal cord** and **neurones**, or nerve cells.

It has **receptors** in the:

- eyes that are sensitive to light
- ears that are sensitive to sound and to changes in position, thus enabling us to keep our balance
- tongue and in the nose that are sensitive to chemicals and enable us to taste and smell
- skin that are sensitive to touch, pressure, pain and to temperature changes.

Waiting for the starting signal.

The nervous system.

Receptors are cells that detect stimuli or changes in the environment. Each receptor cell, e.g. light receptor cells in the eye, like all animal cells, contains a **nucleus** and **cytoplasm** surrounded by a **cell membrane**.

Information from receptors, e.g. in your nose if you smell something burning, passes along neurones to the brain. The information passes along the neurones as signals called **impulses**. The brain then coordinates the response by sending information to the appropriate organs.

There are three types of neurone:

- **sensory neurones** carry impulses from the receptor to the spinal cord
- **relay neurones** carry impulses through the spinal cord and up to the brain and from the brain back along the spinal cord
- **motor neurones** take impulses from the spinal cord to an **effector**.

An effector can be a muscle that is made to **contract,** or a **gland** that secretes a chemical, for example a hormone.

Route to A*

Some drugs are used in medicine because they affect reflex pathways.

- The drug curare prevents muscles from contracting, thereby making surgery easier. At what place in a reflex action does curare probably act?
- Dentists inject the drug procaine into gums so that they can drill into teeth without causing pain. What is the most probable reason for procaine preventing pain?

Neurones are not joined to each other. There is a small gap between them called a **synapse**. When an impulse reaches the end of a neurone, a chemical is released. This travels across the gap, and starts an impulse in the next neurone. This means the message can only travel in one direction (see Figure 1).

Reflex actions

When pain is detected by a sensory receptor in your finger, it sends an impulse along a sensory neurone to a relay neurone in your spinal cord. The relay neurone sends an impulse in an arc via a motor neurone to an effector, a muscle, which contracts, pulling your hand away. This is called a **reflex action**. It is automatic and very quick (see Figure 2). There are other types of reflex actions such as coughing and blinking. These are needed to protect us from being hurt or from damage to our tissues, e.g. foreign bodies in airways or eyes.

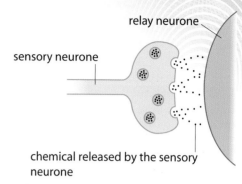

Figure 1 Chemicals released by a sensory neurone travel across the synapse to the relay neurone.

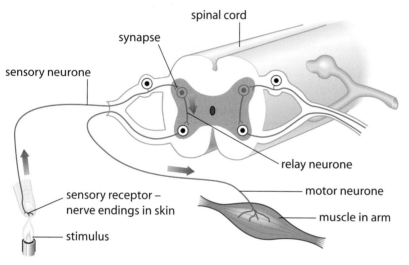

Figure 2 The reflex arc.

Examiner feedback

You should practise looking at different diagrams of the reflex arc and working out what is happening in each part.

Science skills

Design an experiment to measure the width of the pupil under different light intensities. Remember you must not touch the surface of the eye.

a What are the independent, the dependent and the control variables?

b Explain what you will do to make sure your experiment produces reliable results.

Questions

1 Identify six stimuli that you respond to and state where in the body the receptors for these are located.

2 Some people suffer from a disease called motor neurone disease. **(a)** Suggest which part of the nervous system it affects. **(b)** What will people with this disease have difficulty doing?

3 Coughing, sneezing and blinking are examples of reflex actions. **(a)** Identify what part of the body each reflex action protects. **(b)** Identify the receptor in each reflex action. **(c)** Identify the effector in each reflex action.

4 People taking part in motor sports wear head, neck and back protection. Why is it important to protect each of these areas?

5 Suggest how a sprinter might improve his reaction time.

6 The diagram shows the knee-jerk reflex. When the leg is tapped with a hammer just below the knee, the leg straightens. Describe fully the sequence of events in this reflex arc.

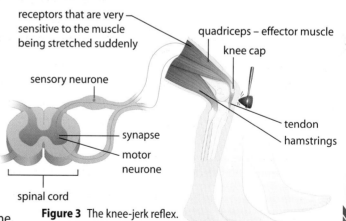

Figure 3 The knee-jerk reflex.

Controlling our internal environment

- describe how water leaves the body via the lungs, skin and kidneys
- describe how ions are lost through the skin as sweat, and the kidneys as urine
- explain why it is important that blood sugar concentration and blood ion concentration are regulated
- explain why body temperature is kept at 37 °C.

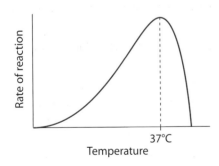

Refuelling during a marathon.

When we exercise

During a marathon, runners top up with sports drinks several times. Why do they need to do this?

Figure 1 compares the rate of heat production and the body temperature of a marathon runner during a race with those of the same athlete at rest.

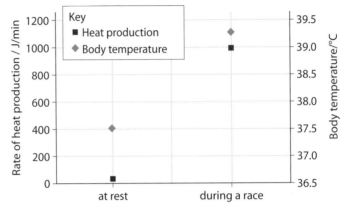

Figure 1 Body changes during a marathon.

Why is our body temperature kept at 37 °C?

Your body tries to stay at a steady internal temperature, around 37 °C. This is the temperature at which enzymes in your body work best. Enzymes speed up chemical reactions in the body. Without enzymes your body would not be able to work properly. The process of keeping things constant and balanced in your body is called **homeostasis**.

Salt (sodium chloride) contains sodium and chloride ions. These are needed to help our body work properly. Too much salt can be dangerous, but so is too little. Sodium and chloride levels in the blood are controlled by the kidneys. These ions are also lost when we sweat.

If the balance of ions and water changes in our bodies, cells do not work so well. Sports drinks help to replace both the water and the ions.

Sports drinks also contain **glucose**. This helps to top up the athlete's blood sugar levels during the marathon. To work properly, body cells need a constant supply of glucose for their energy needs. This glucose is supplied by the blood.

Figure 2 How temperature affects the rate of a reaction involving an enzyme.

Figure 2 shows the effect of temperature on the rate of an enzyme-controlled reaction. If our bodies were cooler than 37 °C, the chemical reactions in our cells would be much slower. Above 37 °C these reactions rapidly slow down. If we heat enzymes above 45 °C, their structure changes and they stop working.

Heat exhaustion and heatstroke

Heat exhaustion and heatstroke are two heat-related health conditions. Both can be very serious.

Heat exhaustion is when the core temperature rises to 40°C. At that temperature, the levels of water and salt in the body begin to drop. This causes symptoms such as nausea, feeling faint and heavy sweating. If left untreated, heat exhaustion can sometimes lead to heatstroke.

Heatstroke happens when a person's core temperature rises above 40°C. Cells inside the body begin to break down and important parts of the body stop working. Symptoms of heatstroke can include confusion, rapid shallow breathing and loss of consciousness. If left untreated, heatstroke can cause multiple organ failure, brain damage and death.

If a person with heat exhaustion is taken quickly to a cool place and given plenty of water to drink, they should begin to feel better within half an hour and experience no long-term effects. Heatstroke is very serious and should be treated immediately. Treatment involves quickly cooling down the body to lower the core temperature by using ice packs or a cold bath/shower.

Balancing the water budget

To stay healthy, the body needs to balance the gain and loss of both water and ions. Besides losing water when we urinate, pass faeces and sweat, we lose water in the air we breathe out. This is why a mirror becomes misty if we breathe on it.

The **kidneys** control the balance of water and ions in the body. They do this by producing a fluid called **urine**. Urine contains the excess salts and water that the body does not need. It also contains other waste materials.

Science skills

The amount of water entering the body should balance the amount of water leaving the body.

a How much water would this person have to drink to compensate for the amount of water lost?

b What proportion of water loss was via the skin?

c Construct pie charts to show the water budget.

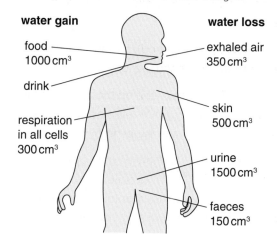

water gain
food 1000 cm³
drink
respiration in all cells 300 cm³

water loss
exhaled air 350 cm³
skin 500 cm³
urine 1500 cm³
faeces 150 cm³

Figure 3 The water budget.

Questions

1 Looking at Figure 1:
   (a) By how much does body temperature rise during a marathon?
   (b) Calculate the percentage increase in heat production by a marathon runner during a race.

2 **(a)** If you sweat a lot, what will happen to your: **(i)** salt levels **(ii)** water levels? **(b)** Why might this be dangerous?

3 Why does an athlete's blood sugar level fall during a race?

4 A person suffering from severe dehydration continues to produce urine, making the body even more dehydrated. Suggest why the body continues to produce urine under these conditions.

5 Many drinks cause the body to lose more water in the urine. These drinks are called diuretics. Alcohol, caffeine and fizzy drinks are all diuretics. Why is it not a good idea to drink these when you feel thirsty?

6 Describe in detail how conditions in the body are kept constant.

Controlling pregnancy

Hormones

Many of our body processes are controlled by chemicals called **hormones.** These are produced by organs called glands. The hormones pass from glands into the bloodstream, which transports them around the body. Each hormone affects one or more organs, known as the target organs.

The menstrual cycle

Every month, an egg (**ovum**) develops inside a female ovary. At the same time, **oestrogen** causes the lining of the womb (**uterus**) to become thicker, ready to receive a growing embryo. If the egg is not fertilised, the womb lining breaks down, causing bleeding from the vagina. The monthly cycle of changes that take place in the ovaries and womb is called the **menstrual cycle**. The menstrual cycle is controlled by several hormones. The action of the hormones involved is summarised in Figures 1 and 2.

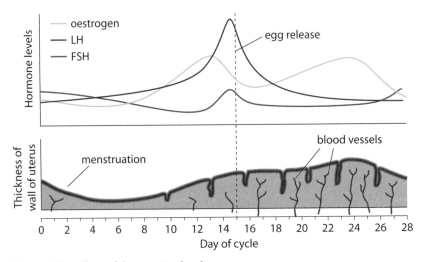

Figure 1 The effects of the menstrual cycle.

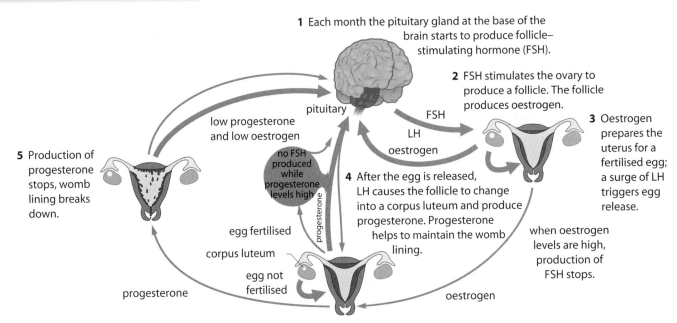

1 Each month the pituitary gland at the base of the brain starts to produce follicle–stimulating hormone (FSH).

2 FSH stimulates the ovary to produce a follicle. The follicle produces oestrogen.

3 Oestrogen prepares the uterus for a fertilised egg; a surge of LH triggers egg release.

4 After the egg is released, LH causes the follicle to change into a corpus luteum and produce progesterone. Progesterone helps to maintain the womb lining.

5 Production of progesterone stops, womb lining breaks down.

low progesterone and low oestrogen

no FSH produced while progesterone levels high

when oestrogen levels are high, production of FSH stops.

egg fertilised

corpus luteum

egg not fertilised

pituitary

FSH

LH

oestrogen

progesterone

progesterone

oestrogen

Figure 2 The menstrual cycle.

The contraceptive pill

A woman can take the contraceptive pill to stop her from becoming pregnant. The pill contains hormones that have the same effect on the pituitary gland as oestrogen. These hormones stop the pituitary gland making the hormone **FSH**. This means that no eggs will mature in the ovaries.

Benefits and problems

The first contraceptive pills contained large amounts of oestrogen. These resulted in women suffering significant side effects such as the formation of blood clots, which can block vital arteries.

There are now two types of contraceptive pill available, 'combined' and 'mini pill'. The combined pill contains a much lower dose of oestrogen along with another hormone called progesterone. The mini pill contains progesterone only. The mini pill causes fewer side effects but must be taken punctually in order for it to work and is less reliable than the combined pill.

The combined pill decreases the chance of getting cancer of the womb by 50% and cancer of the ovaries by 40%. There is an increased risk, however, that women taking the pill will develop blood clots.

Fertility drugs

If a woman's own level of FSH is too low, her ovaries will not release eggs and she cannot become pregnant. Infertility can be treated by injecting FSH into the blood. FSH acts as a fertility drug by stimulating the ovaries to produce mature eggs.

Unfortunately, the treatment does not always work, or sometimes it may cause more than one egg to be released. This can result in twins, triplets, quadruplets or even more.

Science skills

a Imagine you are a doctor. Using the data in the table, what would you say to a woman who wanted to go on the pill and was worried about side effects?

Table 1 The risk of blood clots.

Situation	Risk in cases per 100 000 women
women not on the pill	8
women taking combined pill	25
women taking mini pill	15
women who smoke	100
pregnant women	85

Questions

1. **(a)** How many days are there in a typical menstrual cycle?
   (b) On which day does the concentration of FSH peak?
2. What causes menstruation?
3. What is the role of FSH in the menstrual cycle?
4. What is the relationship between oestrogen concentration in the blood and the thickness of the lining of the womb?
5. The most difficult time for a female athlete to race well is the week before menstruation and the week after ovulation. The best time for female athletes to race is thought to be just before ovulation, between days 9 to 12.
   (a) Study the changing levels of oestrogen in Figure 1 and explain the connection between the oestrogen level and athletic performance.
   (b) Design a training schedule for a female athlete so that she can train and race at peak performance. Think about the menstrual cycle and how it affects performance.
   (c) How might taking the contraceptive pill help with race training and performance?
6. Explain why:
   (a) FSH can be used as a fertility drug
   (b) oestrogen can be used as a contraceptive drug
   (c) the mini pill is better in some respects, and worse in others, than the combined pill.
7. There are two forms of 'morning-after' pill (emergency contraceptive pill). Pills containing high doses of oestrogen and progesterone will immediately stop ovulation. The other type of pill prevents a fertilised egg from implanting into the lining of the womb. Evaluate the use of these two types of 'morning-after' pill.

Evaluating the benefits of fertility treatment

Interfering with nature?

Sixty-six-year-old Adriana Iliescu became the world's oldest mother when she gave birth to a daughter following fertility treatment.

Ms Iliescu is a retired professor who lives alone. She said she had delayed having a child so she could concentrate on her academic career. Ms Iliescu became pregnant through IVF, using donated sperm and eggs, and this was her third attempt at having a baby.

Figure 1 Interfering with nature?

In vitro fertilisation

Many women are infertile because of blocked oviducts, or fallopian tubes. This means that eggs cannot travel from the ovaries to the womb. Nor can sperm travel upwards to meet an egg. This type of infertility can be treated by using *in vitro* **fertilisation (IVF).** This literally means fertilisation in a test tube, which led to the term 'test-tube baby'.

The first stage of IVF is to obtain eggs from the woman. She is given injections of FSH to stimulate the **maturation** of several eggs. Eggs are then collected just before they are released from the ovary.

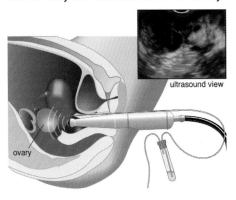

ultrasound view

ovary

Figure 2 Using ultrasound to view the ovary, the doctor inserts the needle through the wall of the vagina into the ovary and removes the eggs for use in IVF.

The eggs are fertilised with sperm from the father outside the body and the fertilised eggs are allowed to divide to form **embryos**, as shown in Figure 3. At the stage when the embryos are still just balls of cells, some are inserted into the woman's womb.

What are the statistics?

The average success rate for IVF treatment using fresh eggs, i.e. eggs that have not been stored frozen, in the UK is shown in Table 1.

The typical cost of a cycle of IVF treatment is approximately £5000–8000. On top of this, the couple will have to pay for the costs of consultation, drugs and tests. The single biggest risk from IVF treatment is multiple births, and particularly triplet births. Many women decide to abort one of these triplets, because multiple births carry potential health risks for both the mother and the unborn children.

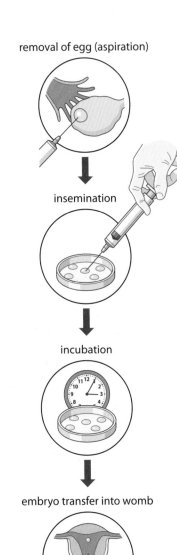

removal of egg (aspiration)

insemination

incubation

embryo transfer into womb

Figure 3 IVF procedure.

Science skills

Multiple birth babies are more likely to be premature and below normal birth mass. Premature babies have a much higher risk of most of the problems associated with early childhood.

The risk of death before birth or within the first week after birth is more than four times greater for twins and almost seven times greater for triplets than for single births.

The incidence of **cerebral palsy**, a form of brain damage, is approximately five times higher for twins and approximately 18 times higher for triplets than for single births.

Table 1 IVF statistics for 2007 in the UK.

Women aged	Success rate (%)
under 35	32.3
35–37	27.7
38–39	19.2
40–42	11.1
43–44	3.4
44+	3.1

a How is the success of IVF treatment affected by age? Suggest an explanation for this.

b Currently 0.5% of IVF births are triplets, down from almost 4% in the early 1990s. Twenty per cent of IVF births are twins. Suggest an explanation for this.

c Imagine that you are a doctor. What advice would you give to a couple who were considering IVF treatment? Use the information above in your answer.

Science in action

Some couples cannot have children because the man's sperm are too weak to penetrate the egg. These couples may be helped by intracytoplasmic sperm injection (ICSI).

As in IVF, the woman is given fertility drugs to stimulate eggs to mature and to be released. Sperm is collected from the man: a semen sample. A single sperm is then injected directly into the woman's egg with a very delicate needle. The egg will reseal itself after the needle is withdrawn, just as it does in natural fertilisation when the sperm breaks through its outer membrane. The fertilised egg is then allowed to develop for a few days before being transferred back into the woman's uterus in the form of an embryo.

Questions

1 Should Ms Iliescu, Figure 1, have been given fertility treatment? Give arguments for and against.

2 Explain why FSH can be used as a fertility drug.

3 A drug called **clomiphine** is often used instead of FSH. This drug blocks the effect of oestrogen on the pituitary gland. Explain how clomiphine works as a fertility drug.

4 Two embryos are sometimes inserted into the mother, even if she only wants one child. Suggest why.

5 Write a leaflet for couples about to have IVF treatment. Describe and explain the procedures involved. Include diagrams where necessary.

6 During normal IVF, a woman undergoes several weeks of hormone injections. The treatment can lead to a condition called ovarian hyperstimulation syndrome, resulting in a build-up of fluid in the lungs and, very rarely, death. The syndrome occurs in about 1% of standard IVF cycles, but in about 10% for some women. An IVF cycle may cost up to £4300.

In *in vitro* maturation (IVM), hormone treatment lasts for less than 7 days. Eggs are collected from the ovaries while still immature, then matured in a laboratory for up to 48 hours before being injected with a single sperm. A few days after fertilisation, the embryos are implanted into the womb. The cost of each IVM cycle is £1700.

In IVM treatment, the risk of abnormalities in the sex chromosomes, and of birth deformities and cancer in the babies, while small, is greater than in IVF.

Evaluate the use of IVM rather than IVF in treating infertility.

Science skills

Think about the ethical implications of IVF. Here are some opinions. Some people are concerned that it is not natural; others think that an older mother will be unable to cope when the child is a teenager. Some people are concerned about the rights of a woman to be a mother against those of unused embryos. Other people ask whether enough is known about the long-term effects of these techniques. Many people ask why it is acceptable for older men to become fathers, when for an older woman to become a mother is seen as unacceptable.

Plant responses

Learning objectives
- describe the responses of plant roots and stems to gravity, light and water
- explain these responses to light and gravity in terms of the distribution of hormones.

Phototropism

Plants need light for **photosynthesis**, but they are rooted in soil so they cannot move from place to place to obtain maximum light.

The photograph shows seedlings that have been grown in three different conditions:
- grown in light coming from the left
- grown in darkness
- grown in all-round light.

The stems in the right-hand pot have grown normally.

The stems in the centre pot have grown straight up, and are much longer than the stems in the other two pots because they received no light.

The stems in the left-hand pot have grown towards the light. This response to directional light is called **phototropism**. Plants stems are **positively phototropic**, that is they grow towards the light stimulus.

Plant stems grow towards the light.

Which part of the stem detects the stimulus?

Charles Darwin did some of the earliest experiments on phototropism. Figure 1 shows one of them.

This experiment showed that the tip of the stem is the receptor for the light stimulus.

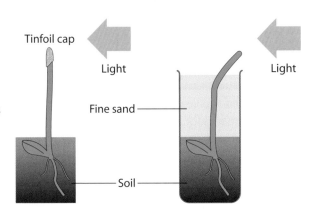

Tinfoil cap

Light   Light

Fine sand

Soil

Figure 1 Darwin's experiment.

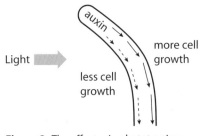

Light ➡

auxin

more cell growth

less cell growth

Figure 2 The effector in phototropism.

What is the effector in phototropism?

The response of growing towards the light is brought about by unequal growth. Cells on the shaded side grow longer than cells on the side nearest the light. Growth of cells in the stem is stimulated by hormones called **auxins**. Auxins are produced by the stem tip and are transported downwards. If the stem is placed in **unidirectional** light, more auxin is transported down the shaded side so the cells on this side grow faster, thus bending the stem towards the light.

Gravitropism

The pot shown in the photograph on the left was placed in the vertical position until the stem was a few centimetres tall. The pot was then placed on its side. One day later the stem had turned to grow vertically as shown.

Stems are **negatively gravitropic** – they grow away from the direction of the force of gravity. Roots are **positively gravitropic** – they grow in the direction of the force of gravity.

Gravitropism.

Growing away from gravity means that a stem beneath the soil will eventually find light. Growing downwards into the soil means that a root will help to keep the plant anchored in the soil.

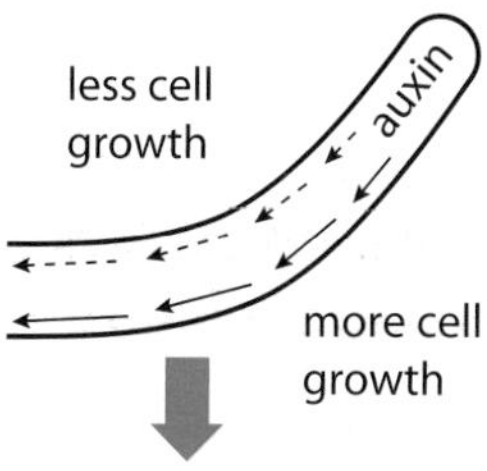

The mechanism for the gravitropic response of stems is similar to the phototropic response in that it is caused by the unequal distribution of auxin. Auxin accumulates on the underside of a horizontal stem in response to gravity. The cells on the underside grow faster than those on the upper side and the stem grows upwards.

If a root is placed in the horizontal position it will grow downwards. This means that the cells on the upper side grow faster than the ones on the underside. However, auxin accumulates on the underside of the root as it does in the stem. So why does the root go downwards? The reason is that the concentration of auxin that stimulates stem growth inhibits root growth, as shown on the graph in Figure 4.

Using agar and mica

Figure 5 shows one of the experiments that scientists did to show that gravity causes unequal distribution of auxin. Agar is **permeable** to auxins but mica is impermeable.

Hydrotropism

Figure 6 shows what happens when a root is stimulated by both the force of gravity and a directional water stimulus. The root grows towards the water. It is **positively hydrotropic**.

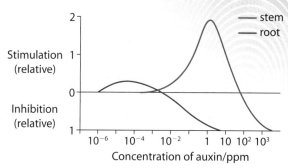

force of gravity

Figure 3 The mechanism of gravitropism in stems.

Figure 4 The effect of auxin concentration on root and stem cell growth.

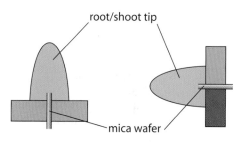

equal amounts of auxin diffuse into both agar blocks

twice as much auxin diffuses into bottom agar block

Figure 5 The distribution of auxins in a gravitropic response.

Examiner feedback

Make sure you understand that stem cells and root cells have different responses to the same concentration of auxin and this is why stems grow upwards and roots grow downwards.

Questions

1. Name the type of substance that brings about plant responses.
2. Why is mica used in experiments on plant responses?
3. Suggest an explanation, other than the effect of gravity, for the root in Figure 6 growing towards the water.
4. What is the receptor in a tropic response?
5. What is the effector in a tropic response?
6. Name the response of a plant organ to: **(a)** directional light **(b)** the force of gravity **(c)** water.
7. Explain fully why roots grow in the direction of the force of gravity, but stems grow away from the direction of the force of gravity.
8. Compare and contrast the response of a plant shoot to light with a pain withdrawal.

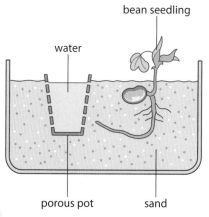

Figure 6 Hydrotropism.

Using plant hormones

The effect of weedkiller.

Selective weedkillers

Most gardens in the UK have a lawn. The biggest problem with lawns is keeping them free of **weeds**. There are two common ways of doing this: pull each weed up by hand or spray the lawn with a **selective weedkiller**.

A selective weedkiller in action on the left.

The most common selective weedkiller is **2,4-D**, short for 2,4-dichlorophenoxyacetic acid.

2,4-D has a chemical structure similar to that of auxins, but it has a much greater effect. 2,4-D is rapidly absorbed by broad-leaved plants. It accumulates in the stem and root tips and causes uncontrolled growth as shown in the photograph.

The growth is so abnormal that the plant dies. 2,4-D is not absorbed by narrow-leaved plants such as grasses, so when it is sprayed on a lawn, the weeds are killed but the grass is unaffected. 2,4-D is a selective weedkiller.

Agent Orange

During the Vietnam war in the 1960s, American aircraft sprayed wide areas of Vietnam with 2,4-D. The codename for this spray was Agent Orange. Agent Orange was an equal mixture of 2,4-D and another hormone, 245T. The concentration of 2,4-D in the spray caused the leaves of the jungle trees to fall off. The purpose of this was to deny hiding places to the North Vietnamese soldiers. Unfortunately the spray came into contact with both Vietnamese and Americans. There was a significant increase in the proportion of children born with birth defects during and after the war. According to the Vietnamese Ministry of Foreign Affairs, 4.8 million Vietnamese people were exposed to Agent Orange, resulting in 400 000 deaths and disabilities and 500 000 children born with birth defects.

Follow-up studies on American soldiers show a higher incidence of several diseases than in the general population.

Rooting powders

Horticulturists use cuttings to produce large numbers of identical plants. Part of a plant shoot is cut off and the end of the stem is dipped in **rooting powder**. The end of the stem is then pressed into damp **compost**. After a few days, roots develop from the cut stem. Rooting powders contain auxins that stimulate the stem cells to develop into roots.

Ripening fruit

The gas **ethene (ethylene)** is a plant hormone. It is produced by fruits as they ripen. One effect of ethylene is to stimulate the reactions that convert starch into sugar. A ripe fruit tastes much sweeter than an unripe one.

Using rooting powder.

Science in action

Bananas grown in the tropics are picked while they are green, which means they are unripe.

They are transported in this state in well-ventilated containers. On arrival at their destination country, the bananas are placed in 'banana rooms'. Ethylene is then pumped into the 'banana room' to ripen them.

Science skills

A student investigated the effectiveness of a rooting powder on three different plant **species**: begonia, geranium and rose. Begonia and geranium are herbaceous (non woody) plants. Rose is a woody bush. The student dipped equal sized pieces of shoots of the three species into rooting powder, then pushed the ends of the stems into damp compost. The student also pushed untreated pieces of shoot from each species into the compost. After two weeks the student measured the total length of roots produced by each species. The results are shown in the table.

a Give two ways in which the student could have improved the investigation.

b Give the two main conclusions that can be drawn from the student's results.

Species	Total length of roots produced/cm	
	Hormone treated shoots	Untreated shoots
Begonia	1.50	0.80
Geranium	0.75	0.40
Rose	0.00	0.00

Practical

Design a controlled investigation to find out if apples ripen faster if stored with bananas.

For 'storage' you could place an unripe apple and a banana into a plastic bag, then seal it.

To compare ripeness of apples, you could cut them in half, then stain with iodine/potassium iodide solution. The more blue/black colour, the more starch.

Questions

1 Name the type of substance used as weedkillers and rooting powders.
2 What is the main difference between the effect of weedkillers on plant stems and that of rooting powders?
3 Suggest why the containers for transporting bananas are well ventilated.
4 Suggest the advantages of transporting bananas in their unripe form, then placing them in 'banana rooms'.
5 Why do selective weedkillers kill only broad-leaved plants?
6 What is the advantage to horticulturists of using rooting powders?
7 Explain the advantages to distributors of using fruit-ripening hormones.
8 How should new weedkillers be trialled before being marketed?

Assess yourself questions

1 Different parts of the body have different functions.
List A gives three organs.
List B gives information about each organ.
Draw one line from each organ in List A to information about the organ in List B.

List A	List B
Organ	Information
gland	produces a fluid that helps to regulate body temperature
kidney	produces hormones
skin	coordinates responses
	produces urine *(3 marks)*

2 A laboratory technician was cleaning out a cupboard. Dust from the cupboard made her sneeze.

(a) In this response, dust is:

A   the coordinator   B   the effector

C   the receptor   D   the stimulus

(b) In this response, the receptor is in:

A   the brain   B   the eye

C   the nose   D   the spinal cord

(c) In this response, the coordinator is:

A   the brain   B   the nose

C   the spinal cord   D   a synapse

(d) Chemical transmitters are involved in:

A   sending impulses along sensory neurones

B   sending impulses across the gap between a sensory neurone and a relay neurone

C   sending impulses from one end of a relay neurone to the other

D   sending impulses from a motor neurone to a relay neurone *(4 marks)*

3 Figure 1 shows the reported number of cases in UK hospitals of an infection with a pathogen called *Clostridium difficile*.

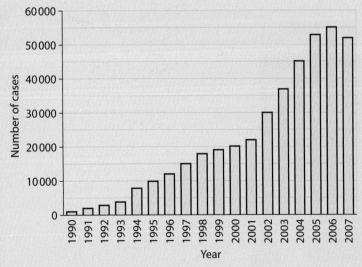

Figure 1 Hospital infections.

(a) Describe as fully as you can the pattern shown by the data in the graph. *(2 marks)*

(b) Suggest an explanation for the change in the number of reported cases of *Clostridium difficile* infection between 1990 and 2005. *(2 marks)*

(c) Suggest an explanation for the change in the number of reported cases of *Clostridium difficile* infection between 2006 and 2007. *(2 marks)*

4 The passage contains information about the 'morning-after' pill.

What does the pill do?

The 'morning-after' pill stops you from becoming pregnant. It is not 100% effective, but the failure rate is quite low – probably about 10%, and rather better than that if you take it as early as possible.

The pill is believed to work principally by preventing your ovaries from releasing an egg, and by affecting the womb lining so that a fertilised egg can't embed itself there.

In Britain and many other western countries, it is not legally regarded as an abortion-causing drug, but as a contraceptive.

Who is the pill for?

It is now very widely used by women (especially young women) who have had unprotected sex. It has proved to be of value to rape victims, couples who have had a condom break and women who have been lured into having sex while under the influence of drink or drugs.

Is it dangerous to use?

You might feel a little bit sick after taking it, but only about 1 woman in 40 actually throws up. Uncommon side effects are headache, stomach ache and breast tenderness.

If the pill didn't work, and I went on and had a baby, could the tablet damage it?

We simply don't know the answer to this question. At present, no one has shown any increase in abnormalities among babies who have been exposed to the morning-after pill. However, past experience does show that other hormones taken in early pregnancy have harmed children.

(a) Some people regard this pill as an abortion-causing drug. Explain why. *(2 marks)*

(b) **(i)** Some people think that this pill should only be available on prescription. Suggest why they think this. *(1 mark)*

(ii) Others say it should be freely available 'over the counter'. Give two reasons why they think this. *(2 marks)*

(c) Scientists are uncertain if the pill might cause abnormalities among unborn children. Suggest why. *(2 marks)*

5 Figure 2 shows the average amount of cholesterol in the blood of people at different ages.

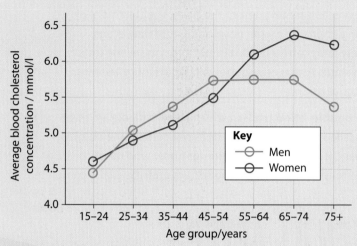

Figure 2 Cholesterol levels.

(a) What is the average blood cholesterol level for a 60-year-old woman? *(1 mark)*

(b) Which group of people has the highest risk of developing heart disease? *(1 mark)*

(c) Give two factors that influence blood cholesterol level. *(2 marks)*

6 Figure 3 shows how the concentrations of the hormones that control the menstrual cycle vary over 28 days.

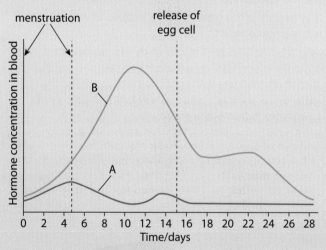

Figure 3 Hormone concentration.

(a) Name:

  (i) hormone A *(1 mark)*

  (ii) hormone B *(1 mark)*

(b) Explain why hormone A can be used as a fertility drug. *(2 marks)*

(c) Hormones similar in their effect to hormone B can be used as contraceptive drugs. Explain why. *(2 marks)*

7 Figure 4 shows the number of cases of influenza in a large city in the UK.

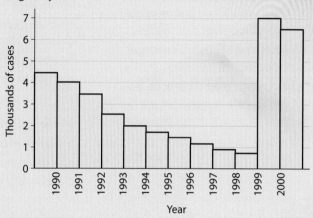

Figure 4 Influenza.

(a) The number of cases of influenza decreased between 1990 and 1998. Suggest an explanation for this. *(2 marks)*

(b) Suggest an explanation for the large increase in the number of cases in 1999. *(2 marks)*

(c) Most people who get flu recover in a few weeks. Explain why. *(2 marks)*

(d) Explain in detail why a person who has been vaccinated against flu may still catch the disease. *(6 marks)*

In this question you will be assessed on using good English, organising information clearly and using specialist terms where appropriate.

8 Figure 5 shows bacteria being transferred from one Petri dish, B, to another, C.

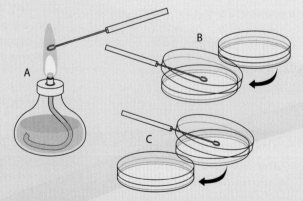

Figure 5 Transfer of bacteria.

Describe fully the procedures you would use with the apparatus shown in the diagram to transfer bacteria from dish B to dish C. Give the reason for each of the procedures you describe. *(6 marks)*

In this question you will be assessed on using good English, organising information clearly and using specialist terms where appropriate.

Developing new drugs

Developing new drugs

Drugs used to treat disease need to be safe, effective, chemically **stable**, and successfully taken in and removed from the body. The treatment of disease is always being improved by the development of new drugs. However, before a new drug can be used, it is put through several tests and has to pass each stage. As the newspaper extract in Figure 1 shows, this is not always without risk.

All **clinical trials** are **double-blind trials** in which some patients are given a dummy medicine, called a **placebo,** which does not contain the drug, as a control group. Neither the doctors nor the patients know who has received a placebo and who has received the drug being tested, until the trial is complete.

Science in action

Animal testing in the cosmetic industry is especially undertaken for make-up and soaps. Rabbits are the main animals used in these tests. Guinea pigs are used to test sunscreen products. The tests are done to find whether the products will produce reactions and allergies .

Many people are uneasy about the use of animals to test make-up and soaps. Scientists have developed 'non-animal' alternatives including the following.

- Human skin model tests are now in use, including EpiDerm™ (cultured human skin) test, which has been accepted almost universally as a total replacement for skin testing in rabbits

- Human skin left over from operations or from people who have donated their bodies to science is used to measure the rate at which chemicals are able to penetrate the skin.

SIX TAKEN ILL AFTER DRUGS TRIAL

Six men remain in intensive care after being taken ill during a clinical drugs trial in north-west London

The healthy volunteers were testing an anti-inflammatory drug at a research unit based at Northwick Park Hospital when they suffered a reaction.

Relatives are with the patients, who suffered multiple organ failure. Two men are said to be critically ill.

An investigation has begun at the unit, run by Parexel, which said it followed recommended guidelines in its trial.

The men were being paid to take part in the early stages of a trial for the drug to treat conditions such as rheumatoid arthritis and leukaemia until they were taken ill on Monday within hours of taking it.

Eight volunteers were involved, but two were given a placebo at the unit, which is on Northwick Park Hospital's grounds, but is run independently.

Figure 1 Drugs tests sometimes go wrong.

Table 1 The main stages in the testing of a new drug.

Stage	Purpose
laboratory	animals or tissues used in a laboratory to find out the level of **toxicity** and to find out if the drug works
phase 1 clinical	low doses are tested on a small group of healthy people to evaluate its safety, and identify side effects
phase 2 clinical	tested on a larger group of people to see if it is effective, to further evaluate its safety and to determine the optimum dose
phase 3 clinical	tested on large groups of people to confirm its effectiveness and monitor side effects

When drug testing fails

Starting in 1957, **thalidomide** was given to women in the first few months of pregnancy to help them sleep and to overcome the effects of morning sickness. Many women who took the drug gave birth to babies with limbs that weren't properly formed. The drug was banned worldwide in 1961 after it was confirmed that it caused tragic birth defects. The testing of thalidomide was incomplete, because it had not been tested on pregnant animals. The total number of babies damaged by thalidomide throughout the world was about 10 000.

Recently, thalidomide has been used very effectively to treat a serious disease called **leprosy**. However, some pregnant women with leprosy have obtained the drug without doctor's advice, and once again children are being born with deformed limbs.

Testing statins

Drugs called **statins** have been developed to lower blood cholesterol levels.

The result of not testing thalidomide.

 **Science skills**

A study into statins was carried out in a leading UK hospital. The study involved 20 536 patients aged between 40 and 80 with heart disease. The health of these patients was monitored closely over a five-year period.

A total of 10 269 of the patients took a **simvastatin** tablet daily, whilst 10 267 received a placebo every day. Patients were randomly placed into the 'statin' group or the 'placebo' or control group.

The main conclusion of the study was that simvastatin is safe and reduces the risk of people having a heart attack or a stroke.

a This type of study is called a **randomised controlled trial**.

  i What feature of the study was randomised?

  ii How was a control used in the study?

b It is important that studies to assess drugs are highly reliable. What features of this study show that the findings are reliable?

Questions

1. **(a)** What conditions was thalidomide designed to treat? **(b)** What test was omitted during the development of thalidomide?

2. What is a double-blind trial?

3. What is a placebo?

4. Suggest why only a few people are used in phase 1 of a clinical trial.

5. Suggest why phase 2 is carried out after phase 1 and not at the same time.

6. Once a drug is on sale, why does it still have to be monitored?

7. Some doctors have used the results of the above statin trial to suggest that all children should be given statins daily. Do you agree with these doctors? Explain the reasons for your answer.

Recreational drugs

What is a drug?

Many drugs are extracted from natural substances. They have been used by people from different cultures for medicines and recreation for thousands of years. **Alcohol** has been fermented from fruit and grain since at least ancient Chinese times, about 9000 years ago.

MAY DAY CELEBRATIONS END IN TRAGEDY

Hundreds of students followed a centuries-old tradition and jumped off Magdalen Bridge at dawn on May Day into the River Cherwell at Oxford.

However, most of them were drunk after all-night parties and they ignored police warnings that the river was too low this year. The result was at least ten students with serious injuries to spines, legs and ankles.

Would students do this if they were sober?

A **drug** is any chemical that alters how our body works. Drugs that affect our **central nervous system (CNS)** control the movement of chemicals across the synapses. The natural chemicals in our nervous system have shapes that fit receptors in our bodies like a key in a lock. Drugs have similar shapes to these chemicals and mimic, or copy, what they do.

People take drugs for recreational or medical reasons. Most drugs were originally used to deal with injury or sickness. Drug abuse occurs when people take too much of a drug or use it for the wrong reasons. Spanish explorers learned from indigenous South Americans to chew on coca plant leaves to keep awake. Today it is used to make cocaine.

If some drugs are used a lot, your body builds up a tolerance to them. This means you must use more of the drug to get the same effect. As a drug is used more often and in greater amounts, your body becomes more dependent on it. This means you will find it difficult to manage without the drug and will need to take it regularly. This leads to addiction. You are addicted when you cannot manage without taking the drug.

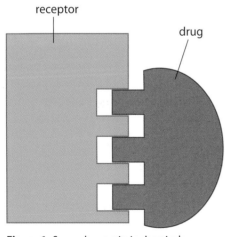

Figure 1 Some drugs mimic chemicals released across the synapses.

When you try to stop taking a drug you are addicted to, you suffer from withdrawal symptoms. These can include feeling sick, headaches and flu-like symptoms. More severe withdrawal symptoms include tremors and fits.

Why do people use drugs?

Drugs are not just taken for medical reasons; some drugs are also taken for pleasure. These drugs are called **recreational drugs**. Some recreational drugs are legal, for example alcohol, **caffeine** and **nicotine** in tobacco, but other recreational drugs are illegal, for example, **cannabis**, **cocaine**, **heroin** and **ecstasy**. Ecstasy, cannabis, cocaine and heroin may have adverse effects on the heart and circulatory system.

Many people smoke cannabis as a recreational drug because it alters their mood. Some of these people think that cannabis is harmless because it is similar to smoking tobacco or drinking alcohol. Many scientists think that the evidence shows that cannabis can cause psychological problems. However, other scientists are uncertain whether cannabis actually causes these problems.

However, it isn't only illegal drugs that can be dangerous. Research has shown that tobacco and alcohol cause thousands of deaths in Britain every year. The NHS has to spend far more money on treating the effects of legal drugs than illegal drugs, because far more people use them. Many people would argue that these drugs should be made illegal. Others argue for the decriminalisation of all drugs, in order to make their use safer, cut down crime associated with the cost of illegal drugs, and to stop criminal gangs from making huge profits from the drugs trade.

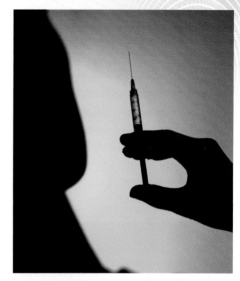

Heroin addicts have to inject themselves frequently or they suffer severe withdrawal symptoms.

Taking it further

There is a 'reward centre' in the brain that affects our behaviour. One cause of a feeling of pleasure is the accumulation of a substance called dopamine in synapses in this centre. Normally, another substance, dopamine re-uptake transporter, causes the dopamine to be reabsorbed. Cocaine blocks the action of the dopamine re-uptake transporter, so dopamine remains in the synapses and the feeling of pleasure persists.

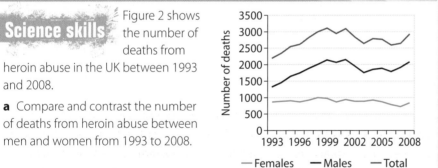

Science skills Figure 2 shows the number of deaths from heroin abuse in the UK between 1993 and 2008.

a Compare and contrast the number of deaths from heroin abuse between men and women from 1993 to 2008.

— Females — Males — Total

Figure 2 Deaths from heroin abuse.

Questions

1 Explain what is meant by a recreational drug.

2 **(a)** Give two examples of legal recreational drugs. **(b)** Give two examples of illegal recreational drugs.

3 Explain why drugs can alter the way we behave.

4 'Tonics' sold to people in America in the 1800s contained heroin. **(a)** What would a person feel having taken this 'tonic'? **(b)** What long-term problems might they have suffered?

5 Why might taking heroin lead to you getting HIV, AIDS or other infections?

6 What is meant by 'withdrawal symptom'?

7 Why do more people die from using nicotine and alcohol than heroin and cocaine?

8 Explain fully how a person becomes addicted to a drug.

Establishing links

Learning objectives

- evaluate evidence for a link between smoking cannabis and mental illness
- evaluate the evidence indicating the possible progression from non-addictive recreational drugs to addiction to hard drugs.

Many people think that smoking a joint is harmless, but is it?

A harmless joint?

Many people smoke cannabis as a recreational drug; it helps them to 'chill out'. However, there is mounting evidence of a link between smoking cannabis and mental illness. There is also some evidence that smoking cannabis can lead to addiction to hard drugs, in other words, that it is a '**gateway**' **drug**.

Science skills Figure 1 shows the government classification of drugs and their harm rating compiled by independent experts.

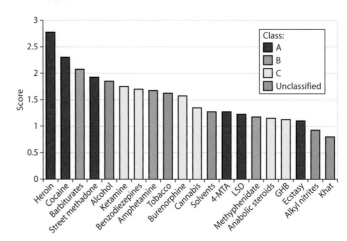

Figure 1 Classification of drugs.

a How does the government classification compare with the harm rating by independent experts?

Is there evidence for a link between cannabis smoking and mental illness?

Patients with mental illness may lose contact with reality or suffer from delusions. Here are some results of research into cannabis and mental illness.

New Zealand scientists followed 1000 people born in 1977 for the next 25 years. They interviewed people about their use of cannabis at the ages of 18, 21 and 25. The questions were about their mental health. The researchers took into account factors such as family history, current mental disorders, and illegal substance abuse.

The scientists' findings were:

- mental illness was more common among cannabis users
- people with mental illness did not have a greater wish to smoke cannabis
- cannabis probably increased the chances of developing mental illness by causing chemical changes to the brain
- there was an increase in the rate of mental illness symptoms after the start of regular use of cannabis.

Examiner feedback

In examination questions you may be given data and asked to draw conclusions from this data. Always read the data carefully and do not make assumptions on what you may believe to be the answer from your knowledge.

Scientists studied 45 000 Swedish male conscripts (men called up for army service). This was 97% of the male population aged 18–20 at that time. They followed these men for the next 15 years. They found the men who smoked cannabis heavily at the age of 18 were six times more likely to develop schizophrenia in later life than those who did not smoke cannabis.

Table 1 Drugs studies.

The Amsterdam Study	The Home Office Study	The view of Drugscope
Four surveys, covering nearly 17 000 people, were carried out in Amsterdam in the 1990s. Amsterdam then had 5000 hard drug users in its population of 700 000 and a much larger proportion of cannabis users. There were 300 'coffee shops' in the city where cannabis was freely available. The surveys showed that cannabis users typically start using the drug between the ages of 18 and 20. Cocaine use usually starts between 20 and 25. However, the study concludes that cannabis is not a stepping stone to using cocaine or heroin. The study also claims that most of the evidence that cannabis is a gateway to the use of hard drugs is circumstantial. It found that there was little difference in the probability of an individual taking up cocaine regardless of whether or not they had used cannabis.	This study used information from the 1998/99 Youth Lifestyles Survey (YLS), which contains information taken from over 3900 interviews with young people on their own experiences of drug use. The study found that the age for use of soft drugs is less than the age for use of most hard drugs. However, there was no significant link between soft drug use and the risk of later involvement with crack and heroin. There was a significant but small link between soft drug use and the use of social drugs ecstasy and cocaine.	A spokesman for the UK charity Drugscope backed the study's findings. He told BBC News Online: 'Sixty per cent of young people aged 20–24 have used cannabis, but only 1% of that age group have used harder drugs.' He said people who used harder drugs were less likely to have 'risk-averse' lifestyles and more likely to have misused other substances, including cannabis, tobacco and alcohol.

Questions

Regarding the Swedish study:

1   What type of scientific research was this?

2   How can the reliability of surveys be improved?

3   What were the control variables in the investigation?

4   What did the investigation show about the link between cannabis and psychosis?

Regarding the Amsterdam Study, the Home Office Study and the view of Drugscope:

5   Do you think that the data from these studies are reliable? Explain the reasons for your answers.

6   Give two conclusions common to all three studies.

7   Give one possible reason for progression from soft drugs to hard drugs.

8   Consider all the evidence on these two pages. Does using soft drugs lead to taking hard drugs? Explain the reasons for your answer.

Science in action

People may not judge evidence on its scientific strength, but on other criteria. For example, a famous scientist may be taken more seriously than an unknown one, and politicians may disregard scientific advice that they know will be unpopular with voters. We are more likely to accept evidence that agrees with our own views than evidence that contradicts them. Did you dismiss any evidence on this page that disagrees with your opinions?

Steroids and athletics

Learning objectives

- describe how steroids can be used as performance-enhancing drugs in athletics
- evaluate the use of drugs to enhance performance in sport and consider the ethical implications of their use
- describe the effects of using steroids on health.

Science skills

Table 1 shows the percentage of American high-school students who admitted to using steroids to build up muscle in the last year.

Table 1

	Percentage of males	Percentage of females
Social class		
Low	2.2	0.8
Low-middle	1.5	2.3
Middle	2.5	1.2
High-middle	0.6	2.3
High	1.6	0.1
Race		
Native American	9.7	0.0
Other Asian	1.4	0.0
Hispanic	0.0	2.6
Black	0.6	3.7
White	1.3	0.2

a Describe the patterns present in the data for steroid use.

Using steroids to cheat in athletics

Marion Jones winning gold in the 2000 Olympics…

At the 2000 Olympics, sprinter Marion Jones became the first female athlete to claim five medals in a single Games, three of them gold. Eight years later, Jones was headline news again. She was sentenced to serve six months in prison for lying to investigators after admitting her performances in Sydney had been enhanced by **steroids**.

'I have no-one to blame but myself for what I've done,' she said after her admission. 'Making the wrong choices and bad decisions has been disastrous.'

What are steroids?

In ancient times it was known that **testes** were required for the development of male sexual characteristics. In 1849 a scientist called Berthold removed the testes from cockerels, which then lost their sexual function. Then he removed the testes and transplanted them into the birds' abdomens. This time the sexual function of the birds was unaffected. Berthold showed that 'male hormones' passed from the testes into the blood.

In the 1930s, the male hormone was identified as **testosterone**. Scientists were then able to synthesise testosterone and other hormones that acted in the same way. These hormones are called steroids.

In 1954, the Soviet Union dominated the World Weightlifting Championships. They also easily broke several world records. It was soon discovered that the weightlifters had used steroids during their preparation. The use of steroids in athletics had begun. By the 1970s most athletics authorities had banned the use of steroids.

In 1996 scientists investigated the effect of high doses of testosterone on the performance of weightlifters. Forty experienced male weightlifters were randomly assigned to one of four groups: two groups were given a placebo, one group with and one without exercise, and two groups were given testosterone, one group asked to exercise, the other not. The investigation lasted six weeks. The scientists tried to match each group for diet, training and weightlifting experience.

The scientists then measured the strength of each weightlifter and his fat-free body mass, which is the total body mass minus the estimated mass of fat in his body. They found that:

- body mass increased only in the two testosterone-treated groups
- fat-free body mass increased only in the exercise groups
- the greatest change in fat-free mass was in the testosterone plus exercise group
- percentage body fat did not change in any group
- muscle size increased more in the testosterone groups than in either placebo group
- strength increased in both testosterone groups, as well as in the exercise group receiving placebo
- strength increase was greater in the exercise group with testosterone than in the exercise group with placebo.

Other scientific studies have shown that there is a significant **placebo effect** in studies with weightlifters. In most of these studies, strength increased considerably in subjects who received placebo, but who were told they were receiving steroids.

Weightlifters need to develop large muscles.

Is it harmful to take steroids?
The poster shows some of the known side effects of steroids.

Questions

1 What is the effect on a male of removing the testes?
2 What conclusions can be drawn from the results of the 1996 study on testosterone about the effectiveness of using steroids in training?
3 What is the natural function of testosterone?
4 Give two ways in which using steroids enhances athletic performance.
5 Give two ways in which using steroids may affect health in women.
6 Explain what is meant by the 'placebo effect'.
7 Suggest a reason for the ban on the use of steroids.
8 Imagine you are an athletics coach. One of your athletes says that she knows that several of her competitors are taking steroids. She does not want them to out-perform her. What advice would you give her?

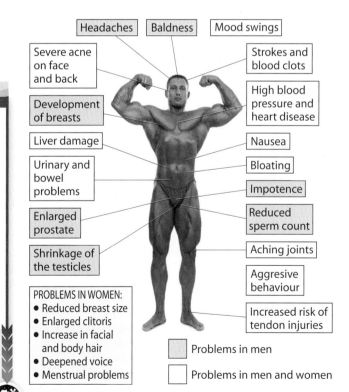

Headaches Baldness Mood swings

Severe acne on face and back

Strokes and blood clots

Development of breasts

High blood pressure and heart disease

Liver damage

Nausea

Urinary and bowel problems

Bloating

Impotence

Enlarged prostate

Reduced sperm count

Shrinkage of the testicles

Aching joints

Aggressive behaviour

Increased risk of tendon injuries

PROBLEMS IN WOMEN:
- Reduced breast size
- Enlarged clitoris
- Increase in facial and body hair
- Deepened voice
- Menstrual problems

Problems in men

Problems in men and women

Figure 1 The possible side effects of using steroids.

ISA practice: testing hand-washes

Scientists are investigating the best hand-wash to use in a hospital. Your task is to do an investigation to compare the effect of antiseptic-based hand-washes and soap-based hand-washes on the growth of bacterial colonies.

Hypothesis

There is a link between the type of antibacterial substance used and the growth of bacteria.

Section 1

1 In this investigation you will need to control some of the variables.

(a) Name one variable you will need to control in this investigation. *(1 mark)*

(b) Describe briefly how you would carry out a preliminary investigation to find a suitable value to use for this variable. Explain how the results will help you decide on the best value for this variable. *(2 marks)*

2 Describe how you are going to do your investigation. You should include:
- the equipment that you would use
- how you would use the equipment
- the measurements that you would make
- a risk assessment
- how you would make it a fair test.

You may include a labelled diagram to help you to explain your method.

In this question you will be assessed on using good English, organising information clearly and using specialist terms where appropriate. *(9 marks)*

3 Design a table that will contain all the data that you are going to record during your investigation. *(2 marks)*
Total for Section 1: 14 marks

Section 2

A group of students, Study Group 1, investigated how effective two different hand-washes were in killing bacteria. They decided to place a drop of each hand-wash onto an agar plate and measured the radius of the clear zone that appeared. They repeated their results three times. Figure 1 shows the results they obtained.

Soap-based hand-wash	Antiseptic-based hand-wash
Radius of the clear zone in cm	Radius of the clear zone in cm
Plate 1	Plate 1
disc 1 0.8, disc 2 0.4, disc 3 0.6	disc 1 1.6, disc 2 1.6, disc 3 1.2
Plate 2	Plate 2
disc 1 0.8, disc 2 0.8, disc 3 0.8	disc 1 1.4, disc 2 1.8, disc 3 1.8
Plate 3	Plate 3
disc 1 0.6, disc 2 0.6, disc 3 0.8	disc 1 1.2, disc 2 1.4, disc 3 1.4

Figure 1 Results from Study Group 1's investigation.

4 (a) (i) What is the independent variable in this investigation?

(ii) What is the dependent variable in this investigation?

(iii) Name one control variable this investigation. *(3 marks)*

(b) Plot a graph to show the link between the type of hand-wash used and the radius of the clear zone. *(4 marks)*

(c) Do the results support the hypothesis? Explain your answer. *(3 marks)*

Below are the results of two other study groups.

Table 1 shows the results of another two students, Study Group 2.

Table 1 Results from Study Group 2.

	Mean radius of clear zone/cm		
	Plate 1	Plate 2	Plate 3
Soap-based hand-wash	0.4	0.6	0.5
Antiseptic-based hand-wash	1.5	1.7	1.2

Study Group 3 is a group of scientists who also investigated the effectiveness of a range of different hand-washes. The scientists investigated how well the 14 different hand-hygiene methods A–N, shown in Table 2, worked.

For their investigation the scientists recruited 70 volunteers. The volunteers were asked to wash their hands only with non-antimicrobial hand soap for seven days before the investigation. Five volunteers used each of the methods A–N during the investigation.

Each volunteer:
- washed hands with non-antimicrobial soap
- spread a standard suspension of a red-coloured bacterium over the hands for 45 seconds
- air-dried the hands for 60 seconds.
- used one of the hand hygiene methods, A–N, for 10 seconds
- rinsed the hands for 10 seconds.

Table 2 Hand hygiene methods used by Study Group 3.

Method	Active ingredient	5p3.568	Method of application
A	60% ethyl alcohol	gel	waterless hand rub
B	61% ethyl alcohol	lotion	waterless hand rub
C	61% ethyl alcohol and 1% CHG	lotion	waterless hand rub
D	62% ethyl alcohol	foam	waterless hand rub
E	70% ethyl alcohol and 0.005% silver iodide	gel	waterless hand rub
F	0.5% parachlorometaxylenol and 40% SD alcohol	wipe 256 cm²	waterless hand wipe
G	0.4% benzalkonium chloride	wipe, 296 cm²	waterless hand wipe
H	0.75% CHG	liquid	hand wash
I	2% CHG	liquid	hand wash
J	4% CHG	liquid	hand wash
K	1% triclosan	liquid	hand wash
L	0.2% benzethonium chloride	liquid	hand wash
M	non-antimicrobial soap	liquid	hand wash
N	tap water	liquid	hand wash

The scientists from Study Group 3 carried out a second investigation using similar techniques, but this time using a virus instead of a bacterium.

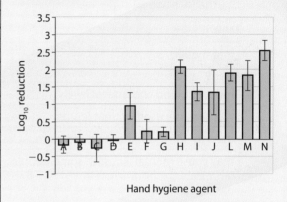

Figure 3 Results from Study Group 3's second investigation.

Each volunteer's hands were then sampled for the red-coloured bacterium by:

- placing each hand into a large latex glove containing 75 cm³ of a sterile sampling solution
- having the glove massaged for 30 seconds.

5 cm³ of the sampling solution was then spread over a nutrient agar plate. The agar plates were incubated at 25 °C for 24 hours, after which the number of colonies of the red-coloured bacterium was counted. Each colony had developed from a single bacterium.

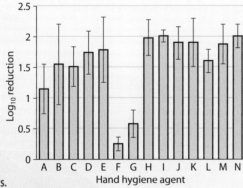

Figure 2 Some of the scientists' results.

A log reduction of 1 means that there are 10 times fewer bacteria in the sample.

A log reduction of 2 means that there are 100 times fewer bacteria in the sample.

A log reduction of 3 means that there are 1000 times fewer bacteria in the sample.

The line associated with each bar on the chart shows the range of results for each hand hygiene method.

5 Describe one way in which Study Group 2's results are similar to or different from the results from Study Group 1, and give one reason why the results are similar or different. *(3 marks)*

6 **(a)** Summarise briefly the results from Study Group 3. *(3 marks)*

(b) Does the data from the study groups support the hypothesis being investigated? To gain full marks you should use all of the relevant data from Study Groups 1, 2 and 3 to explain whether or not the data supports the hypothesis. *(3 marks)*

(c) The data from the other groups only gives a limited amount of information. What other information or data would you need in order to be more certain as to whether or not the hypothesis is correct? Explain the reason for your answer. *(3 marks)*

(d) Use the results from Study Groups 1, 2 and 3 to answer this question. What is the relationship between the type of hand-wash and the effect on bacteria? How well does the data support your answer? *(3 marks)*

7 Look back at Study Group 1's method. If you could repeat the investigation, suggest one change that you would make to the method, and give a reason for the change. *(3 marks)*

8 Suggest how ideas from your investigation and the scientists' investigations could be used to advise hospitals about the type of hand-washes to use. *(3 marks)*

Total for Section 2: 31 marks
Total for the ISA: 45 marks

Assess yourself questions

1 Match drugs A, B and C with the correct statements in Table 1.

A cannabis

B steroid

C thalidomide

Table 1

Information	Drug A, B or C
reduces blood cholesterol levels	
was recently used to treat leprosy	
used by some athletes to build up muscles	
may cause mental illness in some people	

(3 marks)

2 The drug thalidomide was once banned.

Now the drug is being tested to see whether it can be used to treat the disease AIDS.

Match words A, B, C and D, with the numbers 1–4 in the sentences.

A the government

B pregnant women

C research scientists

D volunteers

The trials will be carried out by ... 1 ....

In the trials, the drug will be given to ... 2 ....

The drug should not be given to ... 3 ....

The final decision on whether the drug is licensed for use by AIDS patients will be taken by ... 4 .... *(4 marks)*

3 Caffeine is a drug present in many drinks.

(a) Explain what is meant by 'drug'. *(1 mark)*

Scientists asked 2500 pregnant women to record how much tea, coffee and other foods that contain caffeine they consumed each day. The scientists then compared the results of the survey with the birth mass of the women's babies.

They found that women who consumed more than 200 mg of caffeine per day were more likely to give birth to smaller babies

Following the research, the Food Standards Agency lowered the recommended caffeine intake for pregnant women from 300 mg a day to 200 mg.

(b) Are the results of this survey likely to be reliable? Explain the reason for your answer. *(1 mark)*

(c) Figure 1 shows the amount of caffeine in different drinks

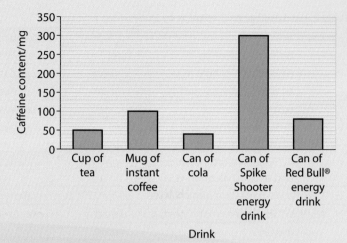

Figure 1 Caffeine concentration.

(i) What is the maximum number of cups of tea a pregnant woman could drink in one day and still be within the new recommended limit? *(2 marks)*

(ii) Caffeine increases heart rate and is linked to high blood pressure. Using the data in the chart, what type of drink would you recommend for a person whilst at work in an office? Explain the reason for your answer. *(2 marks)*

4 Many people become addicted to drugs.

(a) Explain how a person becomes addicted to drugs. *(2 marks)*

Figure 2 shows changes in the number of drug-related deaths in the UK between 1993 and 2007.

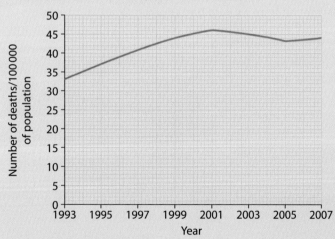

Figure 2 Drug-related deaths.

(b) (i) Describe the pattern shown by the data. *(2 marks)*

(ii) Suggest explanations for the changes in the number of deaths. *(2 marks)*

(c) A city has 2 million inhabitants. How many drug-related deaths would be expected in that city in 2007? *(2 marks)*

5 New drugs have to be extensively tested and trialled before they can be given to patients.

List A gives three stages in drug testing.

List B gives information about each stage.

Draw one line from each stage in List A to information about the stage in List B.

List A	List B
Stage	Information
trials that include a placebo	testing to see if the drug is toxic
trials on small group of volunteers	testing to detect side effects
laboratory trials	trials to determine selling price
	tests in which neither the patient nor doctor knows who has been given the drug

(3 marks)

6 New drugs must be tested before use. A form of ultrasound is being used by scientists to test the effectiveness of drugs designed to break down potentially life-threatening blood clots. Scientists from King's College of Medicine in London claim the technique provides a more reliable measure of the effectiveness of drugs than was previously available, and could remove the need to test new drugs on animals.

They have used the technique to test the effectiveness of a new drug – GSNQ – which dissolves blood clots. This reduces the risk of strokes. GSNQ was compared with the standard treatment of aspirin and heparin in a group of 24 patients who underwent surgery to clean a major blood vessel in the neck. Patients treated with GSNQ were found to have significantly lower numbers of clots during a three-hour period after the operation.

A member of the research team said: 'Before this technique assessing a drug meant either doing animal tests, or taking blood from people and studying it under the microscope. Neither was a very good measure of what would actually happen when the drug was used in people.'

New drugs will still have to be thoroughly assessed in large-scale clinical trials, but the new technique will help scientists to decide which products should go to a full trial.

(a) How did the scientists measure the effectiveness of GSNQ? *(1 mark)*

(b) Give three advantages of the above method of testing GSNQ over traditional drug-testing methods. *(3 marks)*

(c) Explain why GSNQ will still need to be assessed in large-scale clinical trials before it is approved. *(2 marks)*

7 Table 2 Comparing the effects of a number of drugs (3 = highest effect).

Drug	Mean dependence	Mean physical harm	Pleasure	Social harm	Healthcare costs
heroin	3.00	2.78	3.0	3.0	3.0
cocaine	2.39	2.33	3.0	2.5	2.3
barbiturates	2.01	2.23	2.0	1.9	1.7
street methadone	2.08	1.86	1.8	1.9	2.0
LSD	1.51	0.99	1.9	1.3	1.5
ecstasy	1.23	1.13	2.2	1.3	1.1
cannabis	1.13	1.05	1.5	1.0	1.1
anabolic steroids	0.88	1.45	1.1	0.8	1.3

Describe the conclusions that can be drawn from this data. *(5 marks)*

8 Scientists tested the drug thalidomide for effectiveness as a sleeping pill.

They gave tablets to two groups, each of ten volunteers, X and Y.

The tablets given to group X contained thalidomide but the tablets given to group Y did not. Neither group knew which type of tablet they were taking.

The scientists observed the time taken for each person to fall asleep before and after taking the tablets.

The test was repeated a further two times and the mean time taken to fall asleep calculated.

Table 3 The results of the test.

Group	Mean time taken to fall asleep/minutes										
	Person	1	2	3	4	5	6	7	8	9	10
X	Before taking the tablets	47	39	52	37	40	32	30	28	46	48
	After taking the tablets	27	32	19	17	24	36	14	22	29	31
	Person	1	2	3	4	5	6	7	8	9	10
Y	Before taking the tablets	36	48	52	36	44	34	34	26	44	46
	After taking the tablets	36	49	48	33	45	35	28	24	40	41

(a) Give three ways in which the scientists tried to get reliable results. *(3 marks)*

(b) Summarise the results for
  (i) Group X *(2 marks)*
  (ii) Group Y *(2 marks)*

(c) Suggest an explanation for the results of person 10 taking tablet Y. *(1 mark)*

Here are three students' answers to the following question:

Read the information about chickenpox.

Chickenpox is a common, highly infectious disease caused by a virus. Sufferers usually experience a blistering rash accompanied by mild fever, loss of appetite, headache and sore throat. Cases of the disease are not recorded in the UK, but they are thought to number about 600 000 a year, and by the age of 12 some 90% of us will have had it. Children with chickenpox are barred from nursery or school.

Researchers found that in one year in the UK, 112 children had serious complications of chickenpox. Six of these children died. Of these, four had a chronic health problem, such as HIV or cerebral palsy. When compared with other illnesses of childhood, it is less serious than measles, but potentially more problematic than mumps. This is because after the initial infection the virus remains dormant in the central nervous system for the rest of an individual's life and can reappear later as a painful condition called shingles.

All children in the USA are vaccinated against chickenpox. Researchers there have found that vaccinating children has raised the rate of shingles among the elderly by 90%. This is because once a person has had chickenpox, every time they come into contact with an infected child their body's defence system builds up immunity against the disease. If children no longer harbour the disease, a rise in the number of shingles cases in the elderly follows.

A UK government committee is considering whether all children in the UK should be vaccinated against chickenpox.

Using the above information, evaluate the case for vaccinating all UK children against chickenpox.

In this question you will be assessed on using good English, organising information clearly and using specialist terms where appropriate. *(6 marks)*

'Read the three answers below, together with the examiner comments. Then check what you have learned and put it into practice in any further questions you answer.'

B Grade answer

Student 1

> Always use the correct term, in this case vaccination; 'jab' is a colloquialism and should be avoided.

> The answer should not start with a conclusion.

> No credit is gained for copying large amounts of text from the passage.

I think that all UK children should be given a chickenpox jab because there are over 600 000 cases per year. It is a very unpleasant disease in which children experience a blistering rash accompanied by mild fever, loss of appetite, headache and sore throat. Also 112 children got serious complications and six children died. It can also cause shingles in the elderly.

Examiner comment

This candidate stated three reasons for vaccination against chickenpox, but has given no reasons against vaccination so would be limited to two of the five marks. In questions of this type, two marks are allotted for 'pros', two marks for 'cons' and one mark for a conclusion. The conclusion mark is not awarded if the candidate has not given both 'pros' and 'cons'.

Grade answer

Student 2

It is much better to keep 'pros' and 'cons' separate rather than mixing together in one sentence.

It is not fully clear whether this is a 'pro' or a 'con'.

Vaccination would reduce the number of cases of chickenpox, but chickenpox is not a very serious complaint so it might be a waste of money. Also, parents have to take time off work to look after children with the disease. If childhood vaccination is introduced, more elderly people may get shingles. Overall I think that the case against vaccination outweighs the case for vaccination.

No marks are given for a conclusion that does not give a reason and that does not refer to both pros and cons.

Examiner comment

Although the answer has pros and cons jumbled together the candidate did give two reasons in favour of vaccination: the reduction in the number of cases and the fact that parents usually have to take time off work to look after children. The candidate also gave two reasons against vaccination: the fact that it is not usually a serious complaint and that it might increase cases of shingles in the elderly. The candidate should have continued the last sentence with the word 'because' followed by a reason to get the conclusion mark.

 Grade answer

Student 3

The candidate makes it quite clear that they are talking about 'pros'.

The candidate now makes it quite clear that they are moving onto 'cons'.

The case for vaccination is mainly the fact that 150 children a year get serious complications from the disease and that the virus can stay dormant in the body and reappear as shingles in later life. Vaccination would prevent both of these.

The case against vaccination is that the disease is very mild in the majority of cases, so vaccination might not be cost-effective. There is also the likelihood that vaccinating all children will result in an increase in the number of cases of shingles in the elderly.

Overall I think that vaccination should not be given to all children because the increase in the number of cases of shingles in the elderly is far more serious than the mild symptoms experienced by the majority of children who get chickenpox.

The candidate now starts a third paragraph for the conclusion and uses the word 'because' to explain the reason for their decision.

Examiner comment

A well laid out answer that directs the examiner to at least two 'pros', at least two 'cons' and a reasoned conclusion. The candidate has avoided copying out large tracts from the passage. The conclusion refers to both a 'pro' and a 'con' then goes on to differentiate between the effect of the two.

- When answering evaluation questions, first read the passage and mark up 'pros' and cons' as you go through.
- Start your answer with a paragraph containing at least two pros.
- Write a second paragraph including at least two 'cons'.
- Write a conclusion that includes the word 'because' so that you give a reason for your conclusion.
- Refer to at least one 'pro' and at least one 'con' in your conclusion.

Environment and evolution

The world is filled with a breathtaking array of plants, animals and microorganisms, many of which have distinct and obvious adaptations to the physical conditions in which they live and to the organisms that surround them. This section begins with opportunities to explore some of those adaptations and to see how changes, such as those of climate and of pollution, affect organisms and their distribution. It continues with an exploration of the role of microorganisms in the natural cycles of decay and the carbon cycle.

The next chapter introduces the concepts of variation and genes, to provide an understanding from which to explore the developments of genetic engineering and cloning. These techniques offer many opportunities for the future, but have the potential to cause problems as well as raise ethical issues that need to be discussed before decisions can be made.

The final chapter brings together the elements of adaptation and genetic variation in the topics of evolution and natural selection. A discussion of how Darwin's theory of evolution developed provides a framework within which to explore the development of scientific theory in general, and the role of the scientific community in that.

Test yourself

1   What causes variation in living organisms?
2   How do organisms inherit characteristics from their parents?
3   How are organisms affected by the environment and by each other?
4   How is human activity affecting the environment?
5   How do we develop scientific ideas from experiment and investigation?

Objectives

By the end of this unit you should be able to:

- describe a range of adaptations in plants, animals and microorganisms to the environment in which they live
- interpret evidence of changes in the distribution of organisms in terms of changes in their environment
- explain the critical role of microorganisms in nutrient recycling and the carbon cycle
- describe the roles of environment and genes in creating variation
- describe the development of new techniques in cloning and genetic engineering and explain why they are being developed
- make informed judgements about economic, social and ethical issues about cloning and genetic engineering
- explain how natural selection can lead to the evolution of new species
- using evolutionary theory as an example, explain how scientific ideas develop into theories.

Plant adaptations

Learning objectives

- describe some features (adaptations) of plants that help them grow well in different conditions
- describe specific adaptations that help plants survive in dry environments
- explain how different adaptations to the environment help plants to survive.

The leaves and branches of coniferous trees allow snow to slide off quickly without damage.

Science skills

a How would you investigate the effect of different amounts of shade, or different levels of nutrients, on the growth of plants?

Examiner feedback

The conservation of water by plants living in dry conditions and the efficient uptake of water when water is available, through adaptations in the root systems, are ideas that are often questioned in exams.

Adapting to the environment

All organisms need food, water and **nutrients** to grow. They get these from the environment where they live. Different environments have different **physical conditions**, such as temperature, and amounts of light, water and nutrients. To grow well and produce offspring, an organism needs particular features that help it get what it needs from its environment. We call these features **adaptations**.

Growing in the cold

Where it is very cold, such as in the Arctic tundra, few plants can grow because ice forming inside cells can damage them. These plants often have a rounded shape that helps to **insulate** the inner parts and keep them warmer.

In coniferous forests of the northern hemisphere, the temperature is a little warmer, but heavy snow is a danger as it can break branches if it piles up.

Growing in rainforests

In a tropical rainforest, the temperature may be good for growth but rainfall can be so heavy that it damages leaves. Many leaves have shiny surfaces and pointed tips to the leaves to help the rain run off quickly, or are divided into many sections so water can pass through easily. At the top of the trees, there is plenty of light for **photosynthesis**, but the forest is usually so dense that plants growing near the forest floor get little light.

Many plants can grow in a tropical rainforest where it is warm all year round but they need adaptations for other conditions.

The red backs of the leaves help ground-level plants capture more light for photosynthesis.

Growing in the dry

Plants, like cacti, that grow in places where it is dry have very wide root systems to collect as much water as possible when it rains, or very deep root systems that can tap into water far underground. They may also have thick leaves or a thick body that contains tissue for storing water that the plant can use when there is a **drought**.

Tiny holes, called **stomata**, in the surfaces of leaves let in carbon dioxide for photosynthesis, but these holes also let water out. Plants in dry areas must reduce water loss through stomata, so they may have no leaves at all. A few stomata in the stem surface are protected by hairs or by being placed deep in ridges. This reduces the speed of air moving across the stomata and so reduces the rate of evaporation. The plant can continue to photosynthesise because the stems are green.

The effect of soil

The amount of nutrients in the soil will affect plants. Where the soil contains many nutrients, many different kinds of plants may be able to grow. However, few plants grow well on poor acid soil because it contains so few nutrients. For example, sundew plants get extra nutrients by trapping insects on their leaves and digesting them.

The hairy surface of the cactus reduces the speed of air flow across the stomata and so reduces the rate of evaporation of water from the plant.

The sundew plant lives in waterlogged and nutrient-poor soil.

Questions

1. Describe one adaptation of a plant to extreme cold, and explain how this helps the plant to survive.

2. Describe three adaptations of rainforest plants to their environment and explain how they help plants to survive.

3. A rainforest leaf that is split into sections can be bigger than one that isn't split. Explain why this is an advantage.

4. List as many ways as possible that plants which live in dry conditions can make sure they have enough water during long droughts, and explain the importance of each way.

5. In a tropical rainforest the tallest trees are over 60 m, below which are 'layers' of smaller trees and shrubs. Suggest the different adaptations you would expect to see in the tallest trees and the shrubs.

6. Marram grass grows on sand dunes on sea shores and has very deep roots. The leaves are curled, with the stomata tucked inside. Explain as fully as you can how these adaptations help the marram grass to survive.

7. Sundew plants grow slowly. Explain in detail why sundew plants are only found on poor acid soils.

8. The leaves of coniferous trees are thin, waxy needles that remain on the tree all year round. The stomata are hidden in pits in the needle surface. Explain in as much detail as you can why these and other adaptations of conifer trees help them dominate northern landscapes.

Animal adaptations

Science in action

Studying the hollow hairs of caribou, which live in the frozen north of Canada, showed that the air inside the hairs acts as good insulation from the cold. This led to the development of hollow polyester fibres for use in duvets and insulated clothing to keep us warm.

Desert hopping mice can usually only be found on the surface at dawn and dusk.

Examiner feedback

You will not be asked about Bergmann or Allen in an exam. However, you should be able to explain how the surface area to volume ratio of an animal has a direct effect on where it can live and why. Remember that a large animal has a large surface area, but a small surface area to volume ratio.

Staying warm

Where environmental conditions, such as temperature and water availability, are extreme, animals also need particular adaptations to survive and grow well.

Where it is very cold, animals need to reduce heat loss. Land mammals, such as polar bears and caribou, have very thick fur that insulates them from the air so that body heat is lost more slowly to

Before winter, the polar bear grows a thicker coat and eats lots of food. When there is no food, it can reduce its rate of energy use to conserve fat reserves.

the cold environment. Extra fat, in a layer under their skin, increases the insulation and can give the animal energy when food is scarce. During the summer, these animals **moult**, or shed the outer thick layer of fur so that it is easier to lose body heat. Sea mammals, such as seals, need a very thick layer of fat to insulate against heat loss to the water.

Keeping cool and avoiding thirst

In deserts, there is very little water for much of the time. It can also be very hot during the day and very cold at night.

Small desert animals, such as the hopping mice of Australia, live mostly in burrows where the temperature is more constant and not as extreme as above ground. They also do not need to drink water, as they get all the water they need from their food. Their kidneys **excrete** urine that contains very little water. Large desert animals, such as camels, can tolerate higher levels of dehydration than non-desert species.

Science skills

Table 1 The surface area and volume of different sizes of cubes.

Length of one side/cm	Surface area of cube/cm²	Volume/cm³
1	6	1
2	24	8
3	54	27
4	96	64

a Calculate the surface area to volume ratio for each cube.

b Heat is generated in an animal's body by the *volume* of tissue. Heat is lost by an animal from the *surface area* of its body. The larger the surface area to volume ratio, the faster the animal will lose body heat. Which size loses heat faster: the smallest or the largest?

Body size and shape rules

The 19th century biologist Carl Bergmann observed that birds and mammals of the same or similar species tend to be larger and heavier when they live in colder climates. 'Bergmann's rule' states that there is a correlation between body mass and average annual temperature. Bergmann's explanation for the correlation was that animals lose heat at the surface of their bodies so, if two animals are shaped identically, the temperature of the larger one will drop less rapidly.

Science skills How would you test the idea that penguins huddling in Antarctic winters is a behavioural adaptation to the cold?

Huddling penguins.

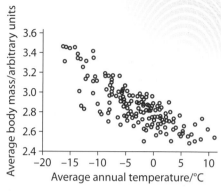

Average annual temperature/°C

Figure 1 Body mass of many different animals compared with temperature where they live.

Joel Allen gathered data relating climate to variation in animals. Allen's rule states that the extremities of organisms (limbs, tails and ears) of animals that need to maintain their temperature, such as mammals, are longer in warm climates than in cold climates because they act as heat-radiating organs.

The kit fox lives in the hot dry regions of Mexico.

Questions

1. Describe the adaptations of the polar bear to life in the Arctic, and explain how they help it survive.

2. **(a)** Explain how small animals can survive life in the desert. **(b)** Suggest what adaptations large desert animals need to survive, and how these adaptations enable them to survive.

3. Use the information about surface area and volume of cubes to predict what impact body size in animals will have in: **(a)** cold climates **(b)** hot climates.

4. Do the data shown in the graph in Figure 1 support Bergmann's rule? Explain your answer.

5. Do the kit fox and Arctic fox comply with Allen's rule? Explain your answer.

6. Use Bergman's rule to help explain why Emperor penguins huddle during polar winter storms.

7. During the Arctic winter, a mother polar bear stays in a den with her cubs. Explain fully why this is an adaptation to living in polar conditions.

8. Whale blubber is not just a layer of fat, but includes blood vessels that can be adjusted to allow more or less blood near to the skin. Explain in as much detail as you can why a whale needs such a complex system.

The Arctic fox lives in northern Canada.

Surviving the presence of others

Learning objectives

- describe some adaptations that plants and animals have to avoid being eaten
- describe some adaptations that help animals and plants to compete for resources
- suggest the factors for which organisms are competing in a habitat
- explain why animals compete for mates and territories.

Keeping others away

The environment of an organism includes not only the physical conditions but also other plants and animals. If an organism is to grow, mature and produce offspring, it must avoid being eaten by other organisms.

Many organisms have special adaptations to avoid being eaten. Many plants, for example, cacti, have physical deterrents such as thick spines to deter herbivores. Other plants, like ragwort, use chemical deterrents such as poisons that taste unpleasant or can kill.

Many animals also use poison to deter predators. They advertise their poison with bright colours. Other animals hide from predators using **camouflage**. The colours and patterns on their bodies make them much more difficult to see against their usual background.

The blue poison dart frog boldly sits in full view of potential predators.

Science skills

a European banded snails come in a wide variety of shell colours and patterns.
How would you test the idea that the variety is the result of camouflage against predation by birds?

Competing for resources

It is rare that there is so much of a resource that all organisms can get what they need. When resources are limited, organisms have to **compete** with each other. Those organisms that are most successful in getting the resource will grow better and produce more offspring.

Plants compete with each other for water, light and nutrients if they are growing close together. Some ground-living plants in woodland, such as bluebells, are adapted to grow, flower and set seed before the trees have fully grown their leaves and block out the Sun.

Animals of different species may compete with each other for the same food. For example, a leopard may kill an antelope to eat, but there will be many other animals, including lions and hyenas, that could take the antelope from the leopard. Leopards often take their kills up into a tree to keep them from other animals.

Animals of the same species may also compete with each other for resources other than food. In species where males mate with many females, competition to father the next generation can be intense.

Bluebells cannot compete with trees in leaf for the light they need.

Many birds have **territories** when they are breeding. They keep other birds out of it to give them enough space to rear their young. Robins need a territory that is large enough to provide all the food they need for their young. However, birds that feed away from the nest site, such as gannets or penguins, will have small nesting territories, just large enough to be out of pecking distance of other adults.

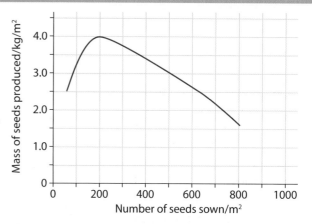

Figure 1 Graph of yield versus density at planting.

Questions

1. Using the graph in Figure 1, describe how the seed yield of a crop depends on the density of plants in the crop.

2. Suggest why polar bears are white.

3. The robin is well known for its red breast and for singing loudly in spring. **(a)** What are the disadvantages of these adaptations? **(b)** What are the advantages?

4. **(a)** Copy the table headings from below and complete your table to show all the resources that animals might compete for. **(b)** Give examples of animals for each resource. **(c)** Explain how each animal is adapted to compete for that resource.

Resource	Example	Adaptation

5. Explain why blue poison dart frogs are blue as well as poisonous.

6. **(a)** It takes a lot of energy for a male peacock to grow his tail feathers and display them. Why does he bother? **(b)** Suggest an advantage to the females (in terms of genes) who mate with the male giving the best display.

7. Annual poppies (plants that live only one year) often suddenly appear on land that has recently been cleared of plants, but not in the following year. Explain this observation as fully as you can in terms of competition.

8. Using examples from what you have learnt so far, describe conditions in which plants may compete for light, water and nutrients.

9. Another strategy for avoiding predation is to look like something dangerous: for example, hoverflies look like wasps, but have no sting. Evaluate the advantages and disadvantages to the hoverfly and wasp of this similarity.

Male peacocks display their huge tail feathers and call when there are females around. The male with the best display will mate with most females.

Extreme microorganisms

Examiner feedback

Be careful not to write that all extremophiles are microorganisms. A few animals are extremophiles, such as the Pompeii worm, which lives in extremely hot water close to deep sea vents (below), and tardigrades (microscopic animals often called water bears), which can survive temperatures as high as 151°C and as low as −270°C.

All the organisms living around this hydrothermal vent deep in the ocean depend on chemosynthetic bacteria.

Extreme temperatures

Organisms that can survive in the most extreme conditions are called **extremophiles**, and they are mostly microorganisms. In such conditions, there are few other organisms to compete with, but the adaptations needed to survive are extreme too.

The single-celled alga *Chlamydomonas nivalis* contains an extra-red pigment that protects it from the intensely bright light in snowy places that would destroy other cells. The colour also absorbs radiation, helping to keep the cells warmer than the snow around them. After the winter, when the cells have been buried by more snow, they grow **flagella** that help them move back up to the surface.

The temperature of the water here is over 60°C, but there are many kinds of bacteria living in the water and around the edges of the hot spring.

Extreme high temperatures can be found in a few places on Earth, such as around hot springs, or around **hydrothermal vents** deep in the ocean. The heat comes from the rocks below ground. Most organisms die above about 40°C because the proteins in their cells break down. Bacteria that survive at higher temperatures have proteins that don't break down as easily.

No light

Deep in the ocean, water pressure is great and there is no light. Amazingly, there are large communities of organisms that can live around hydrothermal vents on the ocean floor. They all depend on bacteria that use **chemosynthesis**, which combine chemicals from the water using heat to make sugars for food. These bacteria are the **producers** in these communities, like green plants on the Earth's surface.

Too many nutrients

Organisms need nutrients to make chemicals inside their cells. If the concentration of nutrients outside the cells gets too high, it draws water out of the cells. For most organisms this is fatal. Some microorganisms, however, have high levels of other chemicals, such as **amino acids** or sugars, inside their cells that stop the water moving out.

This lake is so salty that the man floats. This concentration of salt in his body would kill him, while the bacteria that make the water pink thrive in it.

Too little oxygen

Most large organisms depend on oxygen for **aerobic respiration**, but in a few places there is very little or no oxygen, such as deep below ground. Here there are microorganisms that are adapted to get their energy in other ways. Some use chemicals, such as sulfur, instead of oxygen to release energy in **anaerobic respiration**. Another example of anaerobic respiration is the **fermentation** of glucose by yeast.

Questions

1 List the advantages and disadvantages of being an extremophile.

2 List all the extreme conditions described on these pages, and describe adaptations that make survival possible in those conditions.

3 The ability of microorganisms to live in extreme conditions makes life possible for many other organisms. Explain what this statement means.

4 Two competing theories for the origin of life on Earth are that:

• bacteria from other planets came to Earth on meteorites

• bacteria first originated around hydrothermal vents because the surface of the Earth was too extreme.

(a) Explain why both these theories are possible. **(b)** What else would you need to know in order to evaluate which theory was the more likely?

5 Suggest why microorganisms are more able to live in extreme conditions than larger organisms.

6 A student had some onions. She filled two jars with onions and added pickling vinegar. After six months, the onions she hadn't pickled had gone mushy, but the onions in one jar were still crunchy. After two years she opened the second jar and the onions were mushy. Explain these observations.

7 There are an estimated 10 times more bacterial cells in your body than human cells. Most of these bacterial cells live in your gut and play an important role in digestion. Evaluate the advantages and disadvantages of using antibiotics for curing infections.

(A*)

Many kinds of bacteria live in conditions of low oxygen inside the cow's gut and help to digest the grass. Without them, the cow could not survive on a diet of grass.

The effect of changing environments

Science in action

Many environmental groups are carrying out long-term surveys of organisms to help identify the effects of climate change and to predict what will happen to species in the future. Examples include surveys of birds, butterflies and bees. Some groups ask for help from the public to make their surveys as extensive as possible.

Changing environments

Organisms have adaptations that help them survive well in particular conditions, so if those conditions change it may make it more difficult for them to live in that place, or it may make it easier for other organisms to come into the area and compete. Either way, this may cause a change in the **distribution** of species.

Practical

Using a maximum–minimum thermometer and rainfall gauge, keep a weather diary for a month, recording a range of environmental conditions such as temperature and rainfall. Describe how the weather changed during that month.

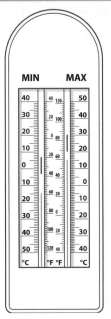

Figure 1 A maximum–minimum thermometer and rainfall gauge.

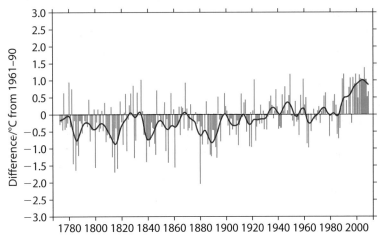

Figure 2 The temperature record for central England since 1772. The blue lines are yearly measurements shown as the difference from the average for 1961–90; the red line is a 20-year running mean of annual-average anomalies.

Environmental conditions are always changing. In the UK weather changes with the seasons. We also get different weather depending on which way the wind is blowing. Organisms that live in the UK can cope with this amount of change, so how much change is needed to affect them?

Short-term changes, such as freak storms that cause flooding, or occasional extreme temperatures, can kill organisms. However, the distribution of a whole species is more likely to be affected by long-term changes in climatic conditions.

Temperature records from thermometer measurements for England suggest that recently there has been an increase in average temperature. Similar changes are being seen in other parts of the world, and scientists think that this explains changes in the distribution of some species.

The effect on birds

In 1996 little egrets started breeding in southern England, expanding their breeding range from Europe. Other changes are happening too. Some birds, such as blackcaps and chiffchaffs, that used to migrate south for winter are now staying all year round as there is usually more insect food still available for them.

Chiffchaffs are mainly insect eaters. Insects either die or hibernate during cold winters.

Other species seem to be suffering a lack of food. In 2008 there were reports that breeding numbers of sea bird species, such as puffins and kittiwakes, that live in the North Sea decreased rapidly in the previous few years. The average temperature of the sea had increased by about 1 °C and scientists linked this to a loss of sand eels, which the birds feed on.

The effect on bees

Recently there has been a rapid decrease in the numbers of bees, both wild and those kept by bee keepers. Many reasons for this have been suggested, including climate change and loss of wildflowers due to increased building and farming. Cold, wet springs make it difficult for bees to get food when they need to start building new colonies. Also, warmer winters make it easier for a mite parasite to survive. This parasite has destroyed bees in many hives. However, loss of a range of food plants due to farming might also be a cause.

Sand eels are the main food source for puffins and their chicks in the summer.

Science in action

Bees are pollinators of many plants, including many of our crop plants. It is estimated that the UK earns about £200 million each year from crops pollinated by bees. Urgent research is needed to explain how quickly numbers are changing, and what the main causes are, if we are to stop an effect on our harvest **yields**.

Bees are essential for the **pollination** of many plants.

Questions

1 The data for the temperature graph in Figure 2 were manipulated in several ways before graphing. Suggest reasons for each of the following: **(a)** only recent data from sites similar to the historical sites were included, not the recent data collected from all over the UK **(b)** the red line is an average of several years, which smoothes out short-term variations.

2 Describe the trends of temperature shown in the graph in Figure 2.

3 **(a)** Suggest one advantage to the blackcap or chiffchaff of staying in the UK over winter. **(b)** Suggest one disadvantage.

4 **(a)** Explain why we cannot be sure that climate change is causing the decrease in numbers of bees. **(b)** Suggest what research should be carried out on bees to identify what is happening to them.

5 Swallows are insect-eating birds that return to the UK in early April to breed; suggest how changes in the climate may affect breeding populations of swallows.

6 Describe as fully as you can, with examples, the possible effects of climate change on species in the UK.

7 Bees fed a diet of five different pollens produced more glucose oxidase than bees fed with only one kind of pollen. Glucose oxidase preserves honey and food for bee larvae from microorganisms that cause disease. Explain as fully as you can how an increase in farming might lead to a decrease in bee numbers.

8 Design a web page highlighting the urgency for finding a solution to the decline in bee numbers. You should provide no more than 100 words and one illustration.

Pollution indicators

- describe some ways in which human activity is changing the distribution of organisms
- explain why lichens can be used to monitor air pollution
- explain how aquatic invertebrates can be used to monitor water pollution.

Pollution changes the environment

Pollution from human activity damages the environment and the organisms that live there. Many industrial processes burn fossil fuels for energy or to release other chemicals for manufacture. Some of the waste gases from this burning are poisonous, or are acidic; when they dissolve in water droplets in cloud, they can form **acid rain**. The acid is damaging to many plants and animals.

We also pollute water by releasing chemicals directly into it, for example when too much fertiliser is put on farmland or when chemicals are released from factories or sewage treatment plants into the water. There are laws against causing air and water pollution, but they can be difficult to monitor and enforce.

Science skills

The lower the pH, the more acidic a solution is.

a Describe the relationship between the number of species of plants and the acidity of the water in a pond.

b Give two explanations for the relationship between number of species of insect larvae and water acidity.

c How could you improve the reliability of your answers?

Table 1 Pond data.

Pond	pH of water	Number of species of insect larvae	Number of species of plants
1	4.4	4	8
2	4.8	5	11
3	5.7	9	16
4	6.6	19	23
5	8.1	14	21

The lichen on the left is a clean-air species. The lichen on the right tolerates some air pollution.

Practical

Carry out a lichen survey in your area, and use the species you find to decide where there is the most air pollution.

If there is a high level of pollution, organisms may be killed and the distribution of species will change. We can use the presence of organisms that are particularly affected by, or tolerant of, pollution as **pollution indicators**.

Lichens and air pollution

Lichens are often found on trees and walls. There are many different species; some can only grow where there is no air pollution while others are tolerant of different kinds of air pollution.

Surveys of lichens can show quickly and easily how polluted the air has become since the lichens started growing. Recent surveys indicate that sulfur-intolerant species are colonising city areas where they had died out, showing that sulfur dioxide pollution in these areas has decreased.

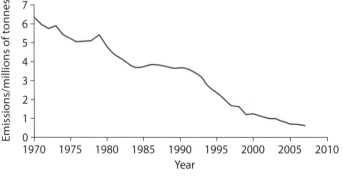

Figure 1 Sulfur dioxide emissions into air in the UK have reduced as we changed to low-sulfur fuels, and because of laws that control emissions from industry.

Aquatic invertebrates as pollution indicators

Most **aquatic** organisms get the oxygen they need for respiration directly from the water they live in, not from air. Fertilisers and sewage contain high levels of nitrogen and phosphate. If they drain into water, they can cause plants, algae and bacteria to grow rapidly and use up the oxygen during respiration.

As oxygen concentration drops, some organisms, such as mayfly nymphs, die because they can't get the oxygen they need. Other organisms can survive in water that has a very low oxygen concentration because they have special adaptations. The bloodworm is red because it contains haemoglobin, which combines with oxygen, as it does in our red blood cells. Different aquatic invertebrates can tolerate different oxygen concentrations, so we can use their presence or absence to indicate how polluted the water is.

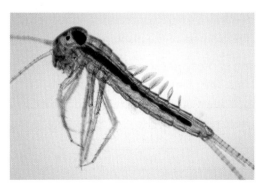 

The mayfly nymph (left) can only live in unpolluted water, but the bloodworm (right) can survive in highly polluted water.

Questions

1. Define the word *pollution* and give examples of air and water pollution.

2. Explain why adding nitrogen to water reduces the oxygen concentration of the water.

3. In the 1970s it was shown that forests in Scandinavia, far from any industrial areas, were being damaged by acid rain. Suggest how this could happen.

4. Explain how bloodworms are adapted to low oxygen concentration.

5. Use the graph in Figure 1 to suggest what you would expect to see from lichen surveys: **(a)** from the Scottish Highlands in 1970 and today **(b)** in the centre of Manchester in 1970 and today. Explain your answers.

6. Compare the use of lichen surveys with roadside air pollution monitoring, and suggest the advantages and disadvantages of each.

7. Explain in detail why it may be easy to identify the source of water pollution caused by a poisonous chemical but difficult to find the source for high levels of nitrate in water.

We can measure the concentration of dissolved oxygen in water using an oxygen meter.

Energy in biomass

About biomass and energy

The amount of 'stuff' that makes up your body is your **biomass**. Your biomass increases when food you eat is used to make more cells and tissues. If we measured the mass of all that food, we would have the biomass of your food.

We can also think in terms of energy. The energy in biomass is in the form of **chemical energy**, stored in the bonds and structures of the chemicals that make up cells.

Making plant biomass

The energy for making more plant biomass comes from the Sun. During photosynthesis, light energy is used to join water and carbon dioxide to make the carbohydrate glucose. Although leaves are adapted for capturing as much sunlight as possible, Figure 1 shows how only a small proportion of light energy is transferred into chemical energy in the biomass of the plant.

Some of the carbohydrates made during photosynthesis are converted into other chemicals, such as proteins and fats. The plant needs energy to build these, so other carbohydrates are broken down during **respiration** to release energy. However, some of the energy from respiration also escapes as heat to the environment.

From plant biomass to animal biomass

When an animal eats, some of the chemicals from its food are absorbed into its body, the rest are egested (expelled from the body) as **faeces**. Absorbed food chemicals may be built up into fats, carbohydrates and proteins and other chemicals that make the cells. These reactions need energy. Energy comes from breaking down carbohydrates during respiration. Respiration also supplies the energy for all the other living processes including movement. As with plants, some of this energy from respiration escapes to the environment as heat. The animal also makes waste products that still contain chemical energy, which it **excretes** into the environment in urine.

Biomass in food chains

Since energy is lost to the environment at each stage of a food chain, there is less biomass in each level of the chain. We can represent this in a **pyramid of biomass**, which shows the amount of biomass at each level of the food chain drawn to scale.

light energy from the Sun

about 30% of the light energy is absorbed by the leaf

most is reflected from the leaf

some light passes straight through

about 54% of absorbed energy is converted to heat and lost in convection and radiation

only about 2% of absorbed energy is converted to chemical energy in photosynthesis

about 44% of absorbed energy is lost in evaporation

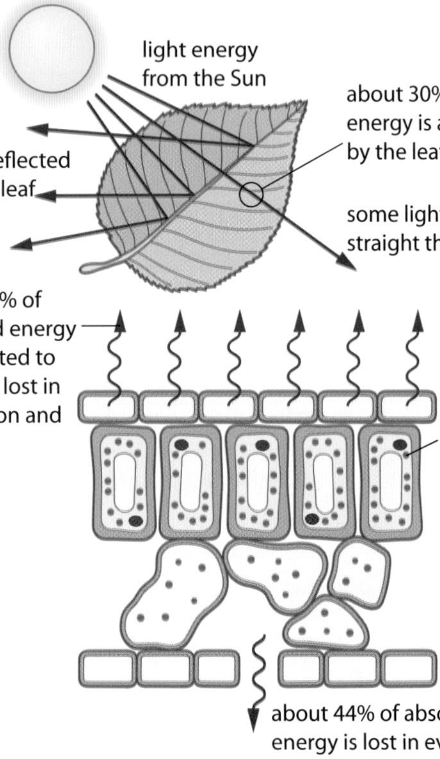

Figure 1 What happens to light energy falling on a leaf.

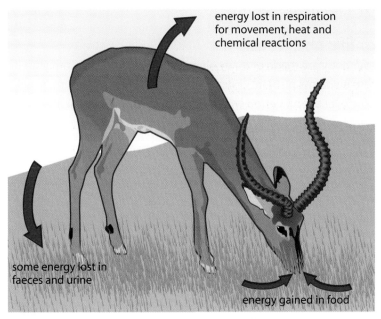

energy lost in respiration for movement, heat and chemical reactions

some energy lost in faeces and urine

energy gained in food

Figure 2 Energy losses from an animal.

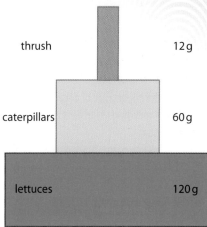

thrush — 12 g

caterpillars — 60 g

lettuces — 120 g

Figure 3 A pyramid of biomass for the food chain lettuce → caterpillar → thrush.

Questions

1. Describe the adaptations of leaves for collecting light energy.

2. **(a)** Identify all the forms of energy shown in the diagram of the leaf in Figure 1. **(b)** Starting with a block that represents all the light energy from the Sun that reaches a leaf, sketch a diagram that shows what happens to all of that energy.

3. Sketch the energy gains, losses and stores of a carnivore, such as a lion.

4. Draw a food chain that includes you and something that you ate today. Identify all the changes in forms of energy through that food chain.

5. On graph paper, draw a pyramid of biomass for the following food chain from the ocean: producers (phytoplankton) 50 g/m², primary consumers (krill) 20 g/m², secondary consumers (penguins, minke whales, crab-eating seals) 5 g/m², tertiary consumers (killer whales, leopard seals) <1 g/m².

6. **Table 1** The percentage of energy taken into an animal's body that is used for making new tissue.

Group	Percentage energy transfer into tissue
ectothermic ('cold-blooded') vertebrates, e.g. reptiles, amphibians	~10%
medium–large **homeothermic** ('warm-blooded') vertebrates, i.e. mammals and birds	1–2%
small homeothermic vertebrates, e.g. wren, shrew	~0.4%

Suggest explanations for the differences between the animal groups.

7. Explain fully how you would evaluate the reliability of data shown in your pyramid of biomass for Question 5.

8. Humans currently use over one-third of all useful plant material that grows on Earth every year. Explain fully the impact of an increasing human population on other life in terms of energy flow.

A*

Science skills

Gathering reliable data to make a pyramid of biomass is not easy.

- Biomass often has to be estimated – how would you measure the biomass of a whale?

- Usually a pyramid shows all the organisms at each **trophic level** of a **food web**, because animals rarely eat just one kind of food.

- It is usually impossible to measure all the organisms in a complete food web, so biomass is usually given in terms of an area, e.g. g/m².

- There is a time element too: think of the mass of food you have at home now, compared with the mass of food you will eat in a year, or your lifetime. How would the pyramid of biomass differ for each of these?

Each of these issues will affect the data that are collected.

Examiner feedback

Remember what you learned about the digestive system at Key Stage 3. It will help you understand this chapter, although you will not be examined on it at GCSE.

Natural recycling

Fungus causing decay of an orange. The white part is a mass of fungal threads, and the grey/green parts are fruiting bodies.

A matter of life and death

The tissues of your body are made of many elements, which you get from your food. We call these elements nutrients because we need them for growth. A lack in any one of these over a long period would affect your growth and health.

Table 1 Important nutrients in a human body.

Nutrients	Percentage of body weight	Role in body
nitrogen	3.2%	forms part of proteins, DNA in all cells
calcium	1.8%	strengthens bones and teeth, needed for nerve and muscle activity
phosphorus	1.0%	part of DNA, also strengthens bones and teeth
sodium	0.2%	needed for nerve and muscle activity
iron	0.007%	haemoglobin in red blood cells carries oxygen

During photosynthesis plants make **carbohydrates**, which contain only carbon, hydrogen and oxygen. To grow well, the plant must have other nutrients, such as nitrogen for proteins and **DNA**, magnesium to make chlorophyll, and calcium to build strong cell walls. Plants absorb these nutrients when they take in water surrounding their roots. This removes the nutrients from the environment and makes it possible for animals to get what they need in their food. However, until the nutrients are returned to the soil, they are no longer available to plants.

Returning the nutrients to the soil only becomes possible when the plants or animals die, or when animals produce waste materials such as faeces and urine. The **decay** of this dead and waste material releases the nutrients back to the environment.

What is decay?

Decay is the digestion, or **rotting**, of complex **organic** substances to simpler ones by microorganisms such as fungi and bacteria. Since microorganisms have no gut, digestion happens outside their cells and the simpler nutrients are absorbed. This gives the microorganisms the nutrients they need for growth. Some of the simpler nutrients are left in the soil which means plants are now able to absorb them through their roots.

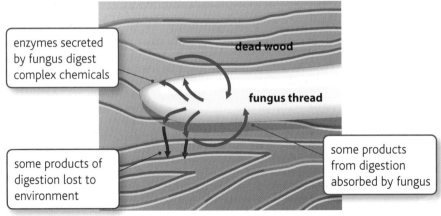

enzymes secreted by fungus digest complex chemicals

dead wood

fungus thread

some products of digestion lost to environment

some products from digestion absorbed by fungus

Figure 1 Decay organisms break down complex chemicals into smaller molecules that they can absorb.

The best conditions for decay

Decay microorganisms don't usually have a thick protective coating, so they easily dry out. They often grow below the surface of the material that they are decaying. However, many microorganisms are more active when there is plenty of oxygen for respiration, so they cannot live far beneath the surface. Like other organisms, the rate of the reactions in the cells of microorganisms is affected by temperature. When it is colder, they cannot grow as quickly, so decay is usually faster in warm, moist conditions.

Science skills

a Which conditions would you test to investigate the best conditions for the decay of plant material?

b How would you carry out your investigation?

c How would you control variables?

In 1991, the body of a man was found in the Italian Alps after the deep ice above it had melted. The remains were dated at 3300 BC and still had skin and some hair.

Essential recycling

Without decay, there would be no recycling of nutrients in the environment, and there would eventually be no life. In **stable** natural communities, where there is little change over time in the plants and animals that live there, there is a balance between the nutrients removed from the soil by plants and the return of nutrients to the soil by decay. The nutrients are constantly cycled.

In winter, dead leaves cover the ground, but by midsummer most of the leaves will have decayed.

Questions

1. Describe one similarity and one difference in the way that microorganisms and animals digest their food.

2. Explain why the only parts of a fungal mould that you can usually see are the fruiting bodies.

3. The leaves in the forest photograph fell in November. Explain why they are still there in February but not in June.

4. **(a)** Draw a diagram to show the cycling of nutrients through the environment and living organisms.
   (b) Use your diagram to explain the essential role of decay in nutrient cycling.

5. Put the following environments in order of decomposition rate of dead material, starting with the fastest, and justify your order: hot desert, Canadian coniferous forest, polar tundra, tropical rainforest.

6. Many gardeners put their garden waste on a compost heap to decay. Explain why the temperature inside the compost heap gradually increases over the first few weeks.

7. Explain fully why the 5000-year-old remains of the ice-man still had skin and hair.

8. Although rainforests are the most productive areas of plant growth on Earth, their soils are nutrient-poor. Explain as fully as you can the reasons for this apparent discrepancy.

Recycling issues

A load of rubbish

In 2009 a report on UK household waste estimated that we throw away about 8.3 million tonnes of food and drink each year. This is the equivalent of an average household throwing away £50 every month. Of the total, over 7.6 million tonnes goes in the waste-bin or down the drain.

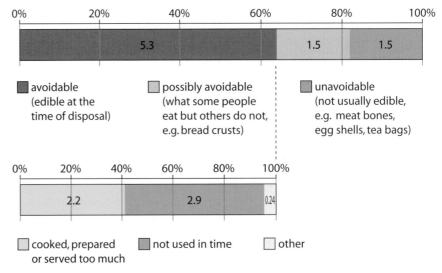

0%	20%	40%	60%	80%	100%
5.3				1.5	1.5

- avoidable (edible at the time of disposal)
- possibly avoidable (what some people eat but others do not, e.g. bread crusts)
- unavoidable (not usually edible, e.g. meat bones, egg shells, tea bags)

0%	20%	40%	60%	80%	100%
2.2		2.9			0.24

- cooked, prepared or served too much
- not used in time
- other

Figure 1 The amount of food and drink waste generated in the UK in 2009 (millions of tonnes per year).

The problem with organic waste

Food and drink wastes are organic, which means they originally come from plants and animals. These wastes decay as bacteria and fungi grow on them. Until recently much of the waste in the UK was disposed of in **landfill sites**. Once organic wastes are buried, the usual decay organisms cannot grow because there is not enough oxygen for aerobic respiration. Other decay microorganisms, called **methanogens**, can grow anaerobically. They release a gas called methane, which is not only highly flammable, but also more active in global warming than carbon dioxide.

In 1999, the European Landfill Directive set out plans to reduce the area used for landfill in all European countries for several reasons, including pollution. This has led to more waste recycling in the UK. Most councils now ask us to separate out garden waste, cans, glass and sometimes plastics for collection, but only a few collect food wastes separately. This is because meat waste is very attractive to pests like rats – the waste needs to be protected while it is waiting to be collected.

Landfill tips need to be vented in a controlled way for many years after tipping has ended, otherwise methane that forms as the refuse decays might explode or create fires that burn below the surface for weeks.

Collecting food waste separately means another separate bin for each house as well as special collection trucks.

A selection of choices

The traditional way of managing garden and vegetable kitchen waste is the **compost heap** in the garden. The waste is piled up and microbial decay breaks it down into compost that you can add to the garden soil. Many councils now collect this as 'green' waste and make compost on a large scale in a process called **windrow composting**. This needs a lot of space, and the composting material must be turned regularly to keep the oxygen level high, but it doesn't need any special equipment.

Other councils collect all garden and kitchen waste, including meat, together. By law, this needs composting in large containers until the meat waste is broken down, in a process called **in-vessel composting**. Composting is then completed using the windrow process. An advantage is that conditions can be monitored inside the containers, and maintained at the correct temperature and moisture levels for more rapid decay in the early stages. The higher temperatures also kill **pathogens** and the seeds of **weed** plants.

Another process uses **anaerobic digestion** by the methanogenic bacteria that cause problems on landfill sites. Food waste is put into large **digesters** and air is excluded. The methanogens break down the material and release methane and other gases. The methane is collected and burnt to produce heat, which can be used to heat buildings or for making electricity. This process can't use wood waste because these microorganisms cannot break it down.

In all these processes, the solid end materials can be used for soil conditioning, in gardens, parks or in agriculture.

Examiner feedback

You need to be able to compare different methods of dealing with organic waste, but the terms 'windrow composting' and 'in-vessel composting' do not need to be remembered for your exam.

A traditional compost heap in the garden can create the right conditions for vegetable waste to decay in a few months.

Questions

1 **(a)** What proportion of the food and drink that we waste in the UK could potentially be avoided? **(b)** Describe methods that would help us to reduce the amount of food and drink waste that we produce.

2 List the problems with disposing of food waste on landfill sites. Explain your choices.

3 Explain why meat waste must be composted in containers for the first part of in-vessel composting.

4 Explain how the recycling of food waste mimics the natural process of nutrient recycling.

5 Another way of dealing with all household waste is to burn it. Argue the environmental advantages of recycling food waste rather than burning it.

6 Draw up a table to show the different ways in which councils are managing waste food. For each way, list the advantages and disadvantages of each process.

7 Using the data in the graphs, create a poster to inform householders how and why they should increase the amount of waste they recycle to the maximum possible.

8 Some councils are considering fining households that put recyclable material into refuse that is not recycled. Prepare a memo for discussion listing the advantages and problems with this.

Science in action

Gardeners need to create the right conditions inside the compost heap to raise the temperature high enough to kill seeds of weed plants, and disease-causing fungi. So the heap must be kept sheltered from rain, and the right balance of fresh and dead material added plus a little soil to bring in the right microorganisms. Turning the heap every few weeks makes sure enough oxygen gets to all parts.

Route to A*

When evaluating a process, make sure you identify the advantages and disadvantages of the various approaches and then compare these to come to a decision about which gives the best result.

The carbon cycle

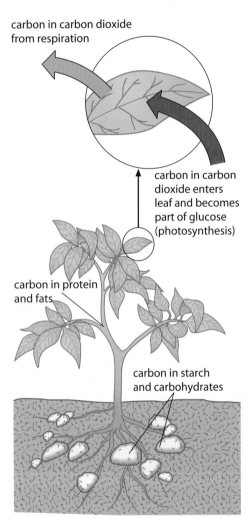

carbon in carbon dioxide from respiration

carbon in carbon dioxide enters leaf and becomes part of glucose (photosynthesis)

carbon in protein and fats

carbon in starch and carbohydrates

Figure 1 How carbon from the air is changed into carbon compounds in a potato plant.

Examiner feedback

Remember that plants photosynthesise during the day, taking carbon dioxide from the atmosphere, and plants respire all the time, releasing carbon dioxide back into the atmosphere.

Capturing carbon dioxide

Imagine a carbon atom that is part of a carbon dioxide molecule in the air. If that carbon dioxide molecule gets too close to a plant, it might be taken into a leaf. There, during photosynthesis, it will be changed into an organic carbon compound called glucose, a carbohydrate. This is known as **fixing** carbon because it removes carbon from the physical environment.

If the glucose is used for respiration, it will be converted to carbon dioxide and released back into the air. However, it might instead be changed into complex carbon compounds, such as the carbohydrates, proteins and fats in plant tissue.

Carbon compounds in animals

If a plant is eaten by an animal, the plant's tissues will be broken down during digestion. Some of the carbon compounds in it will be absorbed through the animal's gut and made into more carbohydrates, proteins, fats or other complex compounds. The rest will leave the animal's body as faeces.

Some of the carbon compounds made inside the animal will be converted to glucose for respiration, then transformed back into carbon dioxide, which will be released into the atmosphere. Other carbon compounds may become part of the animal's body tissues, or may be excreted in urine. If the animal is eaten by a predator, these processes will happen in that animal.

If plants and animals are not eaten, and just die, **detritus feeders**, such as worms and fly larvae, will feed on the dead bodies. They also feed on the faeces and urine excreted by animals. They break down the complex carbon compounds and use them to make more carbon compounds in their bodies, releasing some carbon as carbon dioxide to the air from respiration. Decomposer organisms, such as fungi and bacteria, continue the process of decay. They break down carbon compounds even further, using some to make carbon compounds in their bodies and using some for respiration, releasing carbon dioxide.

The full cycle

When large quantities of organisms, such as trees or plankton, are buried over long timescales, heat and pressure will change them into **fossil fuels**, such as coal and oil.

The **combustion** of fuels formed from organisms, including fossil fuels and wood, releases carbon dioxide into the air.

Whenever the carbon is returned to the atmosphere as carbon dioxide, it is possible that it may be captured by a leaf and fixed again in photosynthesis. This starts the process over again. This constant cycling of carbon through carbon compounds in living organisms and carbon dioxide in the air is called the **carbon cycle**.

In terms of chemicals and energy, we can see that although plants are able to take nutrients and carbon dioxide from the environment, and capture energy from sunlight, only the nutrients and carbon dioxide can be continuously cycled between the environment and living organisms. All the energy that is captured by plants will eventually be transferred as heat to the environment. This energy cannot be used by living organisms, so there is no energy cycle.

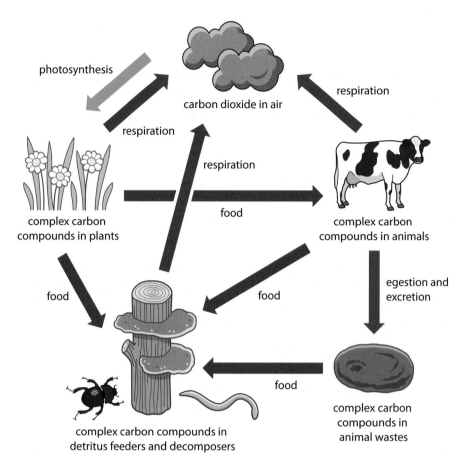

Figure 2 The natural carbon cycle.

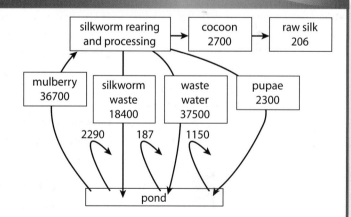

Carbon compounds in this cowpat will be broken down and used by many different kinds of detritus feeders and decomposers.

Examiner feedback

Many different styles of carbon cycle diagram can be used in examination questions. Make sure that you have practised interpreting different styles of diagram.

Questions

1   What is photosynthesis, and what is its role in the carbon cycle?

2   What contribution do plants make to the carbon cycle?

3   Draw a diagram to show what happens to the carbon in an animal that is eaten by a predator.

4   It is possible that one of the carbon atoms in your body was once in the body of William Shakespeare. Explain how this could happen.

5   Explain how human activity modifies the carbon cycle shown in Figure 2.

6   In China, silkworms are grown on mulberry bushes that surround fish ponds. The faeces from feeding silkworms, and waste from the processing of silk, are returned to the ponds. Carp fish feed on water plants in the ponds, and are harvested for human consumption. Figure 3 shows the biomass in kilograms per hectare for the parts of this system. Describe what the diagram shows as fully as possible.

Figure 3 Biomasses.

7   The silkworm/carp pond arrangement is an example of a natural recycling system. Identify which parts of the system are not shown in the diagram and suggest as far as you can why they were not included.

8   Explain as fully as possible why the carbon cycling in the silkworm/carp pond arrangement is self-sustaining, and consider conditions in which this might change.

Assess yourself questions

1 The following methods are used to dispose of organic waste from the home and garden. Choose the correct method to answer each question. Each method can be used more than once.

A windrow composting
B anaerobic digestion
C landfill tipping
D in-vessel composting

(a) Which method is *not* a form of recycling? *(1 mark)*

(b) Which method is *not* suitable for meat wastes? *(1 mark)*

(c) Which method produces methane and other gases that are used for making electricity? *(1 mark)*

(d) Which method is *not* suitable for wood waste? *(1 mark)*

2 Dromedary (one-humped) camels survive better than any other large mammals in dry desert conditions.

(a) Name two conditions of the environment that the camel must survive in a desert. *(2 marks)*

(b) Explain how each of the adaptations shown in Figure 1 improves the camel's chances of surviving in the desert. *(4 marks)*

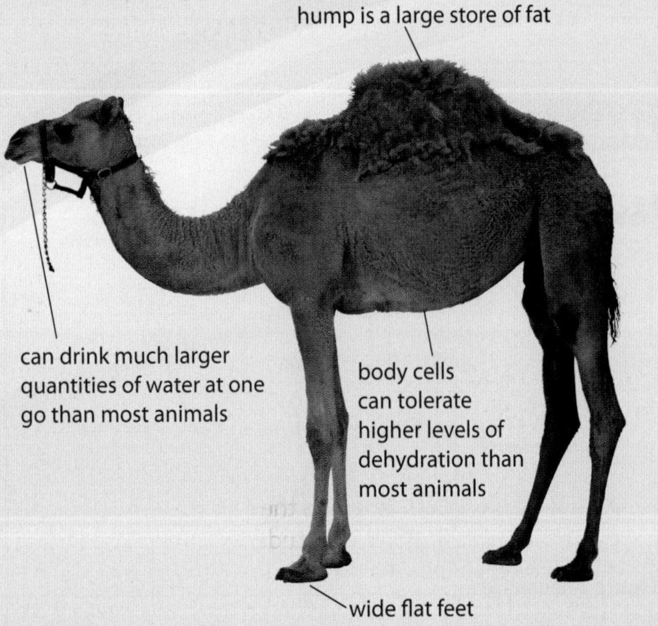

hump is a large store of fat

can drink much larger quantities of water at one go than most animals

body cells can tolerate higher levels of dehydration than most animals

wide flat feet

Figure 1 Camel adaptations.

3 **Table 1** The biomass of organisms at each trophic level living in a marsh.

Trophic level	Biomass / g/m²
producer	800
primary consumers	40
secondary consumers	10
tertiary consumers	2

(a) On graph paper, use these data to draw a pyramid of biomass. *(3 marks)*

(b) Define the terms *biomass* and *trophic level*. *(2 marks)*

(c) Explain why the data produce the shape of a pyramid. *(2 marks)*

(d) What is the source of the energy for the organisms in the marsh? *(1 mark)*

(e) What is the final form of the energy leaving the marsh? Explain your answer. *(2 marks)*

4 Figure 2 shows sewage from a pig farm discharging into a river. It also shows the samples of invertebrates that a scientist caught at different points along the river.

(a) Which of these animals can only live in unpolluted water? *(1 mark)*

(i) rat-tailed maggot
(ii) waterlouse
(iii) mayfly nymph
(iv) leech

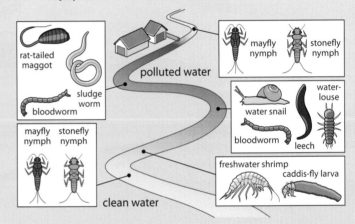

Figure 2 Map of river.

Figure 3 shows the concentration of oxygen in the water at different points along the river.

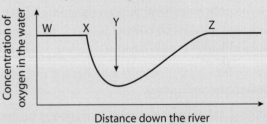

Figure 3 Oxygen concentrations.

(b) Which letter on the graph shows the position of the pig farm? *(1 mark)*

(c) Explain your choice in part b. *(2 marks)*

(d) The bloodworm is a water pollution indicator. Explain what this means. *(1 mark)*

(e) Describe one adaptation of the bloodworm to living in polluted water. *(1 mark)*

5 The herring gull and the Arctic skua are birds that breed in the UK. Figure 4 shows the change in breeding population size for these species since 1986.

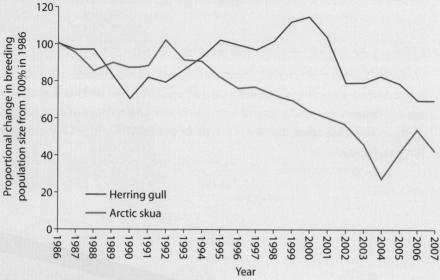

Figure 4 Herring gull and Arctic skua poulation.

Arctic skuas breed only in the north of Scotland and have a population size of about 2100 pairs. Herring gulls breed in many parts of the UK and there are an estimated 130 000 pairs. Both species were put on the 'red' list (birds of concern) in 2009 because of their decline in population size.

Arctic skuas depend on sand eels to feed their chicks. In recent years, the numbers of sand eels have greatly decreased. Some scientists think this is related to an increase in temperature of the North Sea over the past decade. Herring gulls feed their chicks a wide range of food, including fish, worms from fields and scraps from landfill tips.

(a) How does the population change for each of the species between 1986 and 2007? *(2 marks)*

(b) Some people say that climate change is affecting the distribution of animals.

(i) Is this a reasonable explanation for the decline in skuas? Explain your answer. *(1 mark)*

(ii) Is this a reasonable explanation for the decline in herring gulls? Explain your answer. *(1 mark)*

(c) Since 2002, there has been an increase in the amount of food and plant waste that is treated at recycling centres.

(i) Explain how this could affect herring gulls. *(1 mark)*

(ii) Does the graph support this argument? Explain your answer. *(1 mark)*

(d) Do you think that the decline of each of these species should be 'of concern'? Explain your answer. *(4 marks)*

6 Compare the contributions of plants, animals and decomposers to the carbon cycle.

In this question you will be assessed on using good English, organising information clearly and using specialist terms where appropriate. *(6 marks)*

7 During a survey for banded snails, students each searched a different habitat until they had found 15 snails.

Table 2 The students' results.

Snail colour and banding	Habitat		
	long grass	woodland	short grass
brown with bands	1	1	3
yellow with bands	9	2	4
brown no bands	1	9	1
yellow no bands	4	3	7

Assuming that predation was the main factor controlling distribution, the students had predicted that more banded snails would be found in long grass than in the other habitats, where the bands would give better camouflage in stripy shadows. They also predicted that more brown snails would be found in deep shade.

(a) Evaluate the method and suggest how it could be improved. *(2 marks)*

(b) Analyse the results and explain whether they support the two predictions. *(2 marks)*

(c) What other evidence should the students look for to support their idea that predation is a major factor controlling distribution in these areas? Explain your answer. *(2 marks)*

Gene basics

Learning objectives

- describe how genes are small sections of chromosomes in a cell's nucleus
- explain how different genes control the development of different characteristics
- explain how variation in characteristics is caused.

This puppy has inherited some characteristics from each parent.

Examiner feedback

Note that you may see the bands shown here in photographs. They are the effect of staining, not the individual genes. There are many more genes than bands that can be seen.

Examiner feedback

There is often confusion by students in examinations between gametes, chromosomes and genes. Make sure that you know the difference.

Science in action

The Human Genome Project has mapped all of the chromosomes in a human nucleus. Scientists are now trying to identify which part of each chromosome is a particular gene. With this detailed information, scientists hope to speed up the process of looking for cures for human disorders that are caused by faulty genes.

Basic characteristics

All organisms have **characteristics**, for example, coat colour in dogs, and often some characteristics look like those of one parent and others look more like those of the other parent.

Genes control characteristics

We **inherit** some characteristics from our parents. This is because we were formed when a sex cell (a **gamete** called an egg) from our mother fused with a sex cell (a gamete called a sperm) from our father. The nucleus of each gamete contains **chromosomes** that are made up of **genes**. So we receive some genes from each parent.

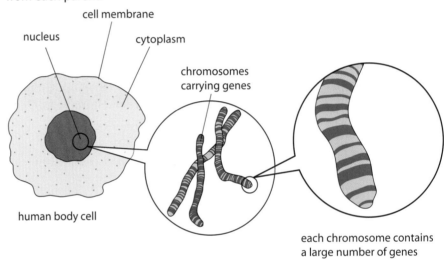

Figure 1 Chromosomes in the nucleus.

Each chromosome carries thousands of genes. There are genes for height, hair colour, blood type, the length and shape of your bones, the size and shape of your hands and so on. Each gene 'codes' for a particular characteristic. Genes are the instructions for making every part of you, and as you grow, so the genes affect the way that you grow. Except for identical twins, we all have slightly different combinations of genes, which is why we all look different.

The cause of variation

Many of our characteristics are controlled by **genes**. One example is a gene called OCA2, which is found on chromosome 15. This gene carries instructions for making the substance that gives eyes, hair and skin colour. As genes can be passed from parent to offspring in gametes, these characteristics are inherited. However, not all of the differences between the characteristics of individuals come from the genes. Some, such as muscle strength, are mainly due to differences in lifestyle and in our environment. These differences cannot be inherited.

Variation that is strongly affected by the environment, such as height, often shows **continuous variation**, where there is a gradual change from one extreme to the other. However, variation caused by a single gene is usually **categoric**, in separate groups.

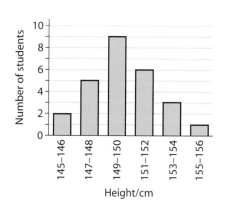

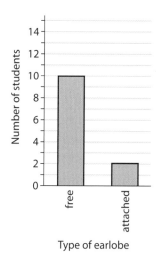

Figure 2 The graph on the left shows continuous variation, and the one on the right shows categoric variation.

Many characteristics are affected by both environment and genes. For example, if you have two tall parents, you are likely to have the genes for tallness, but if you do not grow well as a child (as a result of poor nutrition or illness) you may not grow as tall as your genes would allow. As research continues on human genes, it is becoming clear that many characteristics that we would have previously considered the result of environment, such as obesity, may also be partly the result of inherited genes.

Any differences between these identical twins are the result of the environment.

Science skills If you carried out a survey of human characteristics to see if they were controlled by genes, the environment or both, how would you set up the survey to help you get reliable results?

Questions

1. **(a)** Look at the photograph of the dogs. Identify as many characteristics of the puppy as you can that are from each parent. **(b)** Explain why the puppy has these characteristics.

2. Describe the relationship between nucleus, chromosomes and genes.

3. The parents of a child were both champion marathon runners. Will the child also be a champion marathon runner? Explain your answer.

4. Look at the graphs in Figure 2: **(a)** Which characteristic is the result of genetic factors alone? Explain your answer. **(b)** The graph for types of earlobe shows the results for boys. In the same survey, all 14 girls had free earlobes. Is the conclusion that all girls have free earlobes valid? Explain your answer.

5. Group the following characteristics of rose plants into three groups: variation due to genes, variation due to environment, variation due to genes and environment. For each characteristic, justify your choice of group.
   flower colour, plant height, size of leaf, time of flowering, shape of leaf, presence or absence of thorns

6. Explain how you would investigate whether variation in a human characteristic was the result of genes or the environment, or a combination of the two.

7. Many people think obesity is caused by environmental effects, but research shows there may be a genetic cause too. Explain in detail the importance of this discovery.

Science in action

Some human disorders are caused by genes and some by environment, and some by a mixture of the two. In order to understand why some people have the disorders, scientists compare different aspects of people who have them and people who don't to see if they can find any correlations. For example, comparing people who smoke with those who don't helped to identify the link between smoking and cancer. This kind of study is called epidemiology.

Taking it further

A chromosome is much more than a string of genes that code for characteristics. It includes packaging molecules so genes are only used when needed. The rest of the time the chromosome is neatly folded and protected so that it does not get damaged.

Different types of reproduction

Sexual reproduction

The variation described in lesson B1 6.1 is the result of **sexual reproduction**. This kind of reproduction occurs when the nucleus of a sperm cell (male gamete) fuses with the nucleus of an egg cell (female gamete) to produce a fertilised cell. When the gametes are formed, they only receive half of the chromosomes that are in a body cell. So the fertilised cell gets half its chromosomes from the mother and half from the father. The process of producing gametes ensures that it is highly unlikely that any two gametes will contain the same variations of genes.

Parent cell containing pairs of chromosomes; the two chromosomes in a pair contain different versions of the same genes.

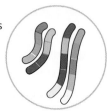

(*Note*: this diagram is highly simplified.)

Four possible different sex cells.

Figure 1 Each sex cell gets one chromosome from each pair in the parent cell.

The variation in the genes in each gamete, and the mixing of genes from the father and mother, make it very unlikely that two offspring from the same parents will be alike, unless they are identical twins formed from the same fertilised cell.

Asexual reproduction

Another way to produce offspring is by **asexual reproduction**. Here the offspring are produced from the division of cells in the parent without the need for **fertilisation** by a sperm cell. So the cells of the offspring contain exactly the same chromosomes as the parent. All the offspring are genetically identical and are called **clones**.

Asexual reproduction can happen much more quickly than sexual reproduction. For example, in one summer, there may be up to 40 generations of cabbage aphid. This is a great advantage for a pest such as aphids that need to reproduce rapidly in the short time when food is available.

Some plants also reproduce asexually. For example, couch grass produces new plants from underground stems, called **runners**, which help it spread quickly in an area to outcompete other plants. Plants that live in places where it is either too hot or too cold for growth during part of the year, may form underground **storage organs**, like potatoes, each of which can form a new plant in the next growing season.

Many species of plants and animals, like these damselflies, use sexual reproduction to produce offspring.

Female aphids can give birth to live young without fertilisation by a male aphid.

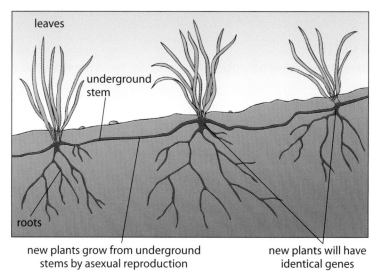

new plants grow from underground stems by asexual reproduction

new plants will have identical genes

Figure 2 When the new couch grass plant has enough roots to grow on its own, the runner may die off.

A tray of leaf cuttings from an African violet plant. The dark leaves were taken from the parent plant. Some of these have formed roots and are starting to grow into new plants with brighter green leaves.

Applications of asexual reproduction

We can make clones of plants artificially by copying the natural asexual process, such as taking potatoes from an old plant and planting them separately. For some plants we can also take **cuttings**. These are parts cut off a plant, usually from a stem or leaf. The cuttings grow roots and develop into new plants. This can produce lots of new plants more quickly than by sexual reproduction, and more cheaply because it is quicker.

Questions

1 Explain why the offspring from sexual reproduction are not identical to:
   (a) their parents **(b)** other offspring from the same parents.

2 Explain why the offspring from asexual reproduction are clones.

3 Draw up a table to show the advantages and disadvantages of sexual and asexual reproduction.

4 A student grows African violet plants. Which technique should he use to: **(a)** try to produce a plant that has a new flower colour? **(b)** produce many plants with this same new colour? Explain your answers.

5 Aphids reproduce asexually all summer, but late in the season winged males and females are produced. These mate and the females lay eggs that overwinter and hatch in spring. **(a)** Are females that hatch from overwintering eggs identical or not? Explain your answer. **(b)** What is the advantage of producing aphids that are able to fly in autumn? **(c)** Explain the advantages of both kinds of reproduction in the aphid life cycle.

6 Use your table from question 3 to suggest the best form of reproduction in the following situations. Justify your answers.
   (a) A weed plant starts growing in cleared soil. **(b)** An aquatic animal produces offspring that will drift downriver to live in other areas.

7 A student has been given a *Bryophyllum* plant to set up an experiment to show as clearly as possible the variation in leaf size caused by temperature. Write a plan for how she should set up the experiment, explaining each step.

Practical

Leaf cuttings can easily be taken from an African violet plant and used to test the best conditions for forming new plants. They can also show how much variation is the result of environment, as the new plants are genetically identical.

Examiner feedback

It is important that you understand why asexual reproduction is so important in economic terms.

Taking it further

Bacteria reproduce mainly asexually, so populations can grow rapidly. Occasionally, they reproduce sexually, producing variation in the offspring. However, they also contain small rings of genetic material called plasmids that they can pass to other bacteria, without reproduction (as no new individuals are formed). Plasmids can carry genes for antibiotic resistance, so resistance can be passed quickly between different types of bacteria.

Cloning plants and animals

Tissue culture

Plant growers have grown new plants from cuttings for many centuries. Now they can also grow new plants using just a few cells from the parent plant. This is known as **tissue culture** and is another form of cloning.

Cells are taken from the tip of a shoot and placed on a jelly that contains nutrients and a chemical that helps the cells to divide. They make a small ball of cells called a **callus**. The callus can be split to make new calluses. Each callus is then put on a jelly that contains different chemicals to encourage roots and shoots to form. When the new plants are large enough, they are planted into compost. Tissue culture makes it easier to grow thousands of new plants from one original one.

Embryo transplants

When animals reproduce, most of the cells in the embryo **specialise** before the animal is born. Specialised animal cells, such as muscle cells, cannot change into other kinds of cell. This means that cloning animals is much more difficult than cloning plants, but it can be done.

One way is called **embryo transplanting**. An egg is fertilised with sperm in a laboratory. When it has divided to make four or eight cells, before they start to specialise, the cells are separated to start making new embryos. These are transplanted into the womb of **host mothers** where they grow until they are ready to be born.

Forming new plants in tissue culture.

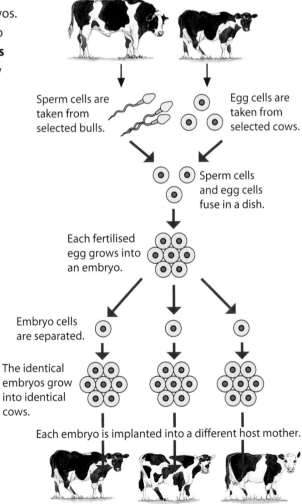

Sperm cells are taken from selected bulls.

Egg cells are taken from selected cows.

Sperm cells and egg cells fuse in a dish.

Each fertilised egg grows into an embryo.

Embryo cells are separated.

The identical embryos grow into identical cows.

Each embryo is implanted into a different host mother.

Figure 1 Embryo transplanting means farmers can get many more offspring from their best animals.

Adult cell cloning

Another animal cloning technique is **adult cell cloning**, where the nucleus of an unfertilised egg cell is removed and replaced with the nucleus of a body cell, e.g. skin cell, from an adult animal. The egg cell can then be given an electric shock so that it starts to divide like a normal embryo. The embryo will contain the same genetic information as the adult body cell. Although this was first done successfully with sheep, it has been repeated for many animal species. People are concerned that it could be used to make human clones, but scientists are using the technique to make replacement cells for problems such as spinal cord damage.

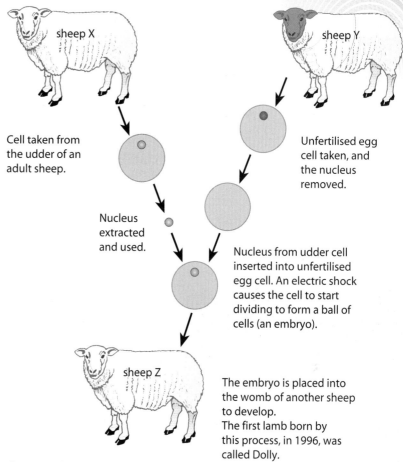

Figure 2 Adult cell cloning.

sheep X

sheep Y

Cell taken from the udder of an adult sheep.

Unfertilised egg cell taken, and the nucleus removed.

Nucleus extracted and used.

Nucleus from udder cell inserted into unfertilised egg cell. An electric shock causes the cell to start dividing to form a ball of cells (an embryo).

sheep Z

The embryo is placed into the womb of another sheep to develop.
The first lamb born by this process, in 1996, was called Dolly.

Science skills

It took 277 attempts using adult cell cloning to create a cell that successfully grew into a healthy sheep. Most attempts fail because the cells do not develop normally. As an adult, Dolly was mated and produced healthy lambs, but she developed arthritis (usually occurs in much older sheep) and was put down at the age of six because of lung cancer. The scientists who bred her said her early death was not the result of being a clone, but other scientists think that using an 'old' nucleus could cause the animal to age faster than normally. What are the pros and cons of continuing adult cell cloning research?

Science in action

Since Dolly the sheep was created, the same technique has been used in many other species, including cats and dogs. For about US$50 000 you could have your pet dog or cat cloned. However, although the clone would look like your pet, it probably wouldn't behave exactly the same way.

Questions

1 **(a)** How is tissue culture different from taking cuttings? **(b)** How is tissue culture the same as taking cuttings?

2 Are all animals produced by embryo transplanting clones? Explain your answer.

3 Why would it make sense for a farmer to use an expensive technique such as embryo transplanting rather than allowing bulls and cows to mate as usual?

4 Look at the diagram in Figure 2, which shows how Dolly the sheep was produced. The three adult sheep were all different species. Which sheep was Dolly a clone of? Explain your answer.

5 Draw a flow chart to show all the steps in tissue culture.

6 Describe how adult cell cloning could be used to create a human clone.

7 Tissue culture is being used increasingly to save rare and endangered plant species. Explain as fully as you can the advantages and disadvantages of using tissue culture for this, rather than collecting seed as scientists used to do.

8 Evaluate the disadvantages of producing a human clone using adult cell cloning.

Modifying the genetic code

Learning objectives

- describe how genes can be cut out and transferred into other cells
- explain why we cut out genes and transfer them into other cells
- explain the result of transferring genes into organisms in the early stages of development
- interpret information about genetic engineering.

Genetic engineering

The genetic information in all organisms works in the same way, whether it comes from a plant, an animal or a bacterium. Therefore, we can take a gene for a particular characteristic from a chromosome of an individual of one species and insert it into an individual of a different species and it will produce the same characteristic. This is called **genetic engineering**. The organism that contains the new gene has been **genetically modified** (GM), and is called a **transgenic organism**.

Genetic engineering has many practical applications. For example, we can transfer the gene for making the hormone insulin from a human cell into a bacterium. Insulin is a hormone that is needed by some diabetic people to prevent them becoming very ill. It is possible to grow many genetically modified bacteria on a large scale in bacterial fermenters. This means we can make a lot of human insulin more cheaply and safely than before. We now use GM bacteria to make human growth hormone and a vaccine to protect against infection by the disease hepatitis B.

This mouse contains a gene from a fluorescent jellyfish that glows under blue light.

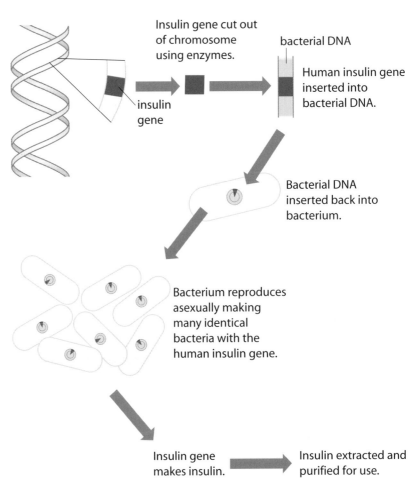

Figure 1 How genetically modified human insulin is produced.

Before we could make GM bacteria to produce human insulin, the insulin was extracted from dead animals, such as pigs. This not only meant there was less insulin available, but the insulin produced was not identical to human insulin and could cause health problems.

Examiner feedback

Although you may come across the term *transgenic* in your research, you do not need to remember it for your exam.

Science in action

The demand for insulin for treating diabetes is very great, so scientists are looking for new, faster and cheaper processes for producing it. One current possibility is to use genetically modified plants, such as safflower.

It is also possible to insert a gene into some of the body cells rather than an early embryo. This means that only those body cells make what the gene codes for, and the gene cannot be passed on to offspring. Scientists are developing ways of treating human diseases caused by faulty genes, such as cystic fibrosis, in this way.

Transferring genes at an early stage

Genes can also be transferred into a plant or animal embryo at an early stage in their development. As the organism grows, all the cells in its body will have a copy of the inserted gene, so all cells can develop the desired characteristics. This technique is most commonly used to make GM food plants. However, it is also very important in research for causes and treatments of human diseases. Mice have been genetically modified so that they can be used to study human cancers, or to investigate the effect of changes to particular genes that cause human diseases. Using mice like this has rapidly increased our knowledge and means treatments will be developed sooner.

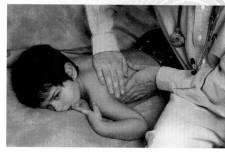

People who have cystic fibrosis need treatment every day to stop them becoming very ill. In the future they might be able to insert the correct genes into their lung cells using an inhaler.

This mouse is genetically modified so that it can be used to find out more about human cancers, how they are caused and how they can be treated.

Science skills Inserting genes into human embryos is illegal. Although it could help cure genetic diseases, there are many arguments against it:

- treatment would be expensive, so would only wealthy people get it?
- the parents choose the treatment not the child who gets it – is this right?
- what if parents could choose other genes for insertion, such as for height or intelligence?

Questions

1. Define the term *genetic engineering* in your own words.
2. Explain why we can transfer a characteristic from one species into a different species.
3. Suggest why the insertion of genes into a human embryo is illegal in most countries.
4. Draw a flow chart to describe how human growth hormone could be produced by genetically modifying bacteria.
5. List as many advantages as you can for producing human insulin from genetically engineered bacteria.
6. Should a parent have the right to choose to have a gene inserted into their embryo so that their child does not have a genetic disease? Justify your answer.
7. Compare as fully as you can the effect of inserting genes into body cells with the effect of inserting genes into embryo cells.
8. Evaluate the ethical and social issues of using GM mice to research the causes and treatment of human diseases such as cancer.

Examiner feedback

It is important that you appreciate the ethical concerns some people have about gene therapy and why it continues to be the focus of much debate.

Taking it further

Plasmids from bacteria are one of the main methods scientists use for transferring genes into bacteria to make genetically modified bacteria. This process copies the natural process that many types of bacteria use for exchanging genetic material.

Making choices about GM crops

Science in action

Evidence from trials carried out by GM seed companies show that herbicide-resistant crops produce greater yields than non-resistant crops. Trials by other scientists working with farmers often show a decreased yield in GM crops. One study in the USA showed that GM soybean produced about 4700 kg/ha compared with over 5170 kg/ha from the nearest similar non-GM variety. These scientists suggest that inserting the gene has damaged other parts of the plant development, which affects yield.

Making GM crops

Plants can be genetically modified by inserting the required gene into the cells of an early embryo. Often a bacterium, called *Agrobacterium*, is used to get the new gene inside the nucleus of the cells where it can join with the cell's DNA.

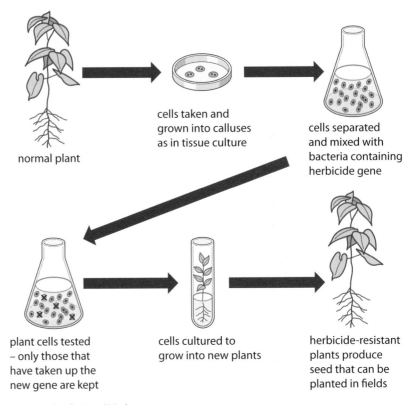

normal plant

cells taken and grown into calluses as in tissue culture

cells separated and mixed with bacteria containing herbicide gene

plant cells tested – only those that have taken up the new gene are kept

cells cultured to grow into new plants

herbicide-resistant plants produce seed that can be planted in fields

Figure 1 Producing GM plants.

Different modifications

Many GM crops have a gene for **herbicide** resistance. While a crop is growing, other plants compete for water and nutrients in the soil. These weed plants can reduce the amount of food harvested from the crop (the **yield**). Farmers use herbicides to kill plants, but these chemicals can damage the crop plants as well. Using crops that are resistant to a particular herbicide means that the crop can be sprayed with that herbicide to kill weeds without damaging the crop.

Some crop plants are modified with a gene for a poison that kills insects that try to eat the plant. Pest damage reduces crop yield, so GM crops should produce a greater yield.

The pros and cons of GM crops

One concern with GM crops is that the seed costs more than normal seed, and the companies that produce seed for herbicide-resistant crops also produce the herbicide that the crop is resistant to. This is good for those companies but not necessarily good for farmers.

In Africa, the maize stalk borer damages plants and reduces crop yields by 20–40% on average.

Another concern is gene transfer through **pollination**. Pollination can happen occasionally between plants that are closely related. As crop varieties were bred originally from wild varieties, if those wild types are weeds growing nearby, then the inserted gene could be transferred to them. Research in Canada has shown that the gene for herbicide resistance has been transferred to weed species within six years of growing GM crops.

Using GM varieties changes the way farmers look after their crops, which can also affect the environment. Growing insect-resistant crops can benefit other species of insects because chemical insecticides, which kill other insect species as well as the pest, are not used. However, where herbicide-resistant varieties have been grown on a large scale, there is no evidence of reduced use of chemicals that kill a wide range of plant species and this means that the variety of wildflowers is reduced, which will affect insect and bird species that feed on them.

People are also concerned about the safety of the foods produced from the crops. Although the foods are tested on animals to make sure they don't cause health problems, we have no idea yet if there are any problems caused by eating GM foods over a long time.

Much more research is needed if GM crops are to help feed the increasing human population.

Spraying a field with herbicide will get rid of not just the weeds, but also the animals that feed on the weeds, and animals that feed on those animals.

Opinion on the value of GM crops is divided because people are not sure about long-term effects.

Questions

1 Explain why plant embryos are used for genetic modification.

2 Sketch a diagram to show how weeds can reduce crop yield.

3 Suggest any disadvantages of using crops that are modified to resist insect attack.

4 Explain how using an insect-resistant crop variety could help the environment.

5 No GM crops are grown for sale in the UK at the moment, but there are licensed scientific trials. Should this be allowed? Justify your answer.

6 A small-scale farmer in Kenya is considering growing GM maize that is resistant to stalk borer. How would you evaluate the advantages and disadvantages of this so that you could advise on the best choice?

7 Genetic engineering and tissue culture are two possible solutions to the problem of creating disease-free bananas. Explain fully why using tissue culture is more likely to be the better approach for poor farmers in Africa.

8 Explain as fully as you can why results for yield in trials on GM crops by the companies that make the seed might be more positive about increased yields than the results from other scientists.

Examiner feedback

You will be expected to understand and present both sides of the ethical debate on GM crops, and not just give your own point of view.

You will be expected to apply the knowledge and understanding you have gained on your course to new examples.

Evolution of life

Life on Earth

The first evidence of life on Earth is found in rocks that are just over 3500 million years old. These rocks contain shapes that look like **fossils** of bacteria.

Scientists estimate that there are over 30 million species of organisms on the Earth today.

Relationships between living organisms

Most organisms can be quite easily classified into three main groups:

- microorganisms – single-celled organisms, such as bacteria
- plants – organisms that photosynthesise, mostly multi-celled
- animals – mostly multi-celled organisms that get their energy from eating other organisms.

Grouping organisms is known as **classification**. Studying the features of organisms carefully can help us decide how to classify them. When we group according to features, we have to be careful about how we interpret the results. Some features are strongly adapted to the environment, so organisms may be a similar shape because they have a similar lifestyle, that is, they show an **ecological relationship**.

Table 1 The main characteristics of mammals and fish.

Mammal	Fish
eggs fertilised inside the body	eggs usually fertilised outside the body
usually give birth to live young	get oxygen from water using gills
mothers make milk for young	body covered in scales
usually have hair or fur	
get oxygen from air using lungs	

Some features, such as the structure of the bones and their arrangement in the skeleton, can help us group organisms in a way that makes better predictions. For example, humans and dolphins share more characteristics than dolphins and sharks, so they are grouped as mammals. If we found an animal that shared characteristics with a human and a dolphin, we could predict that it also had other mammalian characteristics..

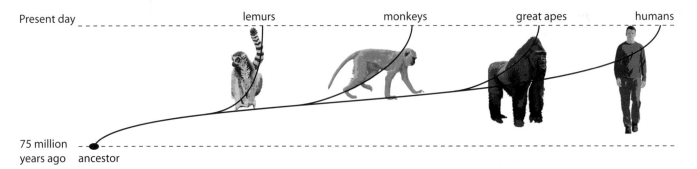

Figure 1 This diagram shows how closely humans are related to some other animals.

If we group animals according to how many similar characteristics they have, we get a diagram like this. This shows that humans are more like apes than monkeys, and more like monkeys than lemurs. This kind of diagram can be interpreted as an **evolutionary relationship**, where the different groups evolved from a **common ancestor**. It doesn't show that the modern great apes became humans, because both apes and humans have evolved since that last common ancestor.

Fossil evidence

Fossils are evidence of organisms that lived in the past. When a new fossil is discovered, scientists use characteristics in the fossil to help classify it with other fossils and with the same groups of organisms that we have today. If fossils are also grouped according to age, we can see that characteristics change over time. For example in fossils of ancient horse-like animals, we can see how the tooth structure and leg bone structure have changed.

The change in species over time is called **evolution**. So arranging similar fossil species to show how they changed over time is called an evolutionary relationship.

From all the fossil species that have been discovered, scientists believe that all the species that are living now evolved by changing gradually from the very simple cells that lived on Earth more than three billion years ago.

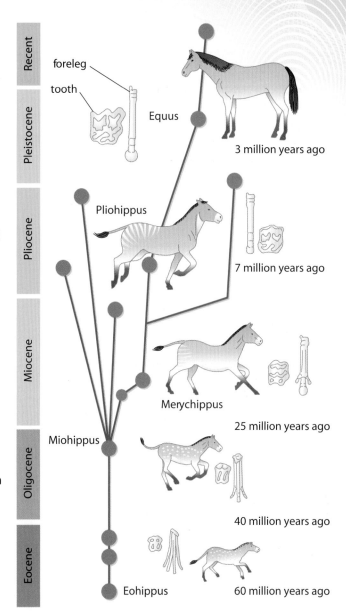

Figure 2 Evolution of the horse, based on teeth and bones from fossils. The tree-like shape is a suggested evolutionary relationship between the species.

Questions

1. An organism contains chlorophyll. How should it be classified, and why?

2. You discover a new fossil skeleton. Explain what would be done so that it could be classified.

3. Explain why dolphins and sharks look similar.

4. In an early classification, snakes were grouped with earthworms. Suggest why this happened.

5. Snakes are now classified as vertebrates (a bony skeleton), and earthworms are invertebrates (no bones). What does this imply about their evolution?

6. Describe the evolutionary tree of humans and other animals in as much detail as you can.

7. Explain in detail what Figure 2 shows.

8. 'Life began on Earth 3500 million years ago.' How accurate do you think this statement is? Explain your answer.

Examiner feedback

You will be expected to explain how evolutionary trees are models that can be used to describe the relationship between organisms through time.

Evolution by natural selection

Evidence for evolution

Fossils show us that there have been other species on Earth than the ones we see today, and that they have changed over time. We can also see from breeding species, such as dogs, that the characteristics we select can be changed over time. These are two lines of evidence for the **theory of evolution**, but they don't help us understand how the change happens.

These dogs belong to the same species, but different characteristics were selected by humans in each breed.

Natural selection

Charles Darwin (1809–1882) spent years carefully observing organisms, asking questions and investigating the answers. What he saw was:

- organisms produce many more offspring than survive to adulthood
- there is variation between the individuals of a species and in the offspring they produce
- characteristics are passed from one generation to the next
- the individuals that are best adapted to the environment are the ones that survive and produce more offspring in the next generation.

Darwin deduced from his observations that the characteristics that were best adapted to the environment were the ones that would increase in the population in the next generation. He called this process **natural selection** because he was suggesting that nature – the environment – was selecting which characteristics were most successful.

How evolution occurs

Darwin suggested that evolution occurred because the environment changed. When the environment changes, different characteristics may be better suited to the new conditions. The individuals with those characteristics will be more likely to survive and breed. Darwin used the evidence of human selection of characteristics in breeding animals such as dogs and pigeons to support this idea.

Darwin thought that after enough time had passed, the characteristics in a population would have changed so much that we would consider those organisms to be a new **species**.

Individuals of the same species may have different characteristics, such as slightly longer legs.

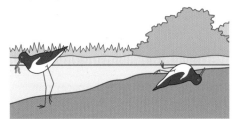

Individuals struggle to survive. Some die because of lack of food or may be eaten by predators.

Individuals with useful characteristics are more likely to survive, and pass on their characteristics to the next generation. The long-legged bird can get food but the short-legged one cannot.

Figure 1 Natural selection results in changes in characteristics.

Genes and mutation in evolution

The idea of genes did not become widely known until 50 years after Darwin published his ideas on evolution. So he could not explain how characteristics were passed from parent to offspring. He also did not know that the variation in inherited characteristics between individuals is caused by their having different forms of genes, and these different forms are caused by random changes, or **mutations**, in the genes.

Many of these mutations have no effect on survival, but some are disadvantageous or fatal, often resulting in a miscarriage during pregnancy, and some can increase survival. For example, DNA evidence suggests that humans (*Homo sapiens*) first evolved in Africa and then spread out across the world. All African populations have dark skins that protect them from the damaging effects of sunlight, but all human societies in northern areas have pale skins. This is the result of random genetic mutation, which improves the health of people in these areas. So it would have been a good adaptation and selected for by the environment in northern areas.

The rate of change in a species is not constant. It depends on how quickly the environment changes and how difficult it is to survive in the new conditions. In difficult conditions, only the few variations that make survival possible will get passed on to the next generation and all other variations will die out. If conditions change so much that no variations can survive then all individuals will die and the species will become extinct.

It has been estimated that a baby has about 100 mutations that are different from its parents' genes.

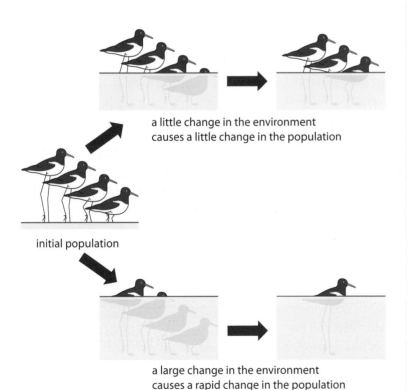

a little change in the environment causes a little change in the population

initial population

a large change in the environment causes a rapid change in the population

Figure 2 Rate of change in a species.

Questions

1. Define the terms *natural selection* and *evolution*.

2. Explain how the evidence from changing characteristics in animal breeding can be used to support the theory of evolution.

3. Mutation can occur anywhere in genes as a cell divides. Explain why only mutations that occur in gametes are important for evolution.

4. Explain how natural selection can change the characteristics of a species.

5. Explain why Darwin deduced from his observations that the best adapted characteristics should increase in a population.

6. Without mutation, there could be no evolution. Explain this statement.

7. Antibiotics are used to kill bacteria. Mutations for antibiotic resistance are rare. Use what you know about natural selection to: **(a)** explain why the increase in bacteria resistant to antibiotics has been so rapid **(b)** suggest ways to limit the increase in antibiotic-resistant bacteria.

8. After heavy fishing using large-mesh nets for many years in the North Sea, scientists have found that the size at which some fish species start breeding has decreased. Use evolutionary theory to explain why.

The development of a theory

Learning objectives

- explain why Darwin's theory was only gradually accepted
- interpret evidence relating to evolutionary theory
- evaluate different theories of evolution
- explain why Darwin's theory is the most commonly accepted theory of evolution.

Other theories of evolution

Two centuries ago, some scientists, other than Darwin, had developed other ways of explaining the diversity of species on Earth. Most people at the time thought that God had created everything. Richard Owen (1804–1892) was a biologist who tried to explain the similarities between species by suggesting that God created basic plans that were developed in different ways. The problem with Owen's theory is that it could not be tested scientifically using experiments.

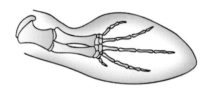 

Figure 1 Owen used the examples of a bat's wing and a whale's flipper as evidence for his theory.

An important theory in Darwin's time had been suggested by Jean-Baptiste Lamarck (1744–1829). Lamarck challenged the ideas of his time by suggesting that species can change; most scientists then believed that they were always the same. He developed his idea to say that the environment caused changes in species, and that these changes were passed on to the offspring.

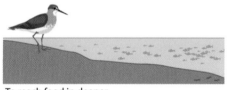

To reach food in deeper water, wading birds stretch their legs. This makes their legs slightly longer.

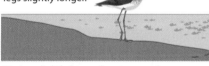

Having slightly longer legs is passed on to the next generation. Birds in this generation also stretch their legs.

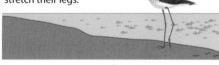

Over many generations, the wading birds' legs become much longer.

Figure 2 How Lamarck's theory explains the evolution of long-legged birds.

The problems with Darwin's theory

When Darwin published his theory in 1859, he knew many people would reject it because it didn't consider God as the creator of species. However, many scientists had difficulty accepting Darwin's theory for other reasons. For them, the problem was that there was little evidence for natural selection causing change and creating new species. This is because it usually takes a long time for a new species to evolve. In addition, Darwin could not explain how characteristics were passed from parent to offspring. This would only be understood after Gregor Mendel's work on inheritance was widely published around 1900, and the concept of genes was developed.

This cartoon of 1871 ridiculed Darwin's idea that apes and humans are related.

The acceptance of Darwin's theory

Darwin's theory has now been used to make predictions that can be tested scientifically. One example was the work of Peter and Rosemary Grant in the 1970s, who used the theory to predict the effect of drought on the beaks of

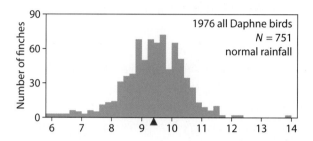

Science skills

The graphs show the sizes of finch beaks in a year after no drought (1976) and a year after drought (1978). The blue arrows show the mean beak depth.

a Describe the results and compare them with the Grants' prediction. Explain how this evidence supports Darwin's theory.

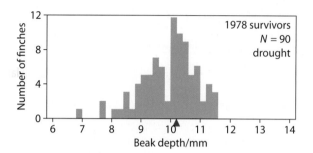

Figure 3 Changes to beak size in finches following drought.

finches in the Galapagos Islands. The Grants saw that drought produced harder seeds. They predicted that the birds that got the most food and produced the most offspring would be those with the larger, stronger beaks so, in years following drought, beak size should increase.

The theory also satisfactorily explains many observations such as why new species evolve rapidly when a new environment occurs. For example, Lake Victoria in Africa is less than 15 000 years old, but contains over 500 species of one kind of fish that are found nowhere else in the world. All these species are most closely related to one species of river fish that lives in the area, and each species is adapted in slightly different ways – some are fast-swimming predators, some graze on weed in shallow water, and others have strong jaws to crush shellfish.

Darwin's theory is now generally accepted as the best explanation for how evolution occurs.

Taking it further

The studies of other scientists have modified Darwin's theory since his death. The theory that is generally held now is called modern Darwinism. Aspects of this theory continue to be debated by scientists as new information is discovered about genes and evolution.

Questions

1 Owen's ideas were not a scientific theory. Explain why.

2 **(a)** Suggest how Owen used the examples of the bat's wing and whale's flipper as evidence for his idea. **(b)** How would Darwin have explained the similarities and differences between the bat's wing and whale's flipper?

3 Compare Lamarck's explanation of the evolution of long legs in birds with Darwin's explanation in lesson B1 7.2. Identify the similarities and differences in the explanations.

4 **(a)** Why do you think the cartoon of Darwin was drawn? **(b)** What assumption does the cartoon make about humans and apes, and how does this differ from Darwin's ideas?

5 Explain why Darwin's theory was only gradually accepted.

6 Look at the graphs of finch beaks in Figure 3. Explain how this evidence supports Darwin's theory.

7 Suggest why Owen, Lamarck and Darwin are all considered to be scientists, but had different theories of evolution.

8 Suggest how the variety of fish species in Lake Victoria may have evolved. Explain your answer.

ISA practice: the growth of mould on bread

Scientists are investigating the best advice to give to supermarkets about storing and displaying bread. Your task is to investigate the effect of temperature on the growth of mould on bread.

Hypothesis

It is suggested that there is a link between temperature and the rate at which bread goes mouldy.

Section 1

1   In this investigation you will need to control some of the variables.
    (a) Name one variable you will need to control in this investigation.   *(1 mark)*
    (b) Describe briefly how you would carry out a preliminary investigation to find a suitable value to use for this variable. Explain how the results will help you decide on the best value for this variable.   *(3 marks)*

2   Describe how you are going to do your investigation. You should include:
    • the equipment that you would use
    • how you would use the equipment
    • the measurements that you would make
    • how you would make it a fair test.

    You may include a labelled diagram to help you to explain your method.

    In this question you will be assessed on using good English, organising information clearly and using specialist terms where appropriate.   *(6 marks)*

3   Think about the possible hazards in your investigation.
    (a) Describe one hazard that you think may be present in your investigation.   *(1 mark)*
    (b) Identify the risk associated with the hazard you have described, and say what control measures you could use to reduce the risk.   *(2 marks)*

4   Design a table that will contain all the data that you are going to record during your investigation.   *(2 marks)*

Total for Section 1: 14 marks

Section 2

A group of students, Study Group 1, investigated the effect of temperature on the growth of mould on bread.

• Their teacher gave them two slices of bread, each of which had a colony of mould growing on it.
• They measured the width of the colonies then placed each of the slices of bread inside separate plastic bags. They placed one plastic bag a shelf in the laboratory. They placed the other plastic bag in a refrigerator.
• On each of the next four days, they removed the slices of bread from the bags, measured the width of the mould colonies then replaced the bread in the bags. The bags were returned to the shelf in the laboratory and the refrigerator respectively.

Figure 1 shows their results.

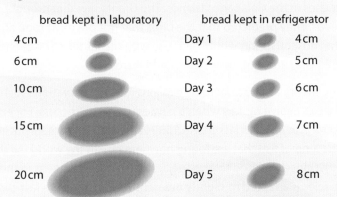

bread kept in laboratory		bread kept in refrigerator
4 cm	Day 1	4 cm
6 cm	Day 2	5 cm
10 cm	Day 3	6 cm
15 cm	Day 4	7 cm
20 cm	Day 5	8 cm

Figure 1 Group 1's investigation.

5   (a) (i)   What is the independent variable in this investigation?
        (ii) What is the dependent variable in this investigation?
        (iii) Name one control variable this investigation.   *(3 marks)*

    (b) Plot a graph to show the link between temperature, time and the diameter of the mould colony.   *(4 marks)*

    (c) Do the results support the hypothesis? Explain your answer.   *(3 marks)*

Below are the results of three other study groups.

Table 1 shows the results of another group of students, Study Group 2.

Table 1 Results from Study Group 2.

Temperature at which bread was stored/°C	Number of days the bread stayed mould-free
0	10.0
10	5.0
20	3.5
30	2.4
40	1.6
50	1.0

A third group of students, Study Group 3, also investigated the hypothesis. Figure 2 is a graph of their results.

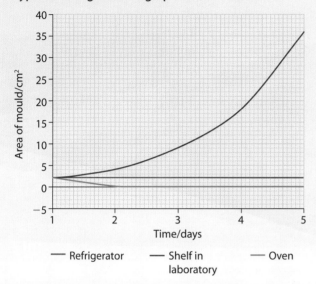

Figure 2 Study Group 3's results.

Study Group 4 was a group of scientists investigating the best conditions for storing bread in supermarkets. They investigated the effect of temperature on the rate at which the bread went stale. Figures 3 and 4 show their results.

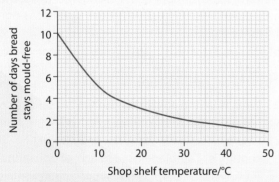

Figure 3 Study Group 4's results: effect of temperature on the rate at which bread goes mouldy.

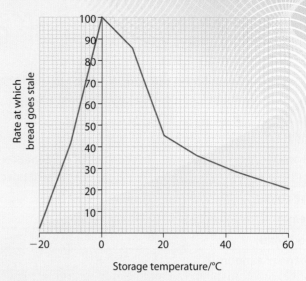

Figure 4 Study Group 4's results: effect of storage temperature on rate at which bread goes stale.

6 Describe one way in which the results of Study Group 2 are similar to or different from the results of Study Group 1, and give one reason why the results are similar or different. *(3 marks)*

7 **(a)** Draw a sketch graph of the results from Study Group 2. *(3 marks)*

(b) Does the data support the hypothesis being investigated? To gain full marks you should use all of the relevant data from the first set of results and Study Groups 2 and 3 to explain whether or not the data supports the hypothesis. *(3 marks)*

(c) The data from the other groups only gives a limited amount of information. What other information or data would you need in order to be more certain as to whether or not the hypothesis is correct? Explain the reason for your answer. *(3 marks)*

(d) Use the results from Study Groups 2, 3 and 4 to answer this question. What is the relationship between the temperature and the growth of mould on bread?
How well does the data support your answer? *(3 marks)*

8 Look back at the investigation method of Study Group 1. If you could repeat the investigation, suggest one change that you would make to the method, and give a reason for the change. *(3 marks)*

9 Suggest how ideas from your investigation and the scientists' investigations could be used to advise supermarkets about the best ways of storing and displaying bread. *(3 marks)*

Total for Section 2: 31 marks
Total for the ISA: 45 marks

Assess yourself questions

1 Tick the correct box in each row of Table 1 to show the cause of variation in these human characteristics.

(4 marks)

Table 1 Human characteristics.

Characteristic	Genetic	Environmental	Genetic + environmental
eye colour			
height			
body mass			
shape of earlobe			

2 Complete Table 2 to compare aspects of sexual and asexual reproduction. *(4 marks)*

Table 2 Reproduction.

Aspect	Sexual reproduction	Asexual reproduction
number of parents		
offspring show variation?		
fusion of gametes?		
offspring are clones?		

3 A student took 10 leaf cuttings from one *Streptocarpus* plant.

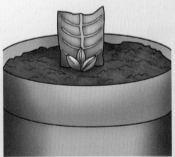

A leaf cutting.

(a) Describe what the student needed to do to the cuttings to grow them into new plants. *(2 marks)*

(b) The student decided to use his new plants to test the effect of light on various characteristics of the plants. Explain why using these plants should give the student more reliable results than using any random 10 *Streptocarpus* plants. *(2 marks)*

(c) Suggest one way that the student could set up this experiment so that light is a quantitative variable. *(1 mark)*

(d) Identify two other variables that the student will need to control. *(2 marks)*

(e) Tissue culture is a more recent method of growing new plants from old ones.

(i) Describe one way in which tissue culture is similar to taking cuttings. *(1 mark)*

(ii) Describe one way in which tissue culture differs from taking cuttings. *(1 mark)*

4 Maize is an important crop plant in parts of Africa and the corn stalk borer is a serious pest, greatly reducing crop yield of maize.

The borer grubs damage the plant stalks, which then fail to produce maize cobs.

A small-scale farmer in South Africa planted 5 hectares of conventional maize and 5 hectares of genetically modified (GM) maize that had been modified to make it resistant to stalk borer. When yields were compared after harvesting, the conventional maize gave her 15 bags/ha as opposed to 40 bags/ha from the GM maize. The GM seed cost more than the usual seed, but the farmer didn't need to use pesticides against the borer so she made a profit.

(a) The gene for resistance to stalk borer comes from a caterpillar. Describe how GM maize could be made. *(3 marks)*

(b) What were the advantages to the farmer of using the GM maize? *(2 marks)*

(c) During a famine in 2002, the neighbouring country of Zambia refused to accept donations of food containing GM maize seed. They eventually accepted seed that had been ground into flour.

(i) What was Zambia worried about? *(1 mark)*

(ii) Give one other concern that people have about GM crops. *(1 mark)*

(d) Some countries, including those of Europe, refuse to buy food made from GM crops. Describe one social and one economic problem facing an African government that is developing policies for growing GM crops in their country. *(2 marks)*

5 Figure 1 shows the giraffes in a population arranged by neck length.

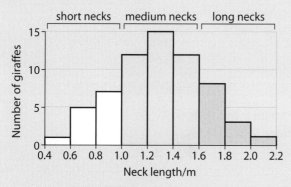

Figure 1 Graph of giraffe necks.

(a) Which is the median neck length? *(1 mark)*

(b) How many giraffes have medium neck length? *(1 mark)*

(c) Lamarck explained the evolution of a long neck from short necks in giraffes with his theory of acquired characteristics. What was his theory? *(1 mark)*

(d) Darwin would have explained the evolution of long necks in giraffes by his theory of evolution by natural selection. Starting with short-necked ancestors, describe how this theory explains long necks now. *(3 marks)*

(e) Give two reasons why Darwin's theory was only gradually accepted by most scientists. *(2 marks)*

6 When the giant panda was discovered in 1869, in the mountains of western China, some scientists decided from its shape that it was a kind of bear. However, it has other characteristics, such as a false 'thumb' that it uses to grasp bamboo stems while it is eating, which bears don't have. Other scientists thought it was more closely

A giant panda.

A red panda.

related to the red panda, a much smaller animal that lives in the Himalayas. The red panda also eats mainly bamboo and it also has a false thumb. Red pandas have never been classified as bears.

(a) What is classification? *(1 mark)*

(b) Explain how classification can indicate evolutionary relationships. *(1 mark)*

(c) Suggest why red pandas have never been classified as bears. *(1 mark)*

(d) Sketch two evolutionary trees:

　(i) one that shows the giant panda more closely related to bears than the red panda *(1 mark)*

　(ii) one that shows the giant panda more closely related to the red panda than bears. *(1 mark)*

(e) Recent evidence using DNA taken from giant pandas, red pandas and bears shows that the two panda species are not closely related at all, and that the giant panda evolved from bears a very long time ago. Suggest why the pandas both have a false thumb. *(2 marks)*

7 (a) Describe how clones are produced by adult cell cloning. *(4 marks)*

(b) Give one advantage of producing an animal clone by adult cell cloning. *(1 mark)*

(c) Give one scientific disadvantage of adult cell cloning. *(1 mark)*

(d) Give one ethical disadvantage of adult cell cloning. *(1 mark)*

GradeStudio Route to A*

During its life the rabbit ate a lot of grass. The carbon in the grass became part of the rabbit's body. The rabbit has died and is left and not eaten. How is the carbon recycled back into the grass which other rabbits will eat?

In this question you will be assessed on using good English, organising information clearly and using specialist terms where appropriate. (6 marks)

Read the three different answers together with the examiner comments. Then check what you have learnt and put it into practice in any further questions you answer.

B Grade answer

Student 1

> The correct scientific word is decay.

> It is better to say that the carbon dioxide is released.

> Grass photosynthesises which means it takes in carbon dioxide from the air. The rabbit ate the grass which contained carbon and the rabbit used this to make carbohydrates. The rabbit is now dead so that means its body will start to rot. Microorganisms are involved in this process. The carbon in the grass that the rabbit ate will go back into air as carbon dioxide.
>
> Other rabbits will come along and eat the grass and the whole process will start again.

Examiner comment

This candidate has understood that the process is a cycle, but they should have started with the dead rabbit and ended up with photosynthesis. They have not explained how the rabbit decays, including the role of microorganisms. Microorganisms respire and enzymes are involved; grass photosynthesises and takes in carbon dioxide to make carbohydrates for it to grow; the rabbit eats the grass and takes in carbon; so as the rabbit decomposes carbon dioxide is released into the atmosphere.

A Grade answer

Student 2

> To synthesise carbohydrates would be better.

> It would have been better to use the more scientific terminology digest.

> The rabbit ate and digested the grass which contained carbon. The grass photosynthesised which means it used carbon dioxide from the air to allow it to grow. Now that the rabbit is dead its body will start to decay because microorganisms will eat it. The microorganisms respire so they will use the carbohydrates they have eaten to produce energy. This process releases carbon dioxide back into air.

Examiner comment

Like student 1, this candidate has understood the carbon cycle. However, they have also discussed how the rabbit decays and that microorganisms are involved. They have also pointed out that microorganisms respire, releasing carbon dioxide back into the atmosphere. They should have started with the rabbit decaying first.

A* Grade answer

Student 3

Use of correct terminology.

When a rabbit dies its body is decomposed by soil microorganisms. Some of these microorganisms use enzymes to digest the complex carbon compounds in the rabbit's body into sugars. These sugars are then used by the microorganisms in respiration to produce energy. The carbon dioxide produced during respiration is released into the atmosphere.

carbohydrates produced by photosynthesis is correct.

Respiration of microorganisms correctly mentioned.

Grass absorbs carbon dioxide from the atmosphere during photosynthesis, producing carbohydrates, which contain carbon. When rabbits eat grass, the carbohydrate in the grass is digested, forming sugars. The sugars are absorbed into the rabbit's blood.

Examiner comment

This candidate has covered all the main points in the process: microorganisms use the energy from respiration to decay/digest the rabbit. As they do this, they respire and release carbon dioxide into the atmosphere. Enzymes are involved in this process. Grass uses the carbon dioxide from the atmosphere in photosynthesis to convert the carbon into carbohydrates to help it grow. Rabbits eat the grass, and digest the carbohydrates in the grass.

MOVING UP THE GRADES

- Read the question carefully.
- These questions carry a maximum of either five or six marks.
- Plan your answer by noting at least five/six relevant points you are going to make.
- Put these points into a logical sequence.

Examination-style questions

1 (a) Give two effects of an unbalanced diet on the body. *(2 marks)*

   (i) Explain what is meant by metabolic rate. *(1 mark)*

   (ii) Give two factors that affect metabolic rate. *(2 marks)*

(b) Body mass index (BMI) is used to classify people into different groups.
The table shows the relationship between BMI and obesity.

BMI	Obesity category
less than 18.5	underweight
18.5–24.9	normal
25.0–29.9	overweight
30.0 and over	obese

The chart shows the relationship between mass, height and BMI.

	Mass/kg													
Height/m	50	55	60	65	70	75	80	85	90	95	100	105	110	115
1.35	29	31	34	36	39	41	43	46	48	51	53	56	58	60
1.40	27	29	31	34	36	38	39	43	45	47	49	52	54	56
1.45	25	27	29	31	34	36	38	40	42	44	46	48	50	52
1.50	23	25	27	29	31	33	35	37	39	41	43	45	47	49
1.55	22	24	26	27	29	31	33	35	37	38	40	42	44	46
1.60	21	22	24	26	28	29	31	33	34	36	38	40	41	43
1.65	19	21	23	24	26	27	29	31	33	34	36	37	39	40
1.70	18	20	22	23	24	26	27	29	30	32	34	35	37	38
1.75	17	19	20	22	23	24	26	27	29	30	32	33	35	36
1.80	16	18	19	20	22	23	24	26	27	28	30	31	33	34
1.85	15	17	18	19	21	22	23	24	26	27	28	30	31	32
1.90	15	16	17	18	20	21	22	23	24	26	27	28	29	30
1.95	14	15	16	17	19	20	21	22	23	24	25	27	28	29
2.00	13	14	15	17	18	19	20	21	22	23	24	25	26	28

   (i) What obesity category is a person 1.60 metres tall with a mass of 75 kg? *(1 mark)*

   (ii) Describe the relationship between height, mass and BMI. *(2 marks)*

2 **(a)** Describe fully the process of IVF (*in vitro* fertilisation).

In this question you will be assessed on using good English, organising information clearly and using specialist terms where appropriate. *(6 marks)*

(b) The table shows the effectiveness of IVF treatment in a fertility clinic in one year, 2004–2005.

	Age of women/years			
	Under 35	35–37	38–40	Over 40
Number of IVF treatments	130	100	30	20
Average number of embryos transferred	2.6	2.8	3.3	3.6
Percentage of successful pregnancies	43	30	20	13

(i) Describe the relationship between the age of women and the percentage of successful pregnancies. *(2 marks)*

(ii) Since the data were collected, doctors have been instructed to transfer fewer embryos during IVF treatment.

Suggest an explanation for this instruction. *(2 marks)*

3 **(a)** Describe in detail the stages in the testing of a new drug.

In this question you will be assessed on using good English, organising information clearly and using scientific words correctly. *(6 marks)*

(b) The drug thalidomide was developed as a sleeping pill. Scientists investigated the drug's effectiveness on volunteers.

- Two groups of 10 people, A and B, were given tablets.
- The tablets for Group A contained thalidomide but the tablets for Group B were placebos.
- The time taken for each person to fall asleep before and after taking the tablets is shown in the table.

Group	Mean time taken to fall asleep/min										
A	Person	1	2	3	4	5	6	7	8	9	10
tablets with thalidomide	Before taking the tablets	47	39	52	37	40	32	30	28	46	48
	After taking the tablets	27	32	19	17	24	26	14	22	29	31
B	Person	1	2	3	4	5	6	7	8	9	10
placebo	Before taking the tablets	36	48	52	36	44	34	34	26	44	46
	After taking the tablets	36	49	48	33	45	35	28	24	40	41

(i) What is a placebo? *(1 mark)*

(ii) Why did the scientists measure the mean time for each person to fall asleep? *(1 mark)*

(iii) What conclusions can be drawn from this investigation? *(2 marks)*

4 The diagram shows a food chain from the Antarctic ocean.

tiny green plants → shrimp → cod → seal
1000 tonnes   100 tonnes   10 tonnes   0.5 tonne

The cod is a fish and the seal is a mammal.

(a) Draw and label a pyramid of biomass for this chain. *(2 marks)*

(b) The ratio of the biomass of shrimp to the biomass of the cod is much less than the ratio of the biomass of the cod to the biomass of the seal. Explain why. *(3 marks)*

5 The diagram shows the mass of carbon involved each year in some of the processes in the carbon cycle.

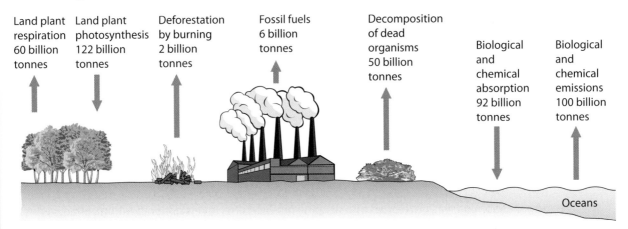

Land plant respiration 60 billion tonnes

Land plant photosynthesis 122 billion tonnes

Deforestation by burning 2 billion tonnes

Fossil fuels 6 billion tonnes

Decomposition of dead organisms 50 billion tonnes

Biological and chemical absorption 92 billion tonnes

Biological and chemical emissions 100 billion tonnes

Oceans

(a) Calculate the net change to the mass of carbon in the atmosphere in one year. *(2 marks)*

(b) Decomposition of dead organisms releases 50 million tonnes of carbon into the atmosphere every year.
Explain how decomposition of dead organisms releases carbon into the atmosphere. *(2 marks)*

6 Lichens are indicators of the concentration of sulfur dioxide in the atmosphere.

Students investigated the distribution of lichens in and around a city. From their results the students divided the city and its surroundings into six zones.

Table 1 shows the range of sulfur dioxide concentrations in the six zones.

Table 2 shows which species of lichen are found in each zone.

Table 1

Pollution zone	Sulfur dioxide concentration / $\mu g/m^3$
1	greater than 75
2	55 to 75
3	45 to 54
4	35 to 44
5	10 to 34
6	less than 10

Table 2

Species of lichens	Pollution zone
Desmococcus viridis	1
Evernia prunastri	2
Physcia adscendens	2
Xanthoria polycarpa	2
Physcia aipolia	3
Melanelia species	3
Cetraria chlorophylla	4
Graphis scripta	4
Menegazzia terebrata	5
Parmotrema arnoldii	5
Usnea rigida	5
Lobaria pulmonaria	6

6 **(a)** Which lichen species can tolerate the highest concentration of sulfur dioxide? *(1 mark)*

   (b) What is the maximum sulfur dioxide concentration that *Graphis scripta* can tolerate? *(1 mark)*

   (c) To carry out their survey, the students travelled by bus. They got off at each bus stop, measured the sulfur dioxide concentration with a meter and identified the lichens growing within 10 metres of the bus stop.

   Evaluate the method used by the students to collect their data. *(3 marks)*

   (d) Which is the better indicator of sulfur dioxide pollution in an area, using a meter or doing a lichen survey?

   Explain the reason for your answer. *(2 marks)*

7 The vole is a small mammal, about the size of a house mouse.

Scientists investigated the size of voles in different parts of Europe. They found that voles in Northern European countries were larger than those found in southern Europe.

Suggest an explanation for the evolution of the differences in size of the voles.

In this question you will be assessed on using good English, organising information clearly and using scientific words correctly. *(6 marks)*

8 Scientists have discovered genes that make plants resistant to attack by fungi in close relatives of potato plants. They have successfully transferred these genes into potato plants. The scientists are planning to grow a trial crop of the genetically engineered potatoes.

   (a) **(i)** Describe how the scientists remove genes from a relative to a potato plant. *(2 marks)*

   (ii) Describe how scientists might clone the genetically engineered potato plant. *(2 marks)*

   (b) Evaluate the issues surrounding the growing of a pilot crop of genetically engineered potato plants.

In this question you will be assessed on using good English, organising information clearly and using specialist terms where appropriate. *(6 marks)*

The Earth provides

Everything we use comes from the Earth in one way or another. A few things can be used directly, such as limestone blocks for building. However, mostly the Earth provides the raw materials that must be turned into useful products by physical or chemical processes.

In this unit you will first learn about the fundamental nature of materials; of atoms and elements, and how they form chemical compounds. It is our understanding of these fundamental ideas that has allowed us to create the products we need. You will then go on to look at three key topics of great importance to the built environment and the way we live in it.

Limestone is a common rock that has been used directly for buildings for thousands of years. Today, millions of tonnes of limestone are dug from quarries every year and chemically processed to make the key building materials cement and concrete. What effect does this have on the environment?

Most metals are found locked up in chemical compounds within the rocks. How can they be extracted, processed and used for buildings, machinery and cables? What are the environmental hazards associated with mining and metal production, and how can we make the most of our finite resources?

Crude oil, an ancient biomass found in the rocks, is the raw material for many useful products. Some of these are important fuels. How can fuels such as petrol be extracted from this complex mixture? What are the advantages and disadvantages of burning these fuels and what alternatives do we have to their use?

Test yourself

1. How are the physical properties of solids, liquids and gases controlled by the way their particles are arranged?

2. What is the difference between an element, a mixture and a compound?

3. What effect does acid rain have on limestone, and how does this compare with the simple acid/base reaction?

4. What is the reactivity series with regard to metals and their reactions?

5. What are fossil fuels and how did they form?

6. How does our use of fossil fuels affect the environment?

Objectives

By the end of this unit you should be able to:

- explain simple chemical processes in terms of the atoms involved and how they form compounds
- describe the chemistry of limestone and limestone products
- evaluate the advantages and disadvantages of our use of limestone and limestone products, including environmental issues
- describe the processes involved in extracting metals from rocks
- explain why some metals are easier and cheaper to extract than others
- analyse data on the properties of different metals and use this to explain their uses
- evaluate the possible ways in which metal extraction may have to develop in the future, as our resources are used up
- explain how useful products may be obtained from crude oil
- evaluate the social, economic and environmental impacts of the uses of fuels.

What are materials made of?

One 3-litre balloon contains 80 000 000 000 000 000 000 000 atoms or 8×10^{22} atoms.

sulfur, S

potassium, K

sodium, Na

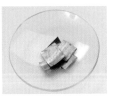

copper, Cu

Some common elements and their symbols.

Route to A*

It is well worth familiarising yourself with the names, symbols and properties of the common elements. Questions will make a lot more sense on first reading, saving you a lot of time.

Atoms

All materials are made up of **atoms** – the paper and ink on this page, the air you are breathing and every part of your body. Atoms vary in size but they are all incredibly small – about 0.000 000 1 mm wide. That means you would need 10 million of them end to end to make 1 mm.

Elements

A substance made up of only one type of atom is called an **element**. There are about 100 different elements. In most elements, like sulfur or copper, the atoms are joined together. In a few, such as the helium inside the balloons in the photo, the atoms are separate.

Each element has a unique, internationally recognised **chemical symbol** of one or two letters. Most symbols clearly derive from the name of the element in English. However some are less obvious, for historical reasons (see Table 1).

Table 1 Some elements and their symbols.

Single letters (always capital)	Double letters (first letter capital)
H Hydrogen	Al Aluminium
C Carbon	Ca Calcium
N Nitrogen	Cl Chlorine
O Oxygen	He Helium
S Sulfur	Mg Magnesium
I Iodine	Zn Zinc
Some 'oddities'	
Na Sodium – from the Latin name *natrium*	
K Potassium – from the Latin name *kalium*	
Fe Iron – from the Latin name *ferrum* (iron and steel are called ferrous metals)	
Cu Copper – from the Latin name *cuprum* (from Cyprus)	
Pb Lead – from the Latin name *plumbum* (plumbers used to work with lead pipes)	

Compounds

Compounds are substances made from two or more types of atom joined together. This joining happens during a chemical reaction. Many familiar substances, for example water and alcohol, are compounds.

Each compound has a **chemical formula**. The chemical formula for a compound contains two types of information. The symbols in the chemical formula tell you which types of atom are present. FeS, for example, is the formula for iron sulfide, which contains iron atoms and sulfur atoms combined together.

The formula FeS also tells us that there is one iron atom for every sulfur atom in the compound. We say that the **ratio** of iron atoms to sulfur atoms is 1 : 1. Some chemical formulae contain small (subscript) numbers after the symbol. The chemical formula for water, for example, is H_2O. The number tells you that there are two hydrogen atoms for every one oxygen atom. The ratio of hydrogen atoms to oxygen atoms in water is 2 : 1.

You can have the same atoms joined together and get different compounds. CO_2 is carbon dioxide and CO is carbon monoxide. Both are gases, but carbon monoxide, CO, is poisonous. Knowing the chemical formula is important.

Inside the atom

In their earliest ideas about atoms, people thought of atoms simply as spheres. We often draw them like this when we are making simple models of chemical reactions. One hundred years ago, however, scientists discovered that the atoms themselves were made of even smaller particles.

Atoms have a central **nucleus**. This is made up of **protons** and **neutrons**. Outside the nucleus are the **electrons**. The shape of the atoms is formed by the moving 'cloud' of electrons that surrounds the nucleus. Protons, and electrons are electrically charged, while neutrons have no charge (see Table 2).

Atoms of the same element always have the same number of protons in the nucleus. If the number of protons is different it is a different element. When atoms are separate, for example in helium, they have the same number of protons as electrons. Helium atoms have two protons, each with a $+1$ change, and two electrons, each with a -1 charge, so the charges cancel out and the atoms are neutral overall.

During chemical reactions electrons in atoms can be lost, gained or shared. This means that atoms that are joined together may have an overall charge. We call charged atoms **ions**; and you will learn more about them later.

sodium chloride, NaCl iron(III) oxide, Fe_2O_3

sodium fluoride, NaF copper(II) sulfate, $CuSO_4$

Some compounds and their formulae.

Table 2 The charge on atomic particles.

Name of particle	Charge
proton	$+1$
neutron	0 (neutral)
electron	-1

Questions

1 What are the symbols for sodium, sulfur, iron, lead and potassium?

2 Brass is a metal containing copper and zinc atoms. Is brass is an element?

3 Copy and fill in the table to show the ratio of the different atoms in each compound. The top one has been done for you.

Chemical formula	Hydrogen atoms	:	Sulfur atoms	:	Oxygen atoms
SO_3	0	:	1	:	3
SO_2		:		:	
H_2SO_4		:		:	
H_2O		:		:	

4 Copy and fill in the table to show the chemical formula for each compound. The top one has been done for you.

Iron atoms	:	Sulfur atoms	:	Oxygen atoms	Chemical formula
1	:	1	:	4	$FeSO_4$
1	:	0	:	1	
2	:	0	:	3	
1	:	1	:	0	

5 A single neon atom has 10 protons.

(a) How many electrons will it have? **(b)** What will be its charge overall?

6 A student stirs iron powder and sulfur powder together in a test tube. She then heats the test tube. A chemical reaction takes place and iron sulphide is made. Write an account of her experiment using the words *element, mixture, compound, symbol* and *chemical formula*.

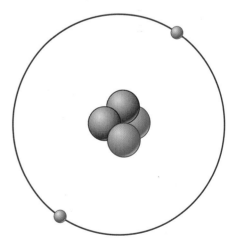

Figure 1 This simple model of a helium atom shows the electrons in orbit around the nucleus. In fact they form a fuzzy cloud, and the scale is very different.

Electrons rule chemistry

Learning objectives

- describe how most materials are made
- describe the formation of ions
- explain why metal/non-metal compounds have ionic bonds
- describe how non-metal compounds are formed and the type of bonding that occurs
- explain what happens to the total mass in chemical reactions.

Electrons control chemical reactions

When a chemical reaction takes place between atoms, electrons may move from one atom to another or be shared between atoms.

When metals and non-metals combine, the metals give up some electrons and the non-metals take them. Because the electrons are negatively charged, the once-neutral atoms become charged particles called **ions**.

- When a metal atom loses an electron it becomes a **positive ion**.
- When a non-metal atom gains an electron it becomes a **negative ion**.

Positive and negative ions are attracted to one another and can form compounds. Sodium and chlorine form a compound in this way, called sodium chloride. This is common salt. The **chemical bonds** between the ions are called an **ionic bonds**.

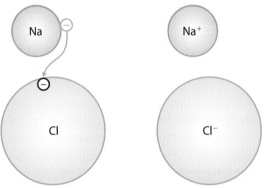

Figure 1 After an electron is transferred from each sodium atom to each chlorine atom, the sodium and chloride ions are arranged in a regular pattern to form a salt crystal.

Share and share alike

When non-metals combine, the atoms share electrons and form **molecules**. One carbon atom and two oxygen atoms can combine in this way to form carbon dioxide: CO_2. Two hydrogen atoms and one oxygen atom form water: H_2O.

Atoms of elements such as oxygen can also share electrons together and make molecules without any other elements. The oxygen in the air forms O_2 molecules from two oxygen atoms.

Strong chemical bonds form when atoms share electrons to make molecules. These are called **covalent bonds**.

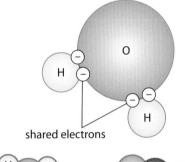

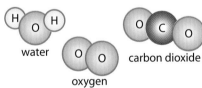

Figure 2 Electrons are shared to make bonds within molecules.

Conserving atoms

When chemicals react, the atoms rearrange themselves. We say they are conserved: that is, no atoms are lost or gained. You always end up with the same number of each type of atom as you started with. You can show this as a **balanced equation**. For example, sodium hydroxide **neutralises** hydrochloric acid to form sodium chloride and water:

$$NaOH + HCl \longrightarrow NaCl + H_2O$$
$$\text{1Na, 1O, 2H, 1Cl} \qquad \text{1Na, 1O, 2H, 1Cl}$$
$$\text{in reactants} \qquad \text{in products}$$

What if it's not that simple?

If an equation does not balance 'first go' you may need more of one reactant or product. To show this, you put a number in front of the formula. For example, $2H_2O$ means two molecules of water: $H_2O + H_2O$.

Balancing more difficult equations

The reaction of hydrogen and oxygen to form water does not balance 'first go'. Here's a step-by-step guide.

Table 1 Balancing equations.

	Step	Reactants		Products	Balanced?
1	Write the word equation	hydrogen + oxygen	⟶	water	
2	Add the formulae	H_2 + O_2	⟶	H_2O	
3	Count the atoms	2H, 2O	⟶	2H, 1O	✗ no
4	Add another water molecule	H_2 + O_2	⟶	$2H_2O$	
5	Recount	2H, 2O	⟶	4H, 2O	✗ no
6	More hydrogen needed	$2H_2$ + O_2	⟶	$2H_2O$	
7	Recount	4H, 2O	⟶	4H, 2O	✓ yes

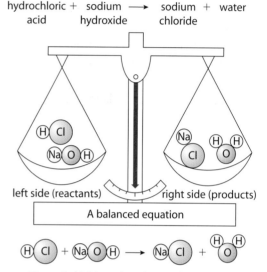

Figure 3 Making salt and water from acid and alkali: it's just a case of rearrangement.

Conserving mass

As the number of atoms does not change during a chemical reaction, it follows that the mass does not change either. For example, when calcium oxide reacts with carbon dioxide to form calcium carbonate:

$$CaO + CO_2 \longrightarrow CaCO_3$$

1Ca, 1C, 3O   1Ca, 1C, 3O   the atoms add up on

in reactants   in products   each side…

… and by experiment you will find the masses add up too:

56 g of calcium oxide and 44 g of carbon dioxide give 100 g of calcium carbonate

or

11.2 g of calcium oxide and 8.8 g of carbon dioxide give 20 g of calcium carbonate.

This is known as the **conservation of mass**.

Questions

1. Describe what happens in terms of electrons when potassium atoms react with fluorine atoms to form potassium fluoride.

2. What type of chemical bonds would you find in: **(a)** magnesium chloride, $MgCl_2$; **(b)** carbon dioxide, CO_2; **(c)** methane, CH_4; **(d)** copper oxide, Cu_2O?

3. Count up the atoms on each side of this equation to check that it balances:
   $$6CO_2 + 6H_2O \longrightarrow C_6H_{12}O_6 + 6O_2$$

4. Balance the equation for the reaction of sodium hydroxide (NaOH) and sulfuric acid (H_2SO_4) to form sodium sulfate (Na_2SO_4) plus water (H_2O).

5. Balance the equation $CO + Fe_2O_3 \longrightarrow Fe + CO_2$

6. 100 g of calcium carbonate gives 56 g of calcium oxide when heated. What mass of carbon dioxide is driven off in this reaction if no other products are formed?

7. Treating 56 g of calcium oxide with water makes 74 g of dry calcium hydroxide. What mass of water has reacted with the calcium oxide to make this?

8. Use the balanced equation for the reaction of hydrogen and oxygen to explain how atoms are conserved in a chemical reaction. If 2 g of hydrogen reacts completely with 16 g of oxygen, what mass of water will be formed?

Electrons and the periodic table

Energy levels

The electrons move round the nucleus of an atom forming an 'electron cloud', which gives the atom its shape. The pattern is not haphazard, and the electrons can only fit into certain zones. These zones are called energy levels or **electron shells**.

Atoms have many energy levels but the electrons usually occupy the lowest ones. For the first 20 elements, the pattern is a simple one.

- Level one, next to the nucleus: one or two electrons only
- Level two: up to eight electrons
- Level three: up to eight electrons (for the first 20 elements)
- Level four: any more electrons (for the first 20 elements)

If you know the number of electrons in the atoms, you can work out how they are arranged in the levels. This is called the **electronic structure** of the atom. It can be drawn on a 'flat' version of the atom as in Figure 1, or written as the numbers in each level, in turn.

Filling them up

- Hydrogen's single electron fits in the first level, and helium's two electrons fill up the first level completely.
- At number three, lithium's third electron must start a new level.
- Carbon is number six, so it half-fills the second level.
- Neon has 10 electrons, which fill both levels one and two.
- Sodium has 11 electrons, so the 11th electron starts a third level.
- Elements 12–18 (magnesium to argon) progressively fill this level.
- Calcium, at number 20, is the last element to show this simple pattern; its last two electrons are found in the fourth level.

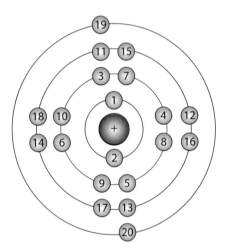

Figure 1 How electrons fill the energy levels of atoms for the first 20 elements. The grey circles represent positions that electrons can fill, numbered in order. You can mark a cross (×) to show the position of an electron, as in Figure 2.

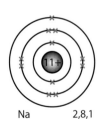
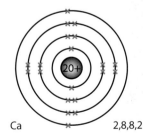

Figure 2 Electrons usually fit into the lowest available energy level.

Different properties

Different elements have different properties. However, there is a pattern to this variation that is controlled by the number of electrons in the highest energy level, or outer shell. You can see this in the **periodic table**. Each vertical column, or **group**, shows elements with similar properties. The group number tells you how many electrons there are in the highest energy level.

The periodic table may look complicated but you don't need to learn it by heart. You simply need to know how to use it. If you know the properties of one element in a vertical group, you know that the properties of other elements in that group are likely to be similar. For example magnesium (Mg) is a reactive metal, so you would expect calcium (Ca) to be a reactive metal too, as it has a similar electronic structure.

Metals are on the left of the table, non-metals on the right, divided by a zig-zag line as shown in Figure 3. Many of the metals you are familiar with from everyday life, such as iron (Fe) and copper (Cu), are found in a block that squeezes in between groups 2 and 3.

The elements are listed in order of their **atomic numbers** – hydrogen has atomic number 1, helium 2, lithium 3 and so on. The atomic number is the number of protons in an atom of the element, which is the same as the number of electrons in an uncharged atom of the element. If you add the number of protons and the number of neutrons in the atom's nucleus, you get the mass number.

Examiner feedback

It is worth becoming familiar with the layout of the periodic table. You will use it over and over again when you study chemistry.

Taking it further

The elements closest to the zig-zag line separating metals and non-metals in the periodic table – the symbols shaded in purple in Figure 3 – often have properties that are between those of metals and non-metals. For example, silicon is a semiconductor.

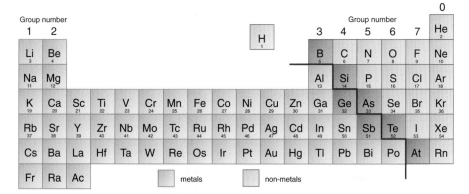

Figure 3 The periodic table of elements.

Questions

1. Magnesium has 12 protons in its nucleus. How many electrons does a magnesium atom have? How many electrons will fit in each energy level?
2. Draw the electronic structures of: oxygen (O: eight electrons), aluminium (Al: 13 electrons), chlorine (Cl: 17 electrons) and potassium (K: 19 electrons).
3. Use the periodic table to see how many electrons each of these elements have in their outer shell: **(a)** oxygen (O); **(b)** iodine (I); **(c)** barium (Ba); **(d)** boron (B).
4. From the periodic table alone, which of these elements are metals and which are non-metals? Kr, Mo, Br, Ba, Rh, Ti, P.

5. Look at the periodic table. **(a)** What do iodine (I), bromine (Br), chlorine (Cl) and fluorine (F) all have in common? **(b)** What is different about their electronic configurations?
6. Oxygen is a reactive non-metal. What chemical properties would you expect the element sulfur (S) to show and why?
7. Calcium is a reactive metal. What chemical properties would you expect the element strontium (Sr) to show and why?
8. Sodium (Na) is a very reactive metal; chlorine (Cl) is a very reactive non-metal. Use their positions in the periodic table and their electron configurations to suggest properties for lithium (Li) and fluorine (F).

A closer look at groups 1 and 0

The exciting group

Group 1 contains very reactive metals such as lithium (Li), sodium (Na) and potassium (K). These all have just one electron in their outer shell, which can be lost to give a positive ion when they react with another element. This happens easily, which is why group 1 metals are so very reactive. Because of this similar electronic structure they all react in a similar way. Group 1 metals react very strongly with oxygen.

The balanced equation for the lithium reaction is:

$$4Li + O_2 \longrightarrow 2Li_2O$$

You could write the balanced equations for sodium and potassium simply by changing Li to Na or K. The atoms combine in exactly the same way in each case.

Practical

When group 1 metals react with oxygen they burn with brightly coloured flames. For example:

lithium + oxygen $\longrightarrow$ lithium oxide (scarlet flame)

sodium + oxygen $\longrightarrow$ sodium oxide (yellow-orange flame)

potassium + oxygen $\longrightarrow$ potassium oxide (lilac flame)

These flame colours are so characteristic that they can be used to test for the elements of group 1.

Lithium emits a characteristic scarlet light.

Keep away from water

Group 1 metals also react violently with water, forming a soluble, strongly alkaline hydroxide compound and giving off hydrogen gas. So much heat energy is produced in this reaction that the hydrogen gas often catches fire.

Sodium + water $\longrightarrow$ sodium hydroxide + hydrogen

$$2Na + 2H_2O \longrightarrow 2NaOH + H_2$$

Again, substitute Li or K for Na and you have the balanced equations for the lithium or potassium reactions.

Sodium in water

Group 0: the dull group?

Group 0 contains the unreactive gases helium (He), neon (Ne) and argon (Ar). Helium has two electrons in its outer level, the other elements in group 0 have eight. This arrangement is very stable and makes the gases unreactive.

The unreactive nature of these gases, called the noble gases, is sometimes exactly what is needed. One hundred years ago, airships were filled with reactive hydrogen, which proved disastrous on many occasions when they exploded.

Modern airships, and 'floaty' party balloons, are filled with helium. Its density is low enough for it to float up through air, but its extreme lack of reactivity makes it perfectly safe.

A bright idea

Old-style light bulbs work by heating a thin filament of tungsten metal to 2000 °C. In air the tungsten would quickly react and burn out. The solution was to put the wire in a glass bulb full of unreactive argon gas.

Neon is also chemically unreactive – but it glows red-orange if electricity is passed through it. This property is used in brightly coloured neon lights. Neon has a very low boiling point, – 246 °C, and liquid neon is used as a very low temperature refrigerant. Krypton (Kr) and argon (Ar) are used in some lasers.

The noble gases were hard to spot

Air contains approximately 20% reactive oxygen and 80% 'unreactive' nitrogen. What was not suspected until just over 100 years ago was that, hidden within the nitrogen, there was about 1% truly unreactive gas…

In 1892, scientists discovered they could make nitrogen react with hot magnesium. However, when this reaction was performed with the nitrogen from the air, about 1% would not react. They realised that they must have discovered something new and called it 'noble gas', after the similarly unreactive 'noble metal' gold. It was later found that most of this 1% noble gas in air is argon, along with smaller amounts of neon. Helium was discovered in the Sun by analysis of sunlight before it was found on Earth.

This could never happen to a helium-filled airship, or balloon.

A neon sign

Science in action

Filament light bulbs are not very efficient, so they are being phased out. This means that companies producing argon have had to search for new uses for their product or go bankrupt. One new use is in food packaging. Food lasts much longer if it is kept surrounded by inert argon.

Questions

1   Rubidium (Rb) is in group 1. How will it react with water?

2   Write the balanced chemical equation for the reaction of sodium with oxygen.

3   Write the word and balanced chemical equations for the reaction of potassium with water.

4   Sodium and potassium are always kept stored in oil. Why do you think that is?

5   Krypton (Kr) is in group 0. Describe its likely chemical properties.

6   Explain why argon is used in filament light bulbs.

7   Explain why the noble gases remained undiscovered for so long.

8   Hydrogen is cheaper to produce industrially than helium. A nitrogen/oxygen mixture comes free in the air. So why do we fill party balloons with helium instead of cheaper hydrogen and fill deep-sea divers' tanks with an expensive helium/oxygen mixture instead of cheaper compressed air?

A*

Earth provides

Many old buildings in Oxford are built from limestone.

Science skills

About 70 million tonnes of limestone were quarried in Britain in 2008. We used:

- 20 million tonnes for road 'chippings'
- 21.5 million tonnes as aggregate for concrete
- 17.5 million tonnes crushed for construction ballast
- 7 million tonnes to make cement
- 2 million tonnes for the chemical industry
- 1.5 million tonnes for agriculture – neutralising soils
- 0.5 million tonnes as straight building stone.

Use the data provided above to draw a pie chart showing the uses of quarried limestone.

Rock of ages

Almost everything we use comes from the Earth in one way or another. Rock is a material that we can sometimes use straight from the ground. Blocks of stone are cut out from quarries. One example is limestone, a common rock with many uses. It has been used in building for thousands of years. Today, most limestone is crushed and used as chippings or changed by chemical processes into other useful products such as **cement**. Limestone is a very important raw material.

The effects of extraction

Digging out rocks leaves big holes – quarries. Quarries are noisy and dirty. Rock is blasted from the quarry face by explosives, spreading dust far and wide. Wildlife habitats can be destroyed as the dust and other pollutants settle over the surrounding countryside. Unfortunately, the best limestone is often found in scenic areas, such as the Peak District or the Yorkshire Dales. Quarries can be ugly places that spoil the natural beauty of the landscape, damaging tourism and upsetting local people. Rock-crushing and sorting machinery rattles away all day and huge lorries rumble down local roads. Most people wouldn't like a quarry next to their home.

However, we need the limestone for making concrete and other important materials. So we have to have quarries somewhere if we are to maintain or improve our standard of living in Britain. Quarries also provide employment for local people, which can be very important in rural areas. They also bring money into the community, which helps the local economy by supporting local shops and services.

This quarry in Yorkshire produced some of the 70 million tonnes of limestone used in Britain in 2008.

A company wishing to open up a quarry might meet local opposition on environmental grounds yet get support from the local council for providing work. They will need to weigh things up carefully to see if a new quarry is economically as well as environmentally viable. How much rock is available and how easily can it be dug out? Are there good transport links to get their product to their customers? What price can they get for that product and is that price likely to rise or fall? Quarries that make money in economic boom years might go bankrupt during an economic recession, when construction projects across the country slow down or stop.

Of course, once the rock has been removed, the soil can be replaced and trees planted. Some old quarries have been successfully turned into nature reserves or country parks. Elsewhere, old quarries have been used to build shopping malls, such as Bluewater in Kent. More imaginatively, an old clay pit in Cornwall has been turned into the amazing Eden Project.

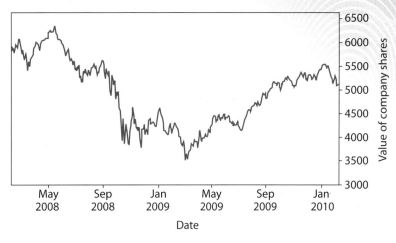

Figure 1 FTSE 100 graph. 2008 ended in a business slump that badly affected construction projects across the country.

Questions

1 Roofs used to be made from slate, a rock quarried in Wales. Why do you think cement tiles are used instead these days?

2 2008 ended in an economic slump.

   (a) How do you think that will have affected the amount of limestone used in Britain? **(b)** What effect might that have had on the price that limestone could be sold for? **(c)** How might this have affected quarrying companies?

3 The problem with quarrying is that it affects everything around it. Before a new quarry is opened, the owners have to consider a lot of different factors. These include:

   - the cost of extracting the rock
   - the availability of people living nearby to work in the quarry
   - the amount of noise that will result from blasting away the rock
   - the dust and dirt that will be produced
   - the impact of quarrying on the landscape
   - the impact of the quarry on the local wildlife
   - the extra traffic generated
   - the effect on local shops
   - the effect on tourism if the quarry is in a tourist area
   - the need for new roads to transport the stone away
   - the price for which the rock could be sold
   - what could be done with the quarry after all the rock has been removed.

   (a) Sort out the factors in the list into those that affect the environment directly, indirectly or not at all. Put them in a table. **(b)** What effect would a large quarry have on: **(i)** the local shops? **(ii)** tourism? **(c)** Who would make money from having a quarry? Explain your answer.

4 A company wants to open a new quarry in a scenic part of the Yorkshire Dales. Write a balanced report for the local council on the pros and cons of this.

The Eden project near St Austell in Cornwall was built in a disued clay pit.

Route to A*

In your exam, you may well get case-study questions related to problems around the exploitation of the Earth's mineral resources. Make sure that you justify any statements you make and bring in examples to back up your arguments.

Limestone chemistry

Learning objectives

- explain that limestone is made from calcium carbonate ($CaCO_3$)
- describe how limestone and other carbonates react with acid
- explain why limestone is so badly affected by acid rain
- explain how and why limestone is used to neutralise acidity in lakes.

The chemical structure of limestone

Limestone is the compound calcium carbonate. Its chemical formula is $CaCO_3$. This means that for every calcium atom there is one carbon atom and three oxygen atoms. All carbonates have one carbon atom and three oxygen atoms arranged like this in a regular arrangement known as a **lattice**. This regular arrangement is reflected in the shape of any crystals that form, as shown for calcite in the photograph.

Calcium carbonate in an irregular, non-crystalline form.

Calcite: the natural crystal form of calcium carbonate.

Limestone reacts with acid

Drop a piece of limestone into acid and it will fizz steadily. The acid reacts with the calcium carbonate to form a salt, water and carbon dioxide. For example, with hydrochloric acid:

calcium carbonate + hydrochloric acid ⟶ calcium chloride + water + carbon dioxide

$$CaCO_3 + 2HCl \longrightarrow CaCl_2 + H_2O + CO_2$$

Acid rain

Rainwater is naturally slightly acidic and, over several million years, it will slowly dissolve limestone. This process can open cracks into fissures or even hollow out gigantic cave systems such as those at Cheddar, in Somerset. Pollution can make rain much more acidic. Sulfur dioxide from power stations can dissolve in rain to form sulfuric acid. Nitrogen oxides from car exhausts can dissolve to form nitric acid. These can make **acid rain**, which is strong enough to dissolve limestone over much shorter timescales.

In polluted areas, old limestone buildings have been badly damaged by acid rain and the fine detail of many statues has been lost forever.

However, limestone can be used to fight back against pollution. Lakes and rivers that have been acidified by acid rain can be restored by adding powdered limestone to neutralise the acid. The calcium sulfate produced is harmless and is in any case not very soluble in water. This is safer than adding an alkali, a base disolved in water, because if you add too much limestone it will simply remain undissolved and settle out harmlessly.

neutralisation

calcium carbonate + sulfuric acid $\longrightarrow$ calcium sulfate + water + carbon dioxide

$$CaCO_3 \quad + \quad H_2SO_4 \quad \longrightarrow \quad CaSO_4 \quad + \quad H_2O \quad + \quad CO_2$$
$$\text{(acid)} \qquad \text{(neutral salt)}$$

A common pattern

Carbonates of other metals such as magnesium, copper, sodium and zinc react in the same way. For example, copper carbonate is a green solid. If you put a piece in sulfuric acid it will fizz and dissolve to form the salt copper sulfate.

copper carbonate + sulfuric acid $\longrightarrow$ copper sulfate + water + carbon dioxide

$$CuCO_3 \quad + \quad H_2SO_4 \quad \longrightarrow \quad CuSO_4 \quad + \quad H_2O \quad + \quad CO_2$$

Copper carbonate (green) and copper sulfate (blue).

This limestone statue has been badly damaged by acid rain.

Questions

1 Why do crystals of calcium carbonate all have a similar shape?

2 **(a)** What is the name of the salt that is formed when limestone dissolves in hydrochloric acid? **(b)** Explain why you need 2HCl to balance the equation.

3 In old churchyards in polluted areas you will find tombstones made from rocks such as limestone or granite. On some the inscriptions are still easy to read but on others you can barely make out any writing. Which type is likely to have been made from limestone? Explain the reason for your choice.

4 Fish tanks containing a lot of fish can get 'self-polluted' and acidic. You can buy solid white blocks to put in the tank that slowly dissolve over time to overcome this. What are the blocks likely to be made from, and how do they help to protect the fish?

5 Powdered limestone can be used to neutralise acid spills in the laboratory. Complete and balance this equation for the reaction that occurs if spilt nitric acid is neutralised in this way.
$$CaCO_3 + HNO_3 \longrightarrow Ca(NO_3)_2 + \rule{1.5cm}{0.4pt} + \rule{1.5cm}{0.4pt}$$

6 **(a)** What would you see happen if you put some copper carbonate into sulfuric acid? **(b)** What is the gas given off? **(c)** The solution turns blue. What chemical causes this to happen?

7 Zinc carbonate ($ZnCO_3$) reacts with sulfuric acid to form zinc sulfate ($ZnSO_4$). Write a balanced chemical equation for this reaction.

8 Fish prefer water to be nearly neutral. What would happen if you tried to neutralise acid lakes with alkali but put too much in? Why is this not a problem with limestone?

A helicopter dropping powdered limestone into an acidified lake.

Ⓐ*

New materials from limestone

Learning objectives

- explain how limestone and other carbonates can be broken down by thermal decomposition
- describe how calcium oxide can be turned into calcium hydroxide
- explain that calcium hydroxide can be used to neutralise acid and improve soils
- describe the test for carbon dioxide.

Route to A* 🄰

Atoms of different elements have different masses. These are shown in the periodic table, and can be used to work out how much of each product you will get in a reaction. Use a periodic table to calculate the masses of the compounds in Figure 1, and compare your figures with the example in the text.

Thermal decomposition

If limestone is heated strongly, the compound is broken down and the atoms are rearranged.

- The carbon atom takes two oxygen atoms to form carbon dioxide.
- The calcium atom is left with just one oxygen atom; this is calcium oxide.

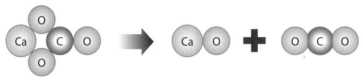

$$\text{calcium carbonate} \xrightarrow{\text{heating}} \text{calcium oxide} + \text{carbon dioxide}$$

Figure 1 Particle model for the quicklime reaction. Note that calcium carbonate and calcium oxide are ionic compounds held together by ionic bonds, whereas carbon dioxide is a molecule with covalent bonds.

As with all chemical reactions, mass is conserved. Yet if you measure the 'before and after' masses for this reaction, the mass will appear to be lower after the reaction. The reason is simple when you think about it: only the calcium oxide remains to be measured. Carbon dioxide is a gas, which escapes into the atmosphere and is lost. So, for example, 100 g of reactant limestone will apparently only give you 56 g of product, but that 'product' is all calcium oxide. The 44 g of carbon dioxide will have escaped unmeasured.

Science in action

The calcium oxide formed in this way, once called lime, glows with a bright white light when heated. This light was used to illuminate the stage in the theatre before electric lights were invented. This is where the phrase 'in the limelight' comes from.

Limelight may be history in the theatre but campers still use it. Camping gas lights have a 'mantle' coated with calcium oxide around the flame to give out a bright white light.

Campers in the limelight.

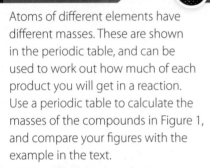

Green copper carbonate breaks down to black copper oxide when heated.

Breaking down a compound by heating it like this is called **thermal decomposition**. All metal carbonates will break down in this way. For example, green copper carbonate breaks down to black copper oxide if heated over a Bunsen burner.

$$CuCO_3 \xrightarrow{\text{heating}} CuO + CO_2$$

For some group 1 metal carbonates, such as potassium carbonate, the temperature needed to make this decomposition happen is too high to achieve with just a Bunsen burner.

Reacting calcium oxide

Calcium oxide is a very strong alkali. It reacts with water to form calcium hydroxide. A lot of heat is given out in this reaction. If you spilt calcium oxide on your skin it would react with the water in your body and give you a bad burn.

$$\text{calcium oxide} + \text{water} \longrightarrow \text{calcium hydroxide}$$
$$CaO + H_2O \longrightarrow Ca(OH)_2$$

 energy given out

Science in action

Farmers have used these reactions for centuries, roasting limestone over charcoal fires in special kilns. They made calcium hydroxide to use as a simple fertiliser to make their soil less acid. Calcium hydroxide also helps to break up the soil so that plants can grow well.

$$\text{calcium hydroxide} + \text{soil acids} \longrightarrow \text{calcium salts} + \text{water}$$
$$\text{(a base)} \qquad \text{(an acid)} \qquad \text{(neutral)}$$

Testing for carbon dioxide

A solution of calcium hydroxide is called limewater. This can be used to test for carbon dioxide. If you bubble carbon dioxide through limewater, it turns cloudy as a precipitate of white, insoluble calcium carbonate forms. Limewater is alkaline – the man in the photograph should wear eye protection.

$$\text{calcium hydroxide} + \text{carbon dioxide} \longrightarrow \text{calcium carbonate} + \text{water}$$
$$Ca(OH)_2 + CO_2 \longrightarrow CaCO_3 \qquad H_2O$$

Questions

1   Copy and complete this equation. Make sure it is balanced.

$$CaCO_3 \longrightarrow CaO + \underline{\hspace{2cm}}$$

2   Why have farmers made calcium oxide from limestone for hundreds of years?

3   Iron carbonate ($FeCO_3$) breaks down just like calcium carbonate. What new chemicals would you get if you heated this? Write a word equation for the reaction.

4   In the thermal decomposition of copper carbonate, the black solid left behind weighs less than the original copper carbonate. Why?

5   Zinc carbonate ($ZnCO_3$) breaks down in the same way to give zinc oxide (ZnO). Write a balanced equation for this reaction.

6   Calcium hydroxide can neutralise acids such as sulfuric acid. Complete this equation and make it balance.

$$Ca(OH)_2 + H_2SO_4 \longrightarrow CaSO_4 + \underline{\hspace{2cm}}$$

7   Describe each stage of the 'limestone cycle' of reactions, giving the balanced equations.

8   Calcium oxide has to be handled very carefully. Explain why, as fully as you can.

A*

Calcium hydroxide fertiliser was made locally by farmers all over the world.

The air we breathe out contains carbon dioxide and turns limewater cloudy.

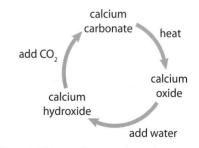

calcium carbonate → heat → calcium oxide → add water → calcium hydroxide → add CO_2 → calcium carbonate

Figure 2 This reaction completes the 'limestone cycle' of reactions.

C1 2.4 New rocks from old

Learning objectives

- describe how cement and concrete are made
- evaluate the advantages and disadvantages of concrete as a building material, including the environmental effects of its production
- explain why concrete needs to be reinforced with steel.

Rock or 'artificial rock'?

These statues look similar. One took a sculptor many weeks to make by chiselling the limestone. The other was made by simply pouring concrete into a mould.

Concrete or rock?

Making cement, mortar and concrete

To make **cement**, limestone is heated with clay in a big oven, called a rotary kiln because it keeps turning to mix everything. Thermal decomposition of the limestone occurs to give calcium oxide, which is mixed with other chemicals from the clay. The roasted product is ground to form a light grey powder. This is cement. Cement forms a paste with water that soon sets solid by a series of chemical reactions. The new compounds form tiny crystals that interlock tightly to make a hard, rock-like material.

Cement can be mixed with sand to make **mortar**, which makes a paste with water for binding bricks together.

Cement is usually mixed with sand, **aggregate** – gravel or crushed rock – and water to make **concrete**, which is cheaper and stronger than pure cement. Concrete forms a thick liquid when first mixed, and can be poured into any shape. Slow chemical reactions make the cement in it set after a few hours and eventually it becomes rock-hard. It is used to make roads, bridges and the frameworks and foundations of buildings.

The aggregate, which makes up the bulk of the concrete, can vary depending on what is available locally, from natural sand and gravel, through crushed rocks and quarry waste, to crushed and recycled building rubble left over from demolition. You can even use ash from power stations. Locally sourced materials help to keep costs down.

Figure 1 A rotary cement kiln.

The Royal Festival Hall was opened in 1951 as part of the Festival of Britain.

Cement and concrete's carbon footprint

Making cement from limestone produces carbon dioxide, which adds to Britain's carbon footprint (this contributes to global warming). The amounts produced are relatively small (just 3% of the total CO_2 emissions of the UK), but are still significant. Fortunately, concrete re-absorbs some of this CO_2 as it continues to harden over a year or so.

Figure 1 labels: limestone and clay, rotating kiln, gas, cement, grinder

Concrete: beauty or the beast?

The architects who designed the Royal Festival Hall in London wanted to show off their building material. They left the concrete exposed for all to see. Some people like it but many find the buildings ugly, especially now that the gleaming white concrete is streaked and dirty.

The Bahá'í Lotus temple in Delhi is also made of concrete. Concrete is so versatile you can build whatever you like from it.

Getting the best out of concrete

Building with quarried stone is a slow, labour-intensive and expensive process. Each block has to be carefully cut to shape and fitted into place by an expert craftsman.

In comparison, building with concrete is quick, cheap and easy.

- Cement is relatively cheap to produce on an industrial scale.
- Powdered cement is easy to store and transport.
- Aggregate of one sort or another can be found almost anywhere and is relatively cheap.
- Liquid concrete can be easily mixed on-site.
- Liquid concrete can be moulded into any shape: floor, girders, domes, ornaments.
- Once it sets, concrete really is rock-hard.

Concrete has one problem that it shares with quarried limestone: it is very strong if you try to squash it, so it can support the weight of very large buildings such as skyscrapers. However, it is brittle, so if you stretch or bend it, it can crack easily. To overcome this problem, concrete beams or girders are reinforced with steel rods that stop the concrete from stretching and cracking.

The Bahá'í Lotus temple in Delhi, India, which was completed in 1986.

Steel rods are used to strengthen concrete.

Questions

1. Every tonne of limestone that is turned into cement releases 440 kg of carbon dioxide into the atmosphere. Suggest one problem caused by cement manufacture.

2. How does concrete reduce this effect as it slowly hardens?

3. Why is concrete used rather than pure cement?

4. How can the choice of aggregate help to keep the concrete costs down?

5. Explain why it would be hard to build a limestone block skyscraper.

6. Many modern buildings now have a concrete framework but are faced with other more expensive materials such as brick or tiles. Why is this?

7. Old buildings often had wooden beams over doors and windows to support the weight of stone or brick above. The wood was strong and could bend slightly without cracking. Today these beams are more likely to be made of concrete. **(a)** What advantage does wood have over simple concrete for this use? **(b)** How could the concrete beam be changed to overcome this problem? **(c)** What is the disadvantage of using wood if you want your building to last a very long time?

8. Explain as fully as you can why concrete has become such a popular and important building material over the last 100 years.

Examiner feedback

You won't be expected to *know* the properties of other building materials: wood, brick, steel or glass. However, in the examination you might be *given* a table of their properties to compare with concrete.

While concrete is a very useful material there are significant environmental effects associated with its production and use. This can also form the focus of examination questions.

Digging up the ore

The Bingham Canyon copper mine, Utah, USA.

Where do metals come from?

Metals are found in chemical compounds in the rocks of the Earth. Some metals are quite common. A field of mud contains tonnes of aluminium and a lot of iron too. The trouble is, the metals are extremely difficult to extract. Fortunately, natural processes sometimes concentrate metals in certain rocks from which it is relatively easy and cheap to extract them. Rocks like this are called **ores**.

Copper ore. Most copper ores contain a very small percentage of copper.

Iron ore. Most iron ore is used to make steel.

Some ores, like iron ore, are relatively common. Others, like copper ore, are very rare, so when we find a big body of concentrated copper ore we just keep on digging until it has all been dug up. The Bingham Canyon mine in Utah, USA, is now nearly 1 km deep. Open-cast mining, which is just digging a big open hole in the ground, presents the same problem for the environment as limestone quarrying; see lesson C1 2.1. Pollution issues may be even greater, as many ores are toxic. Also, only a fraction of the mined rock is useful, so the rest is left in unsightly **spoil** tips. Mining companies have to allow for environmental clean-up costs when working out the economics of their mine. They may have to landscape unsightly areas and remove toxic materials for safe disposal. On the other hand, mining provides work and trade for the local area. It also provides essential raw materials for industry.

Is it worth it?

Ores contain metal compounds in a concentrated form. However, that doesn't necessarily mean that it is worth the cost and effort to extract it. That will depend on:

- how concentrated the ore is
- how easy it is to get the ore out of the ground (cheaper for open-cast mining than deep underground mining)
- how easy it is to extract the metal from the ore
- what price you can get for the metal you extract
- the long-term environmental clean-up costs.

The economics of the process change over time as the demand for the metal and/or its price changes. A mine that is just breaking even might suddenly start making a fortune if the price of its metal rises – or just as suddenly go bankrupt if the price falls.

Science skills A small Welsh gold mine was just about breaking even in 2007. Table 1 shows how the price of gold varied over the next two years.

Table 1 Gold prices (2008–9).

Date	Price of gold / $/oz
03/2008	1000
06/2008	900
09/2008	700
12/2008	890
03/2009	920
06/2009	940
09/2009	1050
12/2009	1200

a Plot a line graph of the gold price over the two years.

b The mining company's costs did not vary much over the period. Explain what would have happened to the finances of the company over this period.

Extracting the metal from the ore

There are four stages in extracting a metal from its ore.

1.	The ore is mined.	Mining can be by open-cast digging or may involve tunnelling down to underground deposits, which is more difficult and expensive.
2.	The ore is separated from impurities.	The waste from these impurities, spoil, is left by the mine. Spoil tips may contain poisonous metals, like copper and lead, that dissolve in rainwater and leak into the soil. Most plants that are sown on spoil tips die.
3.	The ore is converted to the metal.	Usually the ore is heated in air or with carbon. In both cases impurities can react with air to form poisonous substances like sulfur dioxide.
4.	The metal formed is then purified.	See lesson C1 3.3 for examples.

Pure metals such as copper or aluminium are turned into useful products, for example electrical wires, saucepans and bikes. When the product has worn out and is no longer useful, it can be recycled. This is particularly important for metals like aluminium that are expensive to make, and for very rare metals. For example, you can get more gold per tonne out of recycled mobile phones than you can out of the richest gold ore.

Recycling metals:

- saves money
- means that reserves of metal in the ground last longer
- avoids waste and pollution
- lessens the effects of mining on people and the environment
- saves energy.

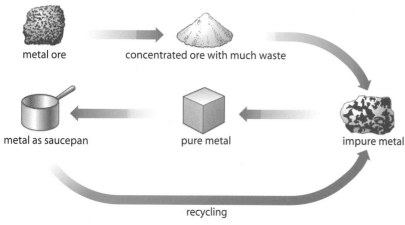

metal ore   concentrated ore with much waste

metal as saucepan   pure metal   impure metal

recycling

Figure 1 Extraction and one use of aluminium.

Aluminium is expensive to make and definitely worth recycling.

Examiner feedback

While there are advantages to recycling metals there are sometimes disadvantages. For example, it may be difficult and expensive to separate out the different metals from complex products, and the processes used might cause pollution in the local environment. You might be given data on these issues to consider in an examination.

Questions

1 What are the similarities between open-cast mining and quarrying for limestone?

2 How do spoil tips affect the environment?

3 Ordinary garden mud contains a few per cent of aluminium. Why is this not used as aluminium ore?

4 A new, important use has been found for a very rare metal. **(a)** What will be the probable effect on the price of the metal? **(b)** Will this make mining the metal more worthwhile?

5 Why do plants growing on spoil tips die?

6 What are the advantages of recycling?

7 Draw a flow chart to show how a copper kettle can be made from copper ore and then recycled.

8 A typical 100 g mobile phone might contain 16 g of copper and 0.03 g of gold. Discuss the potential advantages and disadvantages of recycling the metals in mobile phones.

A*

Metal from the ore

Learning objectives

- explain why some rare metals were discovered before more common metals
- describe how less-reactive metals such as copper and iron can be extracted
- explain why more-reactive metals such as aluminium are much more difficult and expensive to extract than less-reactive metals.

Gold was well known to the ancient Egyptians.

most reactive

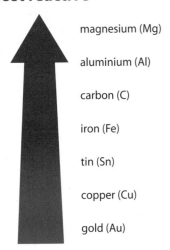

magnesium (Mg)

aluminium (Al)

carbon (C)

iron (Fe)

tin (Sn)

copper (Cu)

gold (Au)

least reactive

Figure 1 The reactivity series of metals.

Which metals are common?

Aluminium and iron are two metals we use a lot. As you can see from Table 1, they are also very common in rocks. Some other important metals, however, such as copper and gold, are really very rare.

Iron is king

Iron is the metal we use most. In 2007, the annual global production of iron peaked at almost 1.5 billion tonnes. That is 20 times as much as all the other metals put together. Production on this scale helps to make iron cheap compared with aluminium, even though aluminium is more common.

Reactivity and metals

Gold is a very **unreactive** metal. It does not react with other elements and so is found in rocks as uncombined metal. It may be rare but, if you are very lucky, you could find a nugget of pure gold.

In contrast, aluminium is a very reactive metal. Because of this, the aluminium atoms are tightly combined in compounds with other atoms such as oxygen. Mud contains plenty of aluminium but you cannot easily extract it. You never find aluminium as a pure element in the Earth's crust.

Table 1 Metals in rocks.

Metal	Percentage of the rocks of the Earth's crust
aluminium	7
iron	4
magnesium	2
copper	0.0045
tin	0.0002
gold	0.000 000 5

Table 2 Metal prices.

Metal	Price/tonne (January 2010)
aluminium	£3600
copper	£4500
iron	£1600

There is plenty of aluminium in this mud. But how could you tell?

Carbon reduction and oxidation

Carbon is more **reactive** than metals such as iron and copper, so it can displace these metals from their compounds, pushing the metal out and taking its place. **Displacement reactions** with carbon are used to get less-reactive metals from their ores.

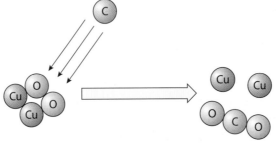

Figure 2 Carbon can displace metals such as copper from their oxide ores.

Many metal ores are oxides. When we react the ore with carbon, the carbon combines with oxygen from the ore to form carbon dioxide. The carbon is oxidised. This is an **oxidation** reaction.

The metal oxide ore has its oxygen taken away. The metal oxide is reduced to the metal only. This process is called **reduction**. Reduction is the chemical opposite of oxidation, so the two reactions always go together. Figure 3 shows an example with copper oxide.

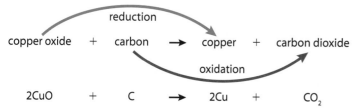

$$\text{copper oxide} \quad + \quad \text{carbon} \quad \longrightarrow \quad \text{copper} \quad + \quad \text{carbon dioxide}$$

$$2CuO \quad + \quad C \quad \longrightarrow \quad 2Cu \quad + \quad CO_2$$

Figure 3 Reduction and oxidation in the copper oxide/carbon reaction.

Many metals, such as iron, tin and lead, as well as copper, have been extracted by this method for thousands of years. Originally the carbon was in the form of charcoal. Today coke, made from coal, is used instead. The oxide ore and coke are heated to very high temperatures in a furnace. As they react, the newly formed metal melts and can be run out through a tap at the bottom.

Why aluminium is so expensive

Aluminium is more reactive than carbon. You can't use the carbon reduction method to get aluminium from its ores. Aluminium ore first has to be heated up and melted. The **molten** ore is then split apart using large amounts of energy in the form of electricity. This process is called **electrolysis**. This is a very costly process that makes aluminium much more expensive than iron.

Figure 4 Molten metal can be run out from the bottom of the furnace.

Questions

1. How much more common is iron than gold?

2. Explain why rare gold was discovered before the much more common aluminium.

3. Tin oxide (SnO_2) reacts with carbon to give tin and carbon dioxide.
   (a) Write this as a word equation, showing the oxidation and reduction arrows. **(b)** Write the equation in symbols.

4. Write a simple word equation for the reduction of iron oxide by carbon.

5. Complete and balance the equation for the reaction of the iron ore magnetite with carbon.
   $$Fe_3O_4 + C \longrightarrow Fe + CO_2$$

6. Why is iron not produced commercially by the electrolysis of molten iron oxide?

7. Aluminium powder and iron oxide react violently to give molten iron.
   (a) Write a word equation for this reaction and explain what is happening.
   (b) Why is this reaction not used to make iron commercially?

8. Aluminium is nearly twice as common as iron in the Earth's crust, yet costs more than twice as much to buy. Use your understanding of the chemistry of the production methods used to explain this.

Developing new methods of extraction

Learning objectives

- describe how iron is extracted from its ore
- explain why copper is easier to get from good-quality ores
- explain why new methods of copper extraction are being developed.

Wanted by all

Iron is the most widely used metal, so we need to produce plenty of it to supply the world. Over the last 300 years scientists have refined the carbon reduction method to make it very efficient. Iron, however, is not as easy to extract as less-reactive metals, such as copper or lead.

Iron plays hard to get

Carbon reduction reactions need a kick-start of energy to get them going. For copper, the heat from a simple fire will do it. However, for iron, much more energy is needed. You can make coke burn at a very high temperature by providing more oxygen. In a **blast furnace**, air is pumped through the burning coke, raising the temperature to 1600 °C or more, hot enough to reduce the ore and melt the iron.

Iron ore (iron oxide), coke (carbon) and limestone are tipped in at the top of the blast furnace. The limestone is only there to remove impurities. The main reaction is the reduction of iron oxide and the oxidation of carbon.

$$\text{iron oxide} + \text{carbon} \longrightarrow \text{iron} + \text{carbon dioxide}$$

Most iron ore used today is only about 50% iron oxide. This will produce about 350 kg of iron per tonne (1000 kg) of ore. However, the impurities from 1 tonne of ore will react with the limestone to make just under 1 tonne of waste material called **slag**, which is dumped. Slag heaps can be unsightly and dangerous.

Molten iron pours from a blast furnace.

Copper's easy – if you can find it

Copper is usually found as copper sulfide crystals scattered through the ore body. In the past, this was converted to copper oxide and then the copper was extracted from the ore by carbon reduction in a furnace. For the best ores, heating alone was enough. However, good-quality, copper-rich ore is getting harder to find. There are just a few major copper mines dotted around the world. Even in these the ore only contains about 1% copper. Separating out the copper by reduction in a furnace is too expensive, so nowadays other methods are used.

Copper sulfide ore.

In one method, acid is sprayed onto the rock. Soluble copper compounds dissolve out of the rock and the **leachate** solution is collected. The copper is then removed from the leachate by electrolysis. This works because the copper forms positive ions in the solution. These positive ions move towards the negative electrode, where they can be collected – see Figure 1.

What is the future?

We use large amounts of copper for water pipes and electrical wiring so the copper mines will soon be exhausted. Many old mines are now reworking their old waste tips to get out more of the copper by **leaching** and electrolysis.

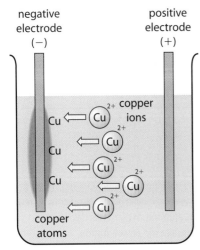

Figure 1 Electrolysis of copper sulfate solution. Positive copper ions move towards the negative electrode.

This process can extract copper from rocks containing just 1% ore. However, scientists are working hard to find ways of extracting smaller and smaller fractions. One new method, called **bioleaching**, involves using special bacteria that 'eat' the copper ions from the rock. They produce a copper-rich leachate. Another method, **phytomining** (see lesson C1 3.4), uses special plants that absorb metals from the soil as they grow.

Even if we find a new source of copper, however, environmentalists have started to object to mining companies ripping great holes in the Earth.

- Mines will inevitably be surrounded by waste heaps.
- Rainwater will naturally leach these, carrying toxic metal salts into surrounding rivers.

A new leaching method that does not affect the environment so much involves drilling down to the ore. Acid is then pumped down to the ore and comes back up to the surface rich in copper for processing: the process is illustrated in Figure 2. You don't need to dig big, ugly holes in the ground at all.

Any old iron will do

In some ore-rich areas the rivers can carry quite high concentrations of dissolved copper salts, or salts of other metals. Iron is more reactive than copper, so if you put scrap iron in these rivers, the iron will displace the copper from solution. The copper can then be collected and refined.

$$\text{copper sulfate} + \text{iron} \xrightarrow{\text{displacement}} \text{iron sulfate} + \text{copper}$$

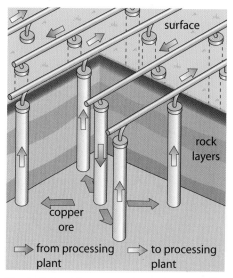

Figure 2 Leaching copper the environmentally friendly way?

Practical

If you put an iron nail into copper sulfate solution, it will soon become coated with copper.

Questions

1. Explain how the blast of air in a blast furnace helps to raise the temperature.

2. Limestone reacts with any sand (SiO_2) in iron ore to form calcium silicate. Complete the balanced chemical equation:

   $CaCO_3 + SiO_2 \longrightarrow CaSiO_3 + \underline{\hspace{1cm}}$

3. **(a)** Write out the simple word equation for the blast furnace and add the oxidation and reduction arrows. **(b)** If the iron oxide is Fe_2O_3, write a balanced equation for this reaction.

4. Explain why copper cannot be extracted from 1% copper ore in a furnace.

5. Explain why copper collects at the negative terminal during electrolysis.

6. Draw a flow chart for the production of copper from low-grade ores by leaching.

7. Complete and balance the equation for the displacement of copper from copper sulfate by iron: $CuSO_4 + \underline{\hspace{1cm}} \longrightarrow FeSO_4 \underline{\hspace{1cm}}$

8. Can you suggest a method for cleaning up rivers polluted with copper salts? Explain how it works. Are there any possible disadvantages to your method?

Finite resources

Scarce resources

We all live on the Earth and get everything we need from it. There are more than six billion people on the planet, and we are consuming the Earth's resources at an ever-increasing rate. Some metal ores will become scarce over the coming decades.

Science skills

a Which metals might run out in your lifetime using today's mining techniques?

b Iron is unlikely to run out in the near future, but steels used for machinery or other high-performance uses are alloyed with metals such as vanadium and manganese that might run out. What problems would society face if we ran out of metals for these important alloys?

c As metals get scarce, the price will rise. How might this help to make more metal available?

Table 1 Summary of common metals and their reserves.

Metal	Uses	Proven reserves will last until…
tin	rust-proofing for steel; also used in bronze and solder	2030
copper	electrical wiring, water pipes; also used in brass and bronze	2030
tungsten	the filament in 'old fashioned' light bulbs; also added to steel to make it very hard and strong	2050
aluminium	cans, saucepans and aeroplanes	2050
nickel	added to steel for acid resistance, and in coinage	2100

Earth from space.

Health and safety rules may not be applied as strictly in some countries as in the West. This man is not wearing any eye protection.

Are we exploiting poorer countries?

Some countries are rich in mineral resources, while others have few. Industrial societies are buying up more than their fair share of the global resources. Sometimes this is because the countries of the developed world have used up their own resources. However, often it is because it is cheaper to mine in developing countries because the wages of the miners are so low. This does have some benefits, as it provides jobs for people in the developing countries. However, sometimes the working conditions are not very good.

Zambia is a poor country. Its economy relies on exports of copper from its huge copper mines. Forty years ago Zambia was encouraged to take out huge loans from the World Bank to develop these mines. They said it would raise the standard of living for all Zambians.

d What happened to the price paid for copper in the late 1970s?

e What effect do you think this had on the people and economy of Zambia?

f Do you think the advice from the World Bank was good or not? Explain your answer.

g In the boom of 2007 the price shot up to $8000 per tonne. What do you think happened to the price in the recession that followed in 2008?

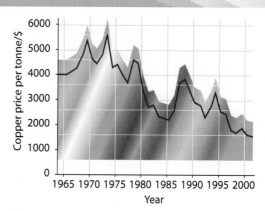

Figure 1 Copper prices.

The economics of recycling

Recycling can help to make our resources last longer and reduce pollution. It also reduces our energy consumption. However, it costs money. One of the problems is that waste material may well contain different metals mixed up. Recycling is only economically viable at the moment for metals that are easy to separate, such as aluminium, iron or steel, or expensive metals such as gold. As technology improves, perhaps we will be able to do this for all metals.

Reclaiming spoilt land

Mines and associated industrial activities can leave great areas of spoilt, contaminated land. How can we reclaim these 'brownfield' sites for housing or recreation? Help is at hand from a surprising source.

Many plants won't grow on soil contaminated with metals, but others do well. The brassicas, a plant family that includes cabbages and sprouts, not only thrive but take up the metals into their leaves. This has led to the development of environmentally friendly **phytomining**. Brassicas are grown on metal-rich soils. As they grow they take any metals out of the soil, cleaning the land. At the end of the season they are harvested and burnt. The metal-rich ash left behind can then be collected and metals such as cadmium, nickel and cobalt may be extracted.

Examiner feedback

You need to understand that new methods of extraction need to be economic and this will partly be determined by how scarce the metal becomes and how much of it is needed.

Questions

1. Brassicas grown on metal-rich soils may contain up to 1% nickel by dry mass. **(a)** If a 1 hectare field gives 10 tonnes of dry biomass, how much nickel could be recovered? **(b)** If the price of nickel were £10 000 per tonne, what would this be worth? **(c)** If the growing and extraction costs were £400 per hectare, would this phytomining be economically viable?

2. Alfacture is a large company that produces one million tonnes of aluminium goods every year. It has its own plant for extracting aluminium from aluminium ore but also uses recycled aluminium. The energy used to extract the metal from its ore costs £100 per tonne.

   The energy used to recycle aluminium costs just £5 per tonne. The company currently uses 40% recycled aluminium in its products. **(a)** Calculate Alfacture's energy costs for its annual production of aluminium goods. **(b)** The company hopes to increase the amount of recycled aluminium it uses to 50%. How much money a year would it save on energy costs? **(c)** Why is it so important to recycle aluminium, which is a common metal? Explain your answer fully.

3. Suggest what will happen when current copper reserves run out. How might we prevent this situation arising?

Heavyweight and lightweight metals

Useful metals

Technology relies on the strength and ease of shaping of metals for everything from aeroplanes to tin cans. Thousands of kilometres of electric cables snake across the country to bring us the power we need for our electrical equipment. Our civilisation is heavily dependent on metals.

The useful properties of metals

- Metals are strong, which makes them good structural materials. We use them to build machines, bridges and the frameworks for large buildings.
- Metals are easy to shape: they can be bent, pressed, drawn and rolled. Car body panels are pressed out of sheet steel.
- Most metals have high melting points. Engines don't melt when they get hot in use.
- Metals also conduct heat and electricity. They are used in electrical wiring and as **heat sinks**, to conduct heat away from microprocessors in computers, to stop them overheating.

The properties of metals make them a useful construction material.

				B		
				Al		
Fe	Co	Ni	Cu	Zn	Ga	Ge
Ru	Rh	Pd	Ag	Cd	In	Sn
Os	Ir	Pt	Au	Hg	Tl	Pb

Figure 1 Iron and copper are transition metals.

Everyday heavyweights

Iron and copper are two of the **transition metals** from the central block of the periodic table. The transition block contains many important, everyday metals.

Iron

Iron, usually used in the form of steel (see lesson C1 3.6), is by far the most widely used metal. It can be made hard and tough for machinery, tools, bridges or girders. Or it can be made into sheets that can be rolled, cut and pressed into shape for anything from car bodies to cans. It is extremely versatile. However, it has one big weakness: it rusts.

Copper

Copper is particularly useful as it is such a good electrical **conductor**. It is also soft and bendy, so it is great for electrical wires. It is also a good conductor of heat. The best saucepans often have copper bottoms. Copper is not very reactive: it does not react with water, and so does not corrode like iron and steel. This makes it useful for pipes for plumbing. It also means it can be used for roofing on important buildings, although it is too expensive for general use in this way.

Copper is our electrical conductor of choice.

The lightweight champions

Steel may be fantastic for cars, trains and ships, but its high density makes it useless for aircraft. An aircraft made from steel would weigh twice as much as a modern plane. It would have to use too much energy to get off the ground. Aluminium is not a transition metal. It is not as strong as steel but its density is very much lower. It can be used to make a plane that is both strong enough *and* light enough to fly. Without aluminium there could be no commercial airliners.

Commercial aircraft rely on lightweight yet strong aluminium.

Table 1 Properties of widely used metals.

Metal	Density / g/cm^3	Strength	Melting point/°C
pure aluminium	2.7	low–medium	660
steel	7.7	high	1540
titanium	4.5	high	1670

Supersonic fighter jets fly so fast that the wings get hot enough to melt aluminium. A new 'supermetal' was needed that was strong and had a low density but a high melting point. Titanium fitted the bill perfectly. Titanium is as strong as steel but less dense, though denser than aluminium. A bonus is that its melting point is higher than that of steel – high enough to withstand the frictional heating caused by supersonic flight. In fact titanium is such a supermetal we would use it to replace steel all the time if it were not so expensive.

High-performance fighters need even stronger (but more expensive) titanium.

Resisting corrosion

Aluminium and titanium share another useful property: they both resist corrosion well. That is why aluminium foil stays shiny. Titanium resists **corrosion** much better than aluminium and stainless steel. It can be used safely where even stainless steel would corrode away, for example in nuclear power stations, or inside the human body.

Questions

1 Suggest three differences between transition metals and group 1 metals.

2 What 'key property' makes the metal useful in each of these cases? **(a)** Iron girders of bridges **(b)** steel used to make car bodies **(c)** copper water pipes **(d)** copper electricity cables.

3 Iron bridges have to be repainted regularly. What would happen if they were not?

4 Why do sheet copper roofs last longer than corrugated iron roofs?

5 Titanium is denser than aluminium. Explain why it is still an excellent material for aircraft manufacture.

6 What would happen in time if the hip replacement shown on the X-ray photograph were made from steel?

7 Given iron's problem with rusting, why don't we use other metals like copper or aluminium for cars and bridges instead?

8 Compare the properties of steel, aluminium and titanium to explain which metals are used in aeroplanes and why. Some lower-performance supersonic planes use titanium for the nose cones and wing leading edges only. Suggest two reasons for this.

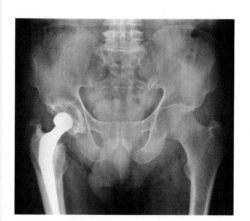

Titanium is used for hip replacement surgery.

Improving metals

Learning objectives

- explain that iron from a blast furnace is impure and has limited uses
- describe how removing these impurities produces pure iron
- describe how the atoms are arranged in pure iron
- describe how and why iron is turned into steel
- explain why the properties of alloys are related to their structures.

Iron straight from the blast furnace

The iron that comes out of a blast furnace is only about 96% pure. It contains impurities like carbon, silicon, sulfur and phosphorus. These impurities make the iron **brittle**, so it is not very useful. To get pure iron these impurities are removed by reacting them with oxygen. Jets of pure oxygen are blasted through molten iron. The oxides formed are then easily separated from the iron.

Like other pure metals, pure iron is soft and easily shaped.

Steel is an alloy

The softness of iron means that it is too soft for many uses. Most iron is converted into steels. Steels are **alloys**. Steel alloys are a mixture of iron with carbon or other metals. The different atoms that are added change the properties of the pure metal, in this case iron. Alloys are harder.

Bronze is an alloy used for statues.

Different types of steel do different jobs.

The best steel for the job

Alloys can be designed to have properties for specific uses. Steels are made by adding carefully calculated amounts of carbon to the pure iron. This affects both the hardness and the strength of the steel, as shown on the graph.

Low-carbon steels are made by adding small amounts (up to 0.25%) of carbon to the molten pure iron. This small amount of carbon makes the iron stronger and a little harder. These steels are easily shaped. They are used for things like wire, nails, cans and car bodies.

As a little more carbon is added, the steel becomes even stronger. However, increased hardness means that the steel can no longer be easily pressed into shape. However, it is good for making hammers.

If slightly more carbon is added (up to 1.5%), **high-carbon steels** are made. These are even harder but the strength drops a little, so they can be brittle. They are used for

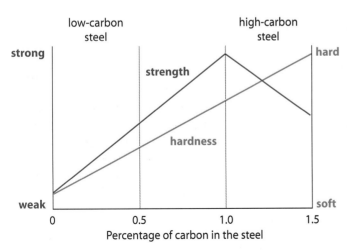

Figure 1 How just a little carbon affects the properties of the steel.

cutting tools, drill bits and masonry nails. Masonry nails are used for hammering into bricks or concrete. Using high-carbon steel nails means that they do not bend as low-carbon iron nails would. However, they can snap if struck incorrectly.

If any more carbon is added the steel becomes very hard but very brittle, just like the 'cast iron' that comes straight out of the blast furnace.

Special steels

Sometimes other metals are added to steel to give new alloys with special properties. Nickel is added to make a steel that is both hard and very strong, for machinery. Tungsten is added to make a very hard steel for cutting tools. Adding 15% or so of chromium produces stainless steel, which does not corrode, making it ideal for cutlery, for example.

Other metal alloys

Aluminium is made stronger for aircraft by adding just 4% copper to make an alloy called **duralumin**. Many other metals are strengthened in this way. Even gold has to have a little copper added to harden it. Without it, gold rings would quickly distort or wear away when used. There are three other important alloys of copper.

Table 1 Important alloys of copper.

Name of alloy	Composition	Special property	Uses
brass	70% copper, 30% zinc	harder than pure copper	electrical fittings, screws
bronze	90% copper, 10% tin	harder than pure copper	bells
cupronickel	75% copper, 25% nickel	harder than pure copper	coins

Masonry nails are made from high-carbon steel.

Modern 'silver' coins are really cupronickel.

Questions

1. What effect do impurities have on iron straight from the blast furnace? How are they removed?

2. Explain how adding different-sized atoms to a metal in an alloy helps to make it harder.

3. Which type of steel would be best for **(a)** scissors and chisels? **(b)** making car body panels? Explain your answer.

4. Why should the builder in the photograph be wearing safety goggles?

5. Why are aircraft built from duralumin, not pure aluminium, and why is copper's high density not a problem?

6. Brass is made from copper and zinc. Why are bolts and hinges made from brass and not copper? Explain the difference in properties.

7. Cupronickel also has the added property that it is more resistant to chemical corrosion. Why does this make it useful for coinage?

8. Explain the effect of adding small amounts of carbon to iron and describe how the metal's properties change with the amount of carbon added.

Examiner feedback

You do not have to remember the details of all these alloys. However, you might get a table of alloys and their properties and have to answer questions about their suitability for different jobs.

Route to A*

You may be given unfamiliar data to work with in examination questions. Practise data questions like those here, which use data from these pages, so that you become good at spotting the relevant information and are able to use it to justify your answers.

Assess yourself questions

1 Complete and balance these chemical equations.

(a) $CaCO_3 \longrightarrow$ ____ $+ CO_2$ (1 mark)

(b) $CaO +$ ____ $\longrightarrow Ca(OH)_2$ (1 mark)

(c) $Ca(OH)_2 + CO_2 \longrightarrow$ ____ $+ H_2O$ (1 mark)

(d) $CaCO_3 + HCl \longrightarrow CaCl_2 +$ ____ $+$ ____ (3 marks)

2

Figure 1 Molecules.

(a) Which of these diagrams in Figure 1 shows a molecule of an element? (1 mark)

(b) Which of these diagrams shows a molecule of a compound? (1 mark)

(c) (i) Give the chemical formulae for molecules A–D. (2 marks)

(ii) Give the chemical names for molecules A–D. (2 marks)

(d) Which subatomic particle is shared between atoms in molecules like these, to make the chemical bonds? (1 mark)

3 Limestone ($CaCO_3$) breaks down to quicklime (CaO) when heated. Three students performed an experiment to see how much quicklime they could get by heating 10 g of limestone. They set their balance to zero with a crucible in place and measured out exactly 10 g of limestone. They then heated the crucible strongly, reweighing it regularly. They kept heating until the mass stopped going down. They each repeated their experiment three times.

Table 1 The students' results.

| | Quicklime produced from 10 g of limestone/g | | | |
	Expt 1	Expt 2	Expt 3	Mean
Student 1	5.6	5.7	5.5	
Student 2	5.65	5.66	5.64	
Student 3	5.62	5.68	6.92	

(a) Why does the mass as measured on the balance go down during this reaction? (1 mark)

(b) Why did they have to keep heating 'until the mass stopped going down'? (1 mark)

(c) Calculate the mean result for each of the three students. (3 marks)

(d) (i) Which student had been given an older, less precise balance to work with? (1 mark)

(ii) How will this have affected their results? (1 mark)

(e) Which student appears to have obtained the most **reliable** results? Explain your answer. (2 marks)

(f) Which student ran out of time and didn't heat their final piece of limestone long enough? Explain your answer. (2 marks)

(g) (i) The theoretical amount of quicklime produced from 10 g of calcium carbonate is 5.6 g. Whose final answer appears to be the most accurate? (1 mark)

(ii) A detailed analysis of the limestone used shows that the residue after heating is indeed slightly greater than 5.6 g. Suggest a possible reason for this. (1 mark)

4 Describe the three reactions that make up the 'limestone cycle', giving the balanced chemical equations for each stage.

In this question you will be assessed on using good English, organising information clearly and using specialist terms where appropriate. (6 marks)

5 Iron is made by heating iron oxide with coal in a blast furnace.

(a) Which element is coal mostly made of? (1 mark)

(b) Complete this word equation:

iron oxide + carbon $\longrightarrow$ iron + ____ ____ (1 mark)

(c) Which reactant is oxidised in this reaction? (1 mark)

(d) Which reactant is reduced in this reaction? (1 mark)

(e) Why can't aluminium be produced from aluminium oxide by this reaction? (1 mark)

6 Laos is a poor country with underdeveloped heavy industry. Bamboo grows well in its hot climate.

In London, scaffolding is built from steel tubes that are screw-clamped together. In Laos, scaffolding is built from bamboo poles lashed together with natural string.

(a) Which do you think would be stronger, the steel or bamboo? (1 mark)

(b) What would you notice if you picked up a steel pole and a bamboo pole? (1 mark)

(c) Suggest *two* reasons why bamboo is used in Laos rather than steel. (1 mark)

(d) Steel scaffolding poles last longer than bamboo poles. Why is that not a problem in Laos? (1 mark)

(e) Broken bamboo poles are simply thrown away. Why is that not an environmental problem? (1 mark)

(f) Large bamboo poles cost more in the UK than their steel equivalents. Suggest *two* reasons for this. (2 marks)

7 **Table 2** Properties of metals.

Metal	Melting point /°C	Strength (1 = low, 50 = very high)	Cost £/tonne	Density g/cm³
aluminium	660	1 (pure) 5 (alloyed)	3600	2.7
steel	1540	20	1600	7.7
titanium	1670	10	12 000	4.5
tungsten	3400	50	9000	15.3

(a) For each use below, suggest a suitable metal and give a reason (from Table 2).
   (i) The barrel of a Bunsen burner. *(1 mark)*
   (ii) The wing of a supersonic fighter *(1 mark)*
   (iii) The filament in a light bulb. *(1 mark)*
   (iv) A commercial aeroplane. *(1 mark)*

(b) Why is aluminium not used in its pure form to make pans, cans or aeroplanes? *(1 mark)*

(c) Explain in simple terms why alloys are harder and stronger than the pure metal. *(2 marks)*

8 The permitted levels of some metal ions in drinking water are:

copper	1 mg/l
lead	0.05 mg/l
zinc	5 mg/l

(a) From these figures, which metal is most toxic, and which is least toxic? *(1 mark)*

Cattle in the fields around the river shown on the map in Figure 2 became ill and metal poisoning was suspected. Water samples taken from the rivers at A, B, C, D and E were analysed.

Table 3 Results of analysis.

	Concentration mg/l		
	copper	lead	zinc
A	0.05	0.001	0.05
B	5.00	0.1	3.0
C	6.0	5.0	10.0
D	1.00	0.02	0.6
E	1.6	1.0	2.0

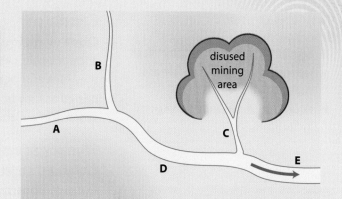

Figure 2 Map of the river system.

(b) (i) Which site would give safe drinking water (in terms of metal content)? *(1 mark)*
   (ii) Which site shows the most polluted water? *(1 mark)*
   (iii) Where do you think this pollution has come from? *(1 mark)*

(c) (i) The rivers flow from A, B and C to E. Why are the metal levels lower at E than at C? *(1 mark)*
   (ii) From the figures, which river carries more water, the main river at D or the side river from C? *(1 mark)*

(d) (i) Site A has a full range of wildlife. How would you expect site E to compare with this? *(1 mark)*
   (ii) You find water snails at site A but they have disappeared from the river at site D. Which metal do you think the snails might be sensitive to? *(1 mark)*

(e) The herd of cattle could only get to the river to drink at E. Which metal is most likely to be responsible for the poisoning? Explain your answer. *(2 marks)*

(f) Scientists have suggested that the pollution problem could be tackled by throwing scrap iron into the rivers at B and C.
   (i) How would this work? *(1 mark)*
   (ii) Which metal would not be affected? *(1 mark)*
   (iii) Which metal ion would increase in the water at E? Would this be a problem? *(2 marks)*

9 Explain why iron and copper can be extracted from their ores by carbon reduction but aluminium cannot be obtained in this way. Describe briefly how aluminium is extracted and explain why this makes aluminium relatively expensive.

In this question you will be assessed on using good English, organising information clearly and using specialist terms where appropriate. *(6 marks)*

Alkanes

Crude oil

Crude oil is a **fossil fuel**. It formed over millions of years from the remains of ancient single-celled plants and animals that lived in the sea. When they died, they sank and were buried in sediments. The remains were compressed and heated as they became more deeply buried. Chemical reactions took place in the absence of air, gradually converting the remains into the oil we use today.

Hydrocarbons

Crude oil is a mixture of a very large number of **compounds**. Most of these are **hydrocarbons**, molecules made from hydrogen and carbon atoms only. The hydrogen atoms are joined to the carbon atoms, and these carbon atoms are joined together in chains. Most of the hydrocarbons in crude oil are **alkanes**.

Alkanes

The atoms in hydrocarbons are joined together by **covalent bonds**, a type of chemical bond. Hydrogen atoms can only make one covalent bond but carbon atoms can each make four. This is why carbon atoms can join up to form chains. All the bonds in alkanes are single covalent bonds. They can be C—C bonds, between two carbon atoms, or C—H bonds, between a carbon atom and a hydrogen atom.

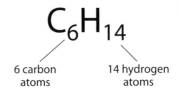

$$C_6H_{14}$$

6 carbon atoms   14 hydrogen atoms

Figure 1 The molecular formula of hexane is written like this.

Crude oil is a liquid containing many different hydrocarbons.

Hexane is an alkane. Its molecules all contain six carbon atoms and 14 hydrogen atoms, so its **molecular formula** is C_6H_{14}. A molecular formula gives information about the number of atoms of each element a molecule contains, but it gives no information about how these atoms are arranged.

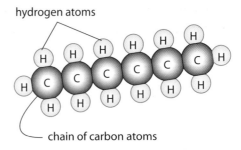

hydrogen atoms

chain of carbon atoms

Figure 2 A simple representation of a hexane molecule.

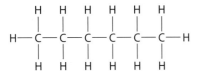

Figure 3 The displayed formula of hexane.

The arrangement of the atoms in a molecule can be shown using a **displayed formula**. In a displayed formula, each atom is shown by its chemical symbol, and each covalent bond by a straight line. It is usual to make all the angles 90° in the displayed formulae of alkanes. It is easiest to write all the carbon atoms first, draw in all the covalent bonds, and then add the hydrogen atoms.

Notice that there are no 'spare' bonds in hexane. The molecule is 'full' of hydrogen and cannot join with any more hydrogen atoms. It is a **saturated** hydrocarbon. All alkanes contain only single bonds, so they are all saturated.

Naming alkanes

The names of alkanes have two parts. The first part shows how many carbon atoms the alkane molecule contains. The second part, 'ane', tells you that the carbon atoms are joined by single bonds. Table 1 shows how this works.

Table 1 Naming alkanes.

Number of carbon atoms	First part of name	Name of alkane	Molecular formula of alkane
1	meth	methane	CH_4
2	eth	ethane	C_2H_6
3	prop	propane	C_3H_8

The number of hydrogen atoms in each alkane is twice the number of carbon atoms plus two. So alkanes have a general formula of C_nH_{2n+2}, where n is the number of carbon atoms.

The alkanes form a **homologous series** or 'family' of compounds. They take part in similar chemical reactions and have a common general formula. The molecular formula of each successive member differs by CH_2.

Science in action

Alkanes and other compounds that contain carbon are named using a system developed and maintained by IUPAC, the International Union of Pure and Applied Chemistry. Some names might look complex. However, chemists everywhere can work out a compound's structure just from its name.

Examiner feedback

The general formula for alkanes is C_nH_{2n+2}. It helps you recognise alkanes and write their formulae.

Science in action

Instead of a straight chain of carbon atoms, it is possible to have 'branched' alkanes. For example, the six carbon atoms in hexane can be arranged in a chain of five carbon atoms, with one attached as a branch. Branched alkanes and cyclic alkanes (like the one in question 7) are included in petrol to help it burn better in car engines.

Taking it further

Compounds that have the same formula, but whose atoms are arranged differently, as described in 'Science in action', are called isomers. The unbranched and branched alkanes described are examples of chain isomers. The cyclic alkane in question 7 is a functional group isomer. It has single bonds like an alkane, but its formula is the same as the formula of an alkene (see C1 5.1).

Questions

1 What are the main compounds in crude oil?

2 Explain what hydrocarbons are.

3 Explain why carbon atoms can form chains of atoms.

4 State the molecular formulae of ethane and propane, and draw their displayed formulae.

5 What is the general formula for alkanes?

6 Icosane contains 20 carbon atoms. Write its molecular formula.

7 The diagram shows the displayed formula of a 'cyclic' alkane.

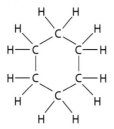

Figure 4 Cyclohexane.

(a) Write the molecular formula of cyclohexane. **(b)** Describe three similarities between cyclohexane and hexane, and three differences.

8 Explain clearly why the alkanes are saturated and form a homologous series. Give relevant examples in your answer.

(A*)

Separating crude oil

Science skills The number of carbon atoms is a categoric variable whose values are restricted to whole numbers. Boiling point is a continuous variable, so the data in Table 1 may be shown as a line graph or as a bar chart.

Table 1 Boiling points of various alkanes.

Formula	Number of C atoms	Boiling point/°C
CH_4	1	−164
C_3H_8	3	−42
C_5H_{12}	5	36
C_7H_{16}	7	98
C_9H_{20}	9	151
$C_{11}H_{24}$	11	196
$C_{20}H_{42}$	20	344

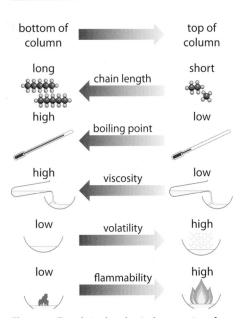

Figure 2 Trends in the physical properties of crude oil fractions.

Separating mixtures

A **mixture** consists of two or more elements or compounds. However, these are not chemically combined. The chemical properties of each substance in a mixture are unchanged, so the substances can be separated by physical methods such as filtration or **distillation**.

Fractional distillation

Fractional distillation is typically used to obtain a liquid from a mixture of liquids that dissolve into one another. The liquid with the lower boiling point **evaporates** first. Its vapours are led away, then cooled and **condensed**, leaving the rest of the mixture behind.

Practical

Ethanol boils at 78 °C and water boils at 100 °C. Fractional distillation is used to separate ethanol from a mixture of the two liquids.

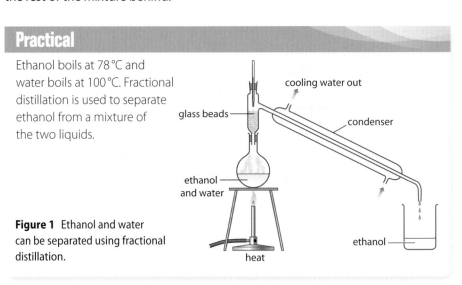

Figure 1 Ethanol and water can be separated using fractional distillation.

Boiling points of alkanes

Short-chain alkanes have low boiling points. They tend to be gases at room temperature. Intermediate-sized alkanes tend to be liquids at room temperature. Long-chain alkanes have the highest boiling points. They tend to be solids at room temperature. This trend in boiling points is the key to separating the hydrocarbons in crude oil using fractional distillation.

Oil fractionation

Crude oil is heated strongly to evaporate it. The hot vapours are led into the bottom of a tower called a **fractionating column**. This is hottest at the bottom and gradually becomes cooler towards the top. The vapours cool down as they rise through it. When the vapours reach a part of the column that is cool enough, they condense. The liquid falls into a tray and is piped out. Fractional distillation is a continuous process. It keeps going as long as vaporised crude oil enters the fractionating column.

Alkanes with the longest chains condense near the bottom of the column. Those with intermediate-sized chains condense at various points further up. Alkanes with the shortest chains remain as gases. They reach the top of the column without becoming cool enough to condense. The separated alkanes are just parts of the original crude oil, so they are called **fractions**. In each fraction, all of the alkane molecules are similar in size.

Useful as fuels?

Alkanes with the longest chains make poor fuels. They are solid at room temperature. They are not very **flammable** and ignite with difficulty, if at all.

Alkanes with the shortest chains, however, are good fuels. They are gases at room temperature and ignite easily. Gases are easily piped to where they are needed but they are bulky to store. So they are often stored under pressure as liquids, like liquefied petroleum gas, LPG.

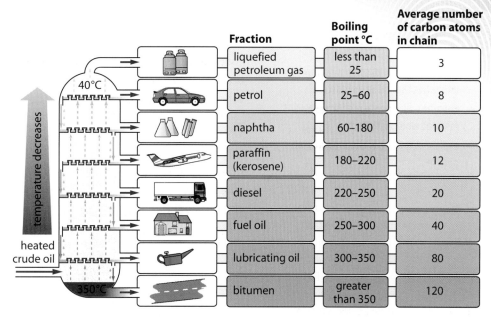

Fraction	Boiling point °C	Average number of carbon atoms in chain
liquefied petroleum gas	less than 25	3
petrol	25–60	8
naphtha	60–180	10
paraffin (kerosene)	180–220	12
diesel	220–250	20
fuel oil	250–300	40
lubricating oil	300–350	80
bitumen	greater than 350	120

Figure 3 The main fractions from crude oil. Naphtha is used in the manufacture of chemicals.

Alkanes with intermediate-length chains also make good fuels. They are liquids at room temperature. They are relatively easy to store and they can be piped to where they are needed. Liquids containing the shorter-chain alkanes are more flammable than those containing the longer-chain alkanes. They are also less **viscous**, which means they flow more easily.

Questions

1. Explain the difference between a compound and a mixture.

2. Why is fractional distillation described as a continuous process?

3. Explain why diesel has a higher boiling point than gasoline (petrol).

4. Use the data in Table 1 on page 132 to plot a line graph of the boiling point against number of carbon atoms. Describe the graph and use it to predict the boiling point of hexadecane, $C_{16}H_{34}$.

5. Describe and explain how crude oil is separated into fractions by fractional distillation.

6. It has been suggested that the sootiness of the flame from a burning alkane depends upon the ratio of carbon atoms to hydrogen atoms. The higher the ratio, the more sooty the flame is. Predict the difference in the flames produced by methane, CH_4, and octane, C_8H_{18}, giving reasons for your answer.

7. **(a)** Explain what is meant by the viscosity of a liquid.

Formula of alkane	Relative viscosity
C_6H_{14}	0.12
C_7H_{16}	0.18
C_8H_{18}	0.24
$C_{10}H_{22}$	0.42
$C_{12}H_{26}$	0.66
$C_{14}H_{30}$	1.00

(b) Plot a suitable line graph of the data in the table.

(c) Describe the relationship between the viscosity of alkanes and the size of their molecules.

8. To what extent does the size of its molecules determine the usefulness of a liquid alkane as a fuel? You should discuss boiling point, viscosity and flammability in your answer.

Burning fuels

Learning objectives

- describe the type of compounds and impurities that make up most fuels
- describe which waste products are released when fuels burn
- explain why these waste products can pose problems.

About 40% of the world's electricity is generated by coal-fired power stations.

Practical

The products of combustion from burning natural gas can be collected and tested. Carbon dioxide turns limewater cloudy white, and water vapour changes anhydrous copper sulfate from white to blue.

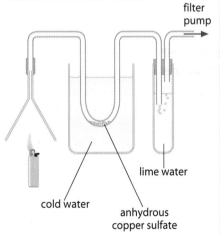

Figure 1 This apparatus is used to collect and test combustion products.

Fuel

Fuels are stores of energy that can be released when needed. When they burn, however, hydrocarbons and other chemical fuels also release particles and various gases.

Burning coal

Coal is a brownish black solid fossil fuel that is mostly carbon. It was formed over millions of years from the remains of ancient swamp plants. **Complete combustion** happens when coal burns completely in a plentiful supply of air. Its carbon is **oxidised** to carbon dioxide:

$$\text{carbon} + \text{oxygen} \longrightarrow \text{carbon dioxide}$$
$$C + O_2 \longrightarrow CO_2$$

Incomplete combustion, also called **partial combustion**, happens instead if the supply of air is not plentiful. As the coal burns, its carbon may be oxidised to carbon monoxide instead of carbon dioxide:

$$\text{carbon} + \text{oxygen} \longrightarrow \text{carbon monoxide}$$
$$2C + O_2 \longrightarrow 2CO$$

Carbon monoxide is a colourless and odourless toxic gas. It attaches to the haemoglobin in red blood cells more strongly than oxygen, reducing the amount of oxygen transported in the bloodstream. Carbon monoxide poisoning causes headaches, sickness and fainting, and even death.

Burning natural gas

Natural gas is a fossil fuel that forms in a similar way to crude oil, and is often found with it. Natural gas is mostly methane, with smaller amounts of ethane and other alkanes. The complete combustion of natural gas oxidises its carbon to carbon dioxide, and its hydrogen to water vapour:

$$\text{methane} + \text{oxygen} \longrightarrow \text{carbon dioxide} + \text{water}$$
$$CH_4 + 2O_2 \longrightarrow CO_2 + 2H_2O$$

The partial combustion of natural gas also causes the production of carbon monoxide. This is why gas fires should have good ventilation.

Burning fuels from crude oil

Petrol, paraffin (also called kerosene), diesel and fuel oil are liquid fuels from crude oil. Carbon dioxide and water vapour are produced when they burn completely. For example, petrol contains octane:

$$\text{octane} + \text{oxygen} \longrightarrow \text{carbon dioxide} + \text{water}$$
$$2C_8H_{18} + 25O_2 \longrightarrow 16CO_2 + 18H_2O$$

Carbon monoxide is produced by the partial combustion of these fuels, too.

Examiner feedback

In the balanced symbol equation for the complete combustion of an alkane, the number in front of CO_2 is the number of C atoms in the alkane, and the number in front of H_2O is half the number of H atoms. The number in front of O_2 is the number before CO_2, added to half the number before H_2O.

Particulates

Particulates are solid particles produced when fuels burn. They contain carbon and unburned fuel and are deposited as soot. The carbon is often noticeable as black smoke from diesel-powered vehicles, particularly if the vehicles are old, accelerating or going uphill. High levels of particulates in polluted air can lead to early deaths and extra cases of asthma, bronchitis and other respiratory diseases.

Other oxides from fuels

Fossil fuels often contain small amounts of sulfur. This is naturally occurring and has not been added deliberately. When the fuel burns, the sulfur does too. It forms sulfur dioxide gas, which escapes along with the other waste products:

sulfur + oxygen $\longrightarrow$ sulfur dioxide

$S + O_2 \longrightarrow SO_2$

At the high temperatures in a furnace or engine, nitrogen and oxygen from the air can react together to produce various oxides of nitrogen. Together, these waste gases are called NO_x. The x in the name shows that different molecules with different numbers of nitrogen and oxygen atoms are possible. Sulfur dioxide and NO_x cause acid rain if they escape into the air.

Science in action

Particulates equal to or smaller than 10 μm in diameter, 10 millionths of a metre, are called PM10s. EU legislation limits the concentration of PM10s allowed in air because of their harmful effects on health.

Taking it further

Catalytic converters fitted to car exhaust systems contain the metals platinum and rhodium. These catalysts can convert nitrogen oxides, NO_x (where x can be 1 or 2) into harmless nitrogen and oxygen, helping to reduce the formation of acid rain:

$2NO_x \longrightarrow N_2 + xO_2$

Questions

1 State the products formed when hydrocarbons burn completely in air.

2 Write the word equation for the complete combustion of butane.

3 **(a)** Which toxic gas is formed during the incomplete combustion of hydrocarbons? **(b)** Explain why this gas is harmful to health.

4 **(a)** Explain, giving an example, what particulates are. **(b)** Describe the problems caused to human health by particulates.

5 Explain why burning fuels may release sulfur dioxide and NO_x.

6 **(a)** Write a balanced symbol equation for the complete combustion of butane, C_4H_{10}. **(b)** Write a balanced symbol equation for the incomplete combustion of methane, CH_4, where the only products are CO and H_2O.

7 Smog, a mixture of smoke from coal fires and fog, covered London for several days in December 1952. Use information from the graph to answer the questions.

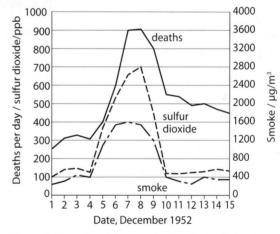

Figure 2 Mortality and atmospheric pollution in London, December 1952.

(a) Explain why sulfur dioxide in the atmosphere is thought to have caused extra deaths. **(b)** Suggest why the death rate remains higher than normal between the 10th and 15th, even though sulfur dioxide levels have returned to normal then. **(c)** To what extent can we be certain that sulfur dioxide was the cause of the extra deaths?

8 To what extent would you agree that it is important to burn fuels in a good supply of air? In your answer, include the products from complete combustion and partial combustion.

Problem fuels

Learning objectives

- explain how carbon dioxide contributes to global warming
- explain what causes global dimming
- explain what causes acid rain
- describe ways in which sulfur dioxide emissions may be reduced
- evaluate the impact on the environment of burning hydrocarbon fuels.

Science in action

Carbon dioxide and water vapour are not the only greenhouse gases. Methane is one, too. It is released as a result of extracting crude oil, natural gas and coal. Large amounts are also produced by cattle and rice paddy fields. Methane has about 25 times the global warming potential of the same amount of carbon dioxide.

Examiner feedback

Take care when answering questions about global warming not to get muddled up with the ozone layer. Carbon dioxide is a greenhouse gas, so it can contribute to global warming but it does not damage the ozone layer.

Examiner feedback

There is no dispute that the Earth and its atmosphere are becoming warmer. It is the causes of this that there is some debate about. You should recognise that people's opinions about global warming may be influenced by economic, ethical, moral, social or cultural considerations. For example, a farmer whose livelihood may be threatened by changing weather patterns might have a different opinion from someone who depends on the oil industry.

Up in smoke?

Around 85 million barrels of oil are used every day in the world, about 2 litres per person on average. Most of it is destined to be burnt as fuel. When it is, waste gases and solid particles are released into the atmosphere. These have significant environmental effects.

Hydrocarbons and global warming

Sunlight reaching the Earth's surface is emitted as **infrared radiation**. **Greenhouse gases** such as carbon dioxide and water vapour absorb this energy, stopping it escaping into space. This is called the **greenhouse effect**: without it our planet would be much colder, and life as we know it would not exist.

Carbon dioxide is released when hydrocarbon fuels burn. Our use of such fuels is releasing carbon dioxide faster than it can be removed by natural processes such as photosynthesis. The concentration of carbon dioxide in the atmosphere increased by around 22% in the second half of the last century. Extra carbon dioxide contributes to an enhanced greenhouse effect, leading to **global warming**.

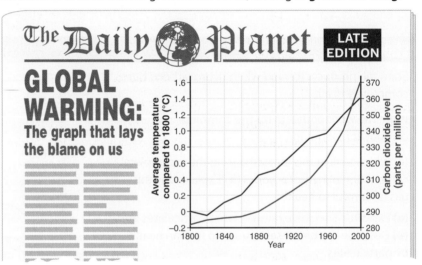

Figure 1 Levels of carbon dioxide and average global temperatures have increased over the last 200 years.

Science in action

Volcanic eruptions and wildfires are natural sources of carbon dioxide. They release much less overall than burning fossil fuels does, but they release it in one go. This makes it difficult for scientists to include the effects of volcanic eruptions and wildfires in computer models of global warming.

Global dimming

Gerry Stanhill, an English scientist working in Israel at the end of the last century, noticed something strange about records of sunlight. Israel received much less sunlight in the 1990s than it did in the 1950s. When he checked, Stanhill found similar results in countries all around the world, with a mean loss of around 2% sunlight per decade. He called this **global dimming**.

Global dimming happens because of the solid particles released from burning fuels. These particles reflect sunlight back into space. In addition, water droplets condense around them, making clouds that are more reflective than normal clouds. Global dimming is likely to have reduced the impact of global warming. It has also reduced the amount of evaporation, interfering with the water cycle and possibly causing droughts.

Acid rain

Sulfur dioxide may be released when fuels burn, particularly when coal is used as a fuel in power stations. This gas dissolves in moisture in the air, forming sulfurous acid, and sulfuric acid if it also reacts with oxygen in the air.

sulfur dioxide + water + oxygen $\longrightarrow$ sulfuric acid

$$2SO_2 + 2H_2O + O_2 \longrightarrow 2H_2SO_4$$

Sulfurous acid and sulfuric acid contribute to **acid rain**, rain that is more acidic than normal rain. Acid rain damages buildings and rocks and it can harm or kill animals and plants.

Sulfur dioxide can be removed from the waste gases at power stations. It is absorbed by powdered calcium carbonate or damp calcium hydroxide, making a less harmful product, calcium sulfate. Sulfur can also be removed from fuels before they are used. Nowadays low-sulfur diesel and petrol are readily available at filling stations. They release less sulfur dioxide when they burn than fuels did in the past.

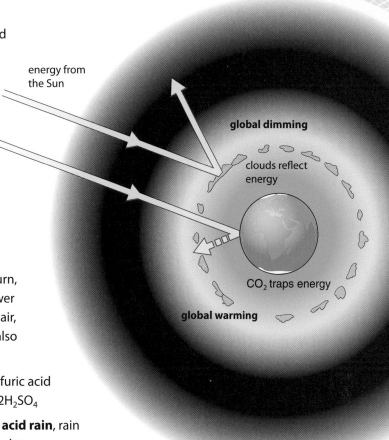

energy from the Sun

global dimming

clouds reflect energy

CO_2 traps energy

global warming

Figure 2 Global warming and global dimming (not to scale).

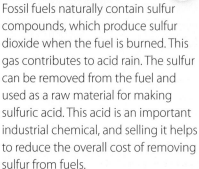

Questions

1   Explain why carbon dioxide is described as a greenhouse gas.

2   Why is global warming believed to be linked to the use of fossil fuels?

3   What is global dimming and how is it caused?

4   Explain why global dimming is likely to have reduced the impact of global warming over the last few decades.

5   How is acid rain formed and what are its effects on the environment?

6   Describe two ways in which the emission of sulfur dioxide may be reduced.

7   **(a)** Write a balanced equation for the reaction between calcium carbonate $CaCO_3$, oxygen and sulfur dioxide, producing calcium sulfate $CaSO_4$ and carbon dioxide. **(b)** Explain why absorbing sulfur dioxide emissions using calcium carbonate may contribute to global warming.

8   Demand for oil continues to increase. Emissions of smoke and soot are decreasing because of clean air laws. Suggest, with reasons, the effect of these two factors on the environment.

Route to A*

Fossil fuels naturally contain sulfur compounds, which produce sulfur dioxide when the fuel is burned. This gas contributes to acid rain. The sulfur can be removed from the fuel and used as a raw material for making sulfuric acid. This acid is an important industrial chemical, and selling it helps to reduce the overall cost of removing sulfur from fuels.

Better fuels

Learning objectives

- evaluate developments in the production and uses of better fuels, for example ethanol and hydrogen.

The end of oil

It is difficult to know how much oil is left. The rate at which we use it varies and new sources continue to be discovered. There are also large deposits of unconventional sources of oil, including a mixture of sand, water and very viscous crude oil, called tar sand. Canada, for example, has as much oil in its tar sands as all the world's conventional oil sources put together. Such unconventional sources are more difficult and expensive to exploit than oil wells. However, when oil prices rise it becomes more commercially viable to use them.

What's left?

Crude oil, coal and natural gas are **non-renewable** resources. They cannot be replaced when they have all been used up. Predictions vary as to how long they will last. However, it seems likely that oil and gas will run out in your lifetime. They will last longer if they are used more efficiently. One way to achieve this is to develop and use alternative fuels.

Examiner feedback

Like all chemical fuels, non-renewable fuels can only be used once. Unlike renewable fuels, once they are all gone, non-renewable fuels cannot be replaced.

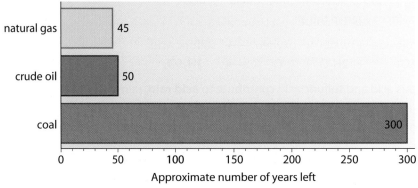

Figure 1 Coal is likely to last much longer than gas and oil at current rates of use.

Ethanol

Ethanol is the alcohol found in alcoholic drinks and antiseptic hand gels. It is also useful as a fuel. Ethanol is made from sugar by a natural process called **fermentation**. The sugar comes from plants, so ethanol made this way is a **renewable** energy resource. Ethanol can be transported, handled and stored in a similar way to petrol and diesel. Modern petrol engines can run on a mixture of 5% ethanol and 95% petrol without any modifications.

Science in action

Using ethanol in fuels may reduce the overall release of carbon dioxide from vehicles. However, scientists have discovered that it may increase the number of people with respiratory problems, such as asthma. Methanal and ethanal are released when such fuels burn. These substances react in the atmosphere to produce ozone, which is harmful at street level.

The complete combustion of ethanol releases the same products as hydrocarbon fuels do:

$$\text{ethanol} + \text{oxygen} \longrightarrow \text{carbon dioxide} + \text{water vapour}$$
$$CH_3CH_2OH + 3O_2 \longrightarrow 2CO_2 + 3H_2O$$

A proportion of the carbon dioxide released is offset by the carbon dioxide absorbed for photosynthesis by the growing crop plants. So using ethanol as a fuel can help to reduce greenhouse gas emissions. However, different plant species grow at different rates, and produce different amounts of material suitable for fermentation.

There is concern that farmland is increasingly being used to grow crops to fuel vehicles rather than to feed people. Scientists are investigating ways to use waste plant materials to produce ethanol more efficiently.

Route to A*

Uranium and plutonium are nuclear fuels. Unlike the fossil fuels, they do not release greenhouse gases or gases that contribute to acid rain when they are used. On the other hand, they are non-renewable resources, just like the fossil fuels.

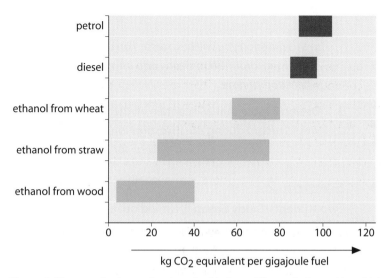

Figure 2 The overall release of carbon dioxide from different fuels used in vehicles.

Hydrogen

Hydrogen gas can be made by passing electricity through water, a process called **electrolysis**. Hydrogen can be a renewable fuel, as long as the electricity to make it is generated using renewable energy resources such as wind or hydroelectric power. When hydrogen burns, the only waste product is water vapour, which does not cause the pollution problems of other fuels. Hydrogen **fuel cells** are the most promising way to use it. These generate electricity by reacting hydrogen with oxygen from the air. The electricity then powers electric motors.

There are problems with the use of hydrogen. It is explosive, so it must be transported and handled with care. Hydrogen is bulky and difficult to store as a gas, so it is usually stored as a liquid at high pressure and low temperature.

This car is fuelled by hydrogen. Its exhaust contains water vapour, but no carbon dioxide.

Questions

1 State which fossil fuel is likely to run out first.
2 Explain why it is difficult to be certain how long fossil fuels will last.
3 State an advantage and a disadvantage of using hydrogen as a fuel.
4 State and compare the combustion products from ethanol, hydrogen and petrol (a hydrocarbon).
5 Write a balanced equation for the production of hydrogen (H_2) and oxygen (O_2) from water by electrolysis.
6 Use the bar chart in Figure 2 to help you answer these questions.
   (a) Explain the benefits of using ethanol from wheat, rather than petrol or diesel, to fuel vehicles. **(b)** Describe two drawbacks of using wheat to produce ethanol. **(c)** Describe two benefits of using straw or wood instead.
7 Hydrogen can be made by reacting steam with coal or natural gas. Suggest why this may not be as sustainable as making it by the electrolysis of water.
8 Describe the benefits and drawbacks of using crops to make fuel such as ethanol. To what extent might this be unethical?

Examiner feedback

You should be able to discuss the benefits and drawbacks of using hydrogen as a fuel in an examination question.

Science in action

Scientists are researching more convenient ways to store hydrogen. For example, metals such as magnesium react with hydrogen to produce metal hydrides. On heating, the reaction reverses and hydrogen is released.

ISA practice: the strength of concrete

Concrete is an important material for all kinds of construction. It is made by mixing water with cement, sand and aggregate – small stones or gravel. Different mixes produce concretes with different strengths. As concrete sets, crystals of calcium carbonate form. These stick the sand and aggregate together. Mortar is made from cement and sand with no aggregate, and is not as strong as concrete.

Your task is to investigate the strength of different concrete mixes. The strength can be measured using a G-clamp to break the concrete. The number of turns needed to crush the concrete is measured and recorded.

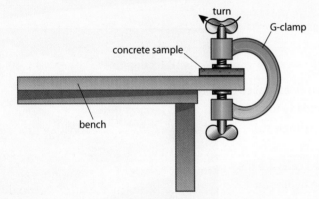

Figure 1 Using a G-clamp to test the strength of concrete.

Hypothesis

It is suggested that there is a link between the mass of aggregate in the concrete and the number of turns of the G-clamp needed to break the concrete.

Section 1

1   In this investigation you will need to control some of the variables.
    (a) Name one variable you will need to control in this investigation. *(1 mark)*
    (b) Describe briefly how you would carry out a preliminary investigation to find a suitable value to use for this variable. Explain how the results will help you decide on the best value for this variable. *(2 marks)*

2   Describe how you would carry out the investigation. You should include:
    - the equipment that you would use
    - how you would use the equipment
    - the measurements that you would make
    - a risk assessment
    - how you would make it a fair test.

    You may include a labelled diagram to help you to explain your method.

In this question you will be assessed on using good English, organising information clearly and using specialist terms where appropriate. *(9 marks)*

3   Design a table that will contain all the data that you would record during the investigation. *(2 marks)*

Total for Section 1: 14 marks

Section 2

Two students, Study Group 1, carried out an investigation into the hypothesis. Figure 2 gives the results of their investigation. They used the same volume of water to make each concrete mix, and the clamp method to break the beams they made.

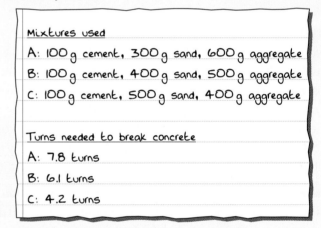

Figure 2 Results from Study Group 1's investigation.

4   **(a)** **(i)** What is the independent variable in this investigation?
        (ii) What is the dependent variable in this investigation?
        (iii) Name one control variable in this investigation. *(3 marks)*
    (b) Put the results from Study Group 1 into the table you designed in answer to question 4. Plot a graph to show the link between the mass of aggregate used and the number of turns needed to break the beam. *(4 marks)*
    (c) Do the results support the hypothesis? Explain your answer. *(3 marks)*

Below are the results of three other study groups. Study Group 2 is another pair of students. Their results are given in Figure 3.

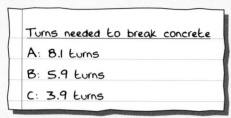

Turns needed to break concrete

A: 8.1 turns

B: 5.9 turns

C: 3.9 turns

Figure 3 Study Group 2's results.

Table 1 shows the results from a third student group, Study Group 3.

Table 1 Results from Study Group 3.

Mix	Cement/ g	Sand/ g	Aggregate/ g	Turns to break beam			
				Test 1	Test 2	Test 3	Mean of Tests 1–3
A	100	100	800	6.1	5.8	5.8	5.9
B	100	300	600	6.3	8.2	6.4	6.9
C	100	500	400	4.8	5.0	4.6	4.8

Table 2 shows the results from Study Group 4, a group of scientists in a building research laboratory. The scientists are testing the force need to break the concrete and the time it takes.

Table 2 Results from Study Group 4.

Mix	Aggregate in the mixture (%)	Force needed to break the beam/N				Time to break/s
		Test 1	Test 2	Test 3	Mean force/ N	
A	75	255	247	245	249	59
B	60	191	201	202	198	42
C	45	138	144	150	144	36

5 Describe one way in which the results of Study Group 2 are similar or different to those of Study Group 1, and give one reason for this similarity or difference.

(3 marks)

6 **(a)** Draw a sketch graph of the results from Study Group 3. (3 marks)

(b) Does the data support the hypothesis being investigated? To gain full marks you should use all the relevant data from the first set of results and Studies 2 and 3 to explain whether or not the data supports the hypothesis. (3 marks)

(c) The data from the other groups only gives a limited amount of information. What other information or data would you need in order to be more certain as to whether or not the hypothesis is correct? Explain the reason for your answer. (3 marks)

(d) Use the results from Study Groups 2, 3 and 4 to answer this question. What is the relationship between the mass of aggregate in concrete and its strength? How well does the data support your answer? (3 marks)

7 Look back at the investigation method of Study Group 1. If you could repeat the investigation, suggest one change that you would make to the method, and explain the reason for the change. (3 marks)

8 A company provides concrete for builders to use for driveways. They need to know the best concrete to use. How could the results of this investigation help the company to decide on the best mixture of concrete for a driveway? (3 marks)

Total for Section 2: 31 marks
Total for the ISA: 45 marks

Assess yourself questions

1 **(a)** State *one* difference between a mixture and a compound (1 mark)
   (b) Name the main type of compound present in crude oil. (1 mark)
   (c) Name the method used to separate the compounds present in crude oil. (1 mark)

2 Alkanes are saturated hydrocarbons.
   (a) What is a hydrocarbon? (2 marks)
   (b) Ethane and propane are two alkanes. What feature of their molecules makes them saturated? (1 mark)
   (c) Table 1 shows the molecular formulae of four alkanes.

   Table 1 Molecular formulae for the first four alkanes.

Alkane	Molecular formula
methane	CH_4
ethane	C_2H_6
propane	C_3H_8
butane	C_4H_{10}

   (i) Which alkane has four carbon atoms in its molecules? (1 mark)
   (ii) Dodecane molecules each contain 12 carbon atoms. Write the molecular formula of dodecane. (1 mark)

   d Figure 1 shows the displayed structural formula of ethane.

   Figure 1 The displayed structural formula of ethane.

   (i) What does each line in the formula represent? (1 mark)
   (ii) Draw the displayed structural formula of propane. (1 mark)
   (iii) What extra information does a displayed structural formula give compared with a molecular formula? (1 mark)

3 Crude oil is separated into fractions using fractional distillation. Table 2 shows six fractions from a fractionating column.
   (a) Describe the main processes that happen in a fractionating column. (4 marks)
   (b) What is the relationship between the boiling point range and the number of carbon atoms per molecule? (1 mark)
   (c) Why does the table show a range of boiling points for each fraction? (2 marks)
   (d) In which fraction would you expect to find propane? Give a reason for your answer. (2 marks)

   (e) Which fraction would you expect to be:
   (i) The least volatile? (1 mark)
   (ii) The least viscous liquid? (1 mark)
   (iii) The easiest to set alight? (1 mark)
   (f) Suggest why diesel burns with a smokier flamer than petrol does. (2 marks)

   Table 2 Crude oil fractions.

Name of fraction	Number of carbon atoms per molecule	Boiling point range/°C
refinery gas	1–4	less than 25
petrol	5–10	25–100
paraffin	11–15	100–250
diesel	16–20	250–350
lubricating oils	21–35	350–500
bitumen	more than 35	more than 500

4 Candles contain waxes, which are hydrocarbons. Figure 2 shows an experiment to collect and test the products formed when a candle burns.

   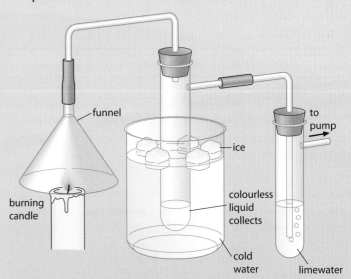

   Figure 2 An experiment to collect and test the products formed when a candle burns.

   (a) **(i)** Name the liquid that collects in the chilled boiling tube. (1 mark)
   (ii) Name the gas detected by the limewater. (1 mark)
   (iii) Which gas is produced when burning happens in a limited supply of air? (1 mark)
   (iv) How could you tell, safely, that heat is released in the reaction? (1 mark)
   (b) Write a word equation for the complete combustion of methane. (2 marks)
   (c) Balance this equation for the combustion of propane:
   $$C_3H_8 + O_2 \longrightarrow H_2O + CO_2$$
   (1 mark)

(d) Nitrogen oxides are produced when petrol burns in a car engine. State one condition needed for these compounds to form. *(1 mark)*

5 Figure 3 shows information about the production of sulfur dioxide from burning different fuels.

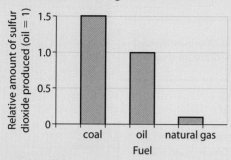

Figure 3 Bar chart of sulfur dioxide released from burning different fuels.

(a) Compare the amount of sulfur dioxide produced by each fuel. Include information from the bar chart in your answer. *(2 marks)*

(b) What environmental problem does sulfur dioxide cause? *(1 mark)*

(c) Describe two ways in which the amount of sulfur dioxide released into the atmosphere may be reduced. *(2 marks)*

(d) What is global dimming and how is it caused? *(3 marks)*

6 Table 3 shows information about the complete combustion of some alkane fuels.

Table 3 Combustion data for alkanes.

Number of carbon atoms per alkane molecule	kJ of energy released per g of fuel burned	mg of CO_2 produced per kJ of energy released
1	55.6	49.4
2	52.0	56.4
3	50.4	59.5
4	49.6	61.2
5	48.7	62.7
6	48.4	63.4

(a) Plot a suitable graph to show how the data in the two right-hand columns depend upon the number of carbon atoms per alkane molecule. Choose a suitable vertical scale so that both sets of data are shown on the same graph, and that the plotted points occupy at least half of the area of the graph. *(5 marks)*

(b) Describe in detail the relationship between the following:
  (i) The energy released per gram of fuel burned and the number of carbon atoms per molecule of fuel. *(2 marks)*
  (ii) The mass of carbon dioxide produced per kJ of energy released and the number of carbon atoms per molecule of fuel. *(2 marks)*

(c) Use your answers to part (b) to explain why methane, with one carbon atom per molecule, could be considered a better fuel than hexane, with six carbon atoms per molecule. *(2 marks)*

(d) Methane is a gas at room temperature but hexane is a liquid. To what extent might this information alter your answer to part (c)? *(2 marks)*

(e) Coal is a solid fuel that is almost pure carbon. When one gram of coal burns completely, it releases 32.8 kJ. Burning carbon produces 112 mg of carbon dioxide per kJ of energy released.

Suggest why hydrocarbons could be considered better fuels than coal. *(2 marks)*

(f) Table 4 shows information about the combustion of ethanol and hydrogen.

Table 4 Combustion of ethanol and hydrogen.

Fuel	kJ of energy released per g of fuel burned	mg of CO_2 produced per kJ of energy released
ethanol	29.7	28.4
hydrogen	143	0

  (i) Use the table to help you describe at least three advantages of using ethanol and hydrogen in cars rather than hydrocarbon fossil fuels, such as petrol. *(3 marks)*
  (ii) Describe at least two disadvantages of using ethanol or hydrogen in cars instead of hydrocarbon fossil fuels such as petrol. *(2 marks)*
  (iii) Ethanol and hydrogen may be described as renewable resources. What does this mean? To what extent may these two fuels be described in this way? *(4 marks)*

7 Read the information about benzene, and then answer the questions.

Benzene is a toxic, colourless liquid with a sweet smell. Its chemical formula is C_6H_6. It was first isolated in 1825 by Michael Faraday from whale oil, which was used as a fuel for lamps. Nowadays most benzene is made from crude oil. It is added to petrol to increase the fuel's 'octane rating'. This helps car engines run more smoothly.

(a) Explain how you know that benzene is a hydrocarbon but not an alkane. *(3 marks)*

(b) Suggest reasons for the following:
  (i) Benzene is made from crude oil rather than whale oil. *(2 marks)*
  (ii) Benzene is becoming increasingly expensive. *(2 marks)*

(c) Write a word equation and a balanced equation for the complete combustion of benzene. *(3 marks)*

(d) Explain why the amount of benzene allowed in petrol is limited by law. *(1 mark)*

Here are three students' answers to the following question:

Titanium is as strong as steel but much lighter. It is produced from titanium dioxide using a batch process that may take several days to complete. The flow chart summarises the main stages involved.

About 1 tonne of titanium is produced per day by a titanium reactor. About 13 000 tonnes of iron is produced per day by a blast furnace, most of which is converted into steel.

Explain why titanium costs more than steel to produce, and why it is better to recycle these metals.

In this question you will be assessed on using good English, organising information clearly and using specialised terms where appropriate. (6 marks)

> Titanium dioxide and chlorine gas react together to produce titanium chloride.

> Titanium chloride reacts with magnesium at 900 °C in a closed reactor for several days, producing titanium.

> The reactor is opened after it cools down, then the titanium is separated by hand from the magnesium chloride.

Figure 1 Flow chart of titanium production.

Read the answers together with the examiner comments. Then check what you have learnt and try putting it into practice in any further questions you answer.

B Grade answer

Student 1

Having better properties is not relevant to the cost of titanium.

The candidate forgets that iron must also be extracted from its ore.

The word 'pollution' is too vague. It would be better to name a particular pollutant.

> Titanium is much better than steel because it is strong and light. Not much titanium is made compared with iron. Steel does not need as much energy to make from iron. Recycling is cheaper than extracting a metal from its ore. Less waste is made and recycling makes less pollution.

Examiner comment

The candidate has not answered the question carefully enough. Their answer lacks detail and they make little use of relevant specialist terms. They mistakenly think that a metal will be expensive just because it has desirable properties. The candidate makes a valid point about the amount of titanium produced compared with the amount of iron and steel produced. However, steel is made from iron, and this also has to be extracted from its ore.

The candidate mentions the cost of recycling but they could have explained why it is cheaper than extracting metals from their ores. They make an attempt to explain why recycling is better for sustainable development. Fewer waste materials will be produced because of recycling, but the candidate should have taken care to name a relevant pollutant, such as carbon dioxide.

A **Grade answer**

Student 2

'It' (titanium) is not extracted using electrolysis.

The candidate mentions limited resources and gives a correct example.

Titanium takes a long time to produce. Even then it is produced in much smaller amounts than iron and steel. It is expensive to produce because it is extracted by electrolysis, which uses a lot of electricity. Recycling saves limited resources such as metal ores. It is cheaper than extracting the metal from its ore because it saves energy needed for extraction and processing.

The candidate gives a correct reason why recycling is cheaper.

Examiner comment

The candidate has answered in detail, giving reasons for several of their statements. Their answer has a clear structure and they use some relevant specialist terms. They give a correct reason why electrolysis is expensive. Unfortunately, they incorrectly state that titanium, rather than the magnesium needed, is extracted using electrolysis. The candidate gives a correct example of a limited resource that will be conserved by recycling. They mention cost and give a correct reason why recycling is cheaper. However, they do not link saving energy to sustainable development, when they could have easily done so.

A* **Grade answer**

Student 3

A correct use of information given in the stem of the question.

A more precise word than 'saves'.

Titanium is produced in a batch process while iron is produced in a continuous process. The production of titanium is more labour intensive and requires several stages. Magnesium and chlorine are needed to produce titanium, and these are expensive.
Recycling conserves limited resources such as metal ores. Less energy is needed for recycling than for extracting the metal from its ore. Fewer waste materials are produced by recycling.

Specific expensive materials are mentioned.

Examiner comment

The candidate has answered in great detail, taking care to give correct reasons for their statements. Their answer is structured well, with a good range of relevant specialist terms used accurately. They correctly compare the different types of processes used to extract titanium and iron. They give two different statements in their second sentence, each of which is valid. They then go on to make a correct statement about the cost of magnesium and chlorine. However, this would be unnecessary and the candidate could run out of time if they wrote too much.

The candidate gives a clearly structured answer about recycling, too. They focus on sustainable development rather than cost, but do make three valid points about this. They give a correct example of a conserved resource, they correctly explain why less energy is used without going into too much detail, and they mention the reduction in waste.

- Read the whole question carefully.
- Put your answers into a logical sequence and make sure you include relevant specialist terms.
- Use both your knowledge *and* the information given to you in the question.
- Make sure you explain all the ideas asked of you in the question.
- Take care not to give an incorrect explanation for a correct statement.

Oils, Earth and atmosphere

The Earth's crust, the oceans and the atmosphere are our only source of raw materials to make everything that we have. In this unit you will learn about the structure of the Earth, including looking at how scientists came to realise that the continents are moving. You will also study the gases in the atmosphere today and how the atmosphere has changed since the Earth was young.

Crude oil is extracted from the Earth's crust. As well as being used as a fuel, crude oil is a very valuable resource from which many important substances are made. In this unit you will look at how chemicals called alkenes are made from crude oil fractions and how these alkenes are used to make polymers. You will look at the properties and uses of different polymers, and how polymers are disposed of. You will also consider the social, economic and environmental advantages and disadvantages of the production and disposal of polymers. The alcohol ethanol, used as a fuel, can also be made from alkenes and you will compare this with its production from crops such as sugar cane.

Crops are also a source of vegetable oils. You will study how these oils are extracted and their uses in food, cooking and to make biodiesel. You will compare the structure and properties of different vegetable oils and their effects on health. You will see how emulsifiers, as an example of food additives, allow vegetable oils and water to mix.

Test yourself

1 What is different about the fractions separated from crude oil?
2 Why is the burning of many fuels thought to be leading to global warming?
3 What gases are in the air?
4 Why do volcanoes and earthquakes only occur in certain parts of the world?
5 Why are additives put in some foods?

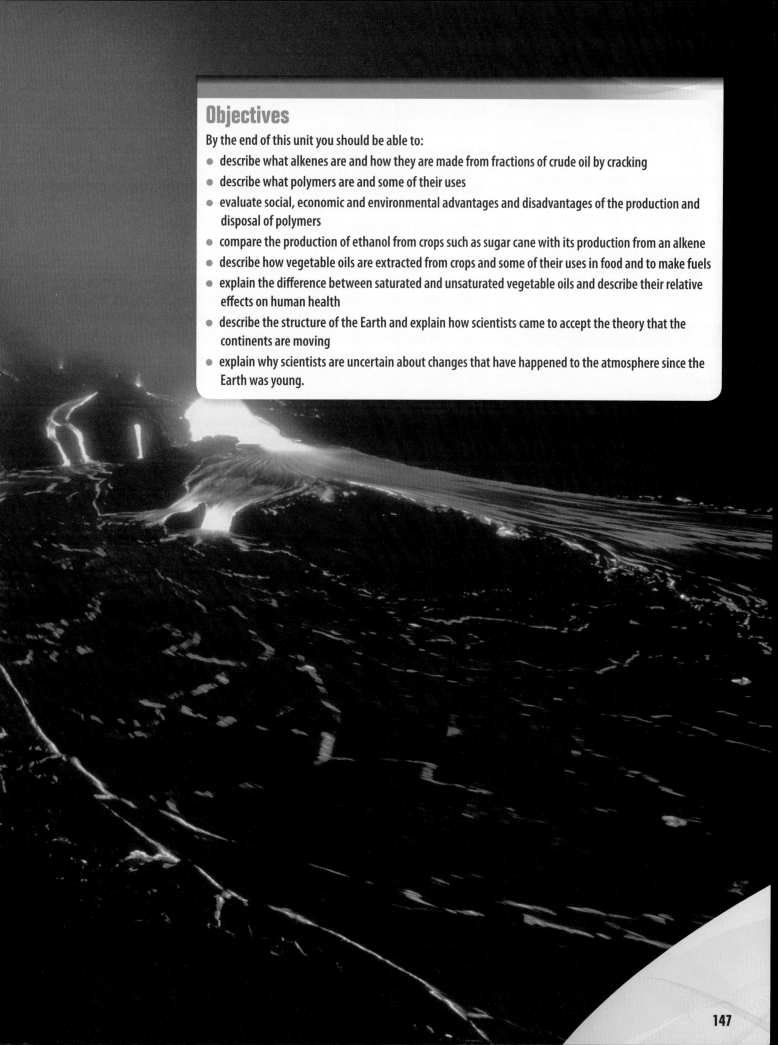

Objectives

By the end of this unit you should be able to:

- describe what alkenes are and how they are made from fractions of crude oil by cracking
- describe what polymers are and some of their uses
- evaluate social, economic and environmental advantages and disadvantages of the production and disposal of polymers
- compare the production of ethanol from crops such as sugar cane with its production from an alkene
- describe how vegetable oils are extracted from crops and some of their uses in food and to make fuels
- explain the difference between saturated and unsaturated vegetable oils and describe their relative effects on human health
- describe the structure of the Earth and explain how scientists came to accept the theory that the continents are moving
- explain why scientists are uncertain about changes that have happened to the atmosphere since the Earth was young.

Cracking

Taking it further

As alkanes get longer, the forces between their molecules increase. This makes it harder for the molecules to move past each other, making longer alkanes more viscous than short ones. In order to burn, alkanes must first be vaporised. Larger molecules are more difficult to vaporise because of the stronger forces between the molecules. The greater viscosity and lower flammability of longer alkanes contribute to the lower demand for them as fuels.

Examiner feedback

When explaining the need for cracking, discuss supply and demand issues for both shorter and longer fractions. Remember that shorter alkanes are more valuable because they are better fuels.

Science in action

The products of cracking are a mixture of different alkanes and alkenes. These need to be separated before they can be used further. This separation is done by fractional distillation.

How useful is crude oil?

Crude oil is a mixture (see lesson C1 4.1) and is separated into useful **fractions** at oil refineries (see lesson C1 4.2). Some fractions, such as petrol, are in greater demand than the supply. Other fractions, such as fuel oil, are in less demand than the supply. This problem is solved by **cracking** the large, less sought-after molecules into smaller, more useful ones. The process of cracking also produces chemicals called **alkenes**, from which many plastics are made.

Supply and demand issues

Crude oil is a mixture of mainly **hydrocarbons**, most of which are **alkanes**. Hydrocarbons are compounds containing carbon and hydrogen only. The different fractions separated from crude oil by **fractional distillation** have different properties. Fractions containing shorter alkanes are less viscous, are easier to ignite and burn with a cleaner flame. These properties make them more useful as fuels and so more valuable than fractions containing longer alkane molecules.

The more useful fractions containing shorter alkanes, for example petrol, are in greater demand than the supply. In other words, more petrol is needed than we produce by the fractional distillation of crude oil. Fractions containing longer alkanes, for example fuel oil, are less useful as fuels, and the supply is greater than the demand.

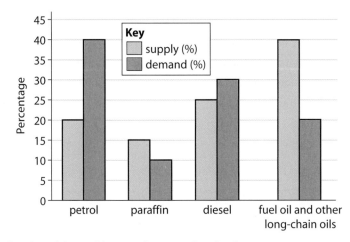

Figure 1 Supply and demand for some fractions of crude oil.

Cracking

To solve the supply and demand problem, longer hydrocarbons can be broken down into smaller ones by a process called cracking. Cracking involves breaking C—C covalent bonds.

The hydrocarbons are heated to vaporise them, turning them into gases. They are then passed over a hot **catalyst**. A catalyst is a chemical that speeds up a reaction but does not get used up. Cracking is a **thermal decomposition** reaction in which molecules are broken down by heating them. Much energy is needed to break the covalent bonds between the atoms.

Cracking produces shorter alkanes and alkenes. The shorter alkanes are used to help meet the demand for fuels such as petrol. The alkenes are used to make plastics.

e.g.

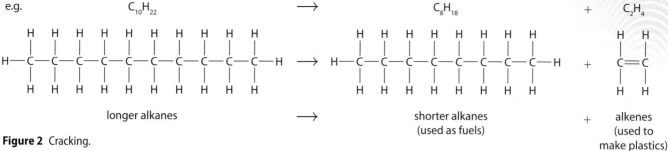

Figure 2 Cracking.

Alkenes

Alkanes are **saturated** hydrocarbons. These contain no C=C double bonds, and have the general formula C_nH_{2n+2}. Alkenes are **unsaturated** hydrocarbons that contain one or more C=C double bonds. Alkenes have the general formula C_nH_{2n}.

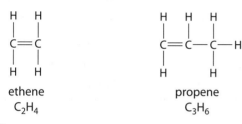

Figure 4 Alkenes.

A simple test for unsaturated hydrocarbons uses bromine water. Bromine water is an orange colour. It turns colourless when it reacts with unsaturated hydrocarbons. However, if it is added to a saturated hydrocarbon, there is no reaction so it stays an orange colour.

Practical

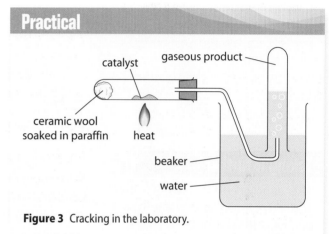

Figure 3 Cracking in the laboratory.

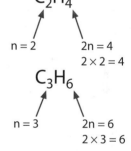

Figure 5 The general formula of alkenes.

Questions

1. Why are shorter alkanes in more demand as fuels than longer alkanes?

2. **(a)** Name one fraction of crude oil that is in greater demand than the supply. **(b)** Name one fraction of crude oil that is in greater supply than the demand.

3. **(a)** Why is cracking carried out? **(b)** How is cracking carried out?

4. What are the main two types of products of cracking and what are they used for?

5. An alkane has the formula $C_{12}H_{26}$. Write a balanced equation to show this alkane being cracked to form propene and an alkane.

6. **(a)** Alkenes are unsaturated molecules. What is an unsaturated molecule? **(b)** Describe a test to show that a molecule is unsaturated. Give the result of this test.

7. **(a)** Give the formula of an alkene that contains four C atoms. **(b)** Draw the structure of an alkene that contains four C atoms.

8. Explain as fully as you can the economic reasons for cracking crude oil. **A***

The bromine reacts with the double bond in the alkenes.

Polymers

Learning objectives

- describe what a polymer is and why they are so useful
- explain how polymers are made from alkenes
- write equations for the formation of polymers
- explain that different polymers have different properties and uses.

Versatile polymers

Polymers (plastics) are used to make many things, including bags, bottles, CDs, DVDs and the casings of electrical items such as computers and mobile phones. Many polymers are made from alkenes. This lesson looks at what polymers are.

Polymerisation

Polymers are large molecules made from lots of small molecules joined together. The small molecules that are joined together are called **monomers**. The process in which monomers join together is called **polymerisation**. For a simple model of polymerisation, imagine joining paper clips together to make a long chain.

Figure 1 A simple model for polymerisation.

Taking it further

Alkenes polymerise by a process called addition polymerisation in which the polymer is the only product. There is another type of polymerisation called condensation polymerisation where small molecules, such as water, are produced, as well as the polymer. Many artificial polymers, such as nylon and polyesters, are condensation polymers, as well as many natural polymers, such as starch and cellulose.

Making poly(ethene)

Many common polymers are made from alkenes. This is because the double bond in alkenes can be broken and used to join the molecule to another alkene molecule. For example, **poly(ethene)** is made by joining several thousand ethene molecules together into long-chain molecules. This polymer is better known as polythene and is used to make things like plastic bags and plastic bottles.

cracking makes small ethene molecules

these can be made to join together to form poly(ethene)

the chains stack up like molecular spaghetti

Figure 2 Making a polymer.

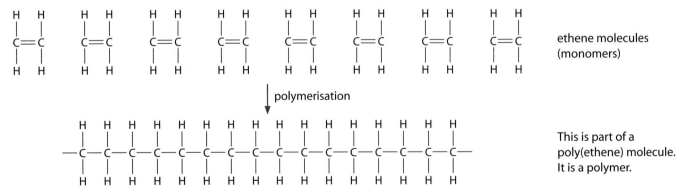

ethene molecules (monomers)

polymerisation

This is part of a poly(ethene) molecule. It is a polymer.

Figure 3 The formation of poly(ethene).

Figure 4 Equation for the formation of poly(ethene).

A balanced equation can be written for the polymerisation of ethene, as shown in Figure 4. The number of molecules that join together is very large. It is often several thousand but the exact number varies. We can use n to mean a large number.

Making other polymers

Poly(propene) is formed from the polymerisation of the alkene propene. Poly(propene) is used to make plastic crates, bins and rope. Polymers are often named by putting *poly* before the name of the monomer in brackets. Poly(propene) is a good example of this.

Many other polymers can be made from monomers containing C=C double bonds. Some examples are shown in the table below. Different polymers have different properties and uses. You will not have to learn these for the exam.

Figure 5 Equation for the formation of poly(propene).

Table 1 Useful polymers.

Polymer	Common name	Properties	Uses
poly(ethene)	polythene	flexible	bags, cling film
poly(propene)	polypropylene	flexible	crisp packets, crates, ropes, carpets
poly(chloroethene)	PVC	tough, hard	window frames, gutters, pipes
poly(tetrafluoroethene)	Teflon/PTFE	tough, slippery	frying pan coatings, stain-proof carpets
poly(methyl 2-methylpropenoate)	Perspex	tough, hard, clear	shatter-proof windows
poly(ethenol)	PVA	dissolves in water	hospital laundry bags

Questions

1   **(a)** What is a polymer? **(b)** What is a monomer? **(c)** Name five different polymers mentioned on these pages.

2   Polymers can be made from alkenes. What do alkenes contain that allow them to react to form polymers?

3   **(a)** Give two uses for poly(ethene). **(b)** Give two uses for poly(propene).

4   Describe what happens to molecules in a polymerisation reaction.

5   **(a)** Name the polymer made from phenylethene. **(b)** Name the polymer made from methylpropene.

6   Draw a diagram to show four molecules of propene reacting together to form poly(propene).

7   Write an equation for the formation of poly(chloroethene), also called PVC, from chloroethene. The structure of chloroethene is shown in Figure 6.

Figure 6 Chloroethene.

8   Explain what polymers are and how they are formed from alkenes. Use poly(ethene) as an example in your answer.

Examiner feedback

Examination questions often provide the structure of an alkene and ask for the polymer formed from this alkene to be drawn.

When drawing the structures of polymers, make sure that the brackets go through the bonds at the ends, that there is a single (not double) bond between the two carbon atoms and that you put the n after the bracket.

New uses for polymers

Designing materials

Many new uses are being found for polymers, and new types of polymers are being developed all the time with new and exciting properties and applications. Scientists are even designing polymers to have very specific properties. This lesson looks at some new uses for polymers.

Smart polymers

Smart materials are materials that have one or more properties, for example shape, colour or size, that change with a change in conditions, for example temperature or pH.

Shape-memory polymers are one example of a smart material. They can change shape as the temperature changes. However, they can go back to their original shape when the temperature gets high enough. Two uses of shape-memory polymers are in heat-shrink wrapping used for packaging and in heat-shrink tubing used to cover bundles of electrical wires. The wrapping or tube is placed over what it is being used to protect and then heated. As it is heated, it shrinks to a tight fit.

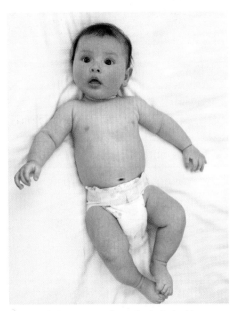

Hydrogels keep urine from the baby's skin.

Polymers that change colour with changes in temperature or light are also smart materials. For example, you can buy plastic bowls and spoons for baby food that change colour if the food is too hot. There are also light-sensitive lenses for spectacles that darken in bright light.

The colour of the spoon changes from purple to pink to show that the food is too hot.

Hydrogels

Hydrogels are polymers that can absorb a lot of water and turn into a gel. One use is in disposable nappies; the hydrogel is built into the nappy to absorb urine to prevent nappy rash. Hydrogels are also used to make soft contact lenses. They are also used in garden plant containers and hanging baskets. The hydrogel is mixed into the compost and absorbs a lot of water. This means that the plants can survive longer without being watered.

Waterproof coatings for fabrics

For many years, waterproof coatings for clothing fabrics kept water out but would not allow water vapour released by the body to escape. This meant that the fabric still got wet on the inside. However, light, waterproof coatings for fabrics have been developed that will keep water out but allow water vapour from sweat to escape, keeping the wearer dry. The pores in the coating are too small to allow droplets of liquid water through but large enough to allow individual molecules in water vapour out.

PTFE layer

water vapour from sweat can escape

PTFE layer

water in raindrops can't get in

Figure 1 How a breathable PTFE coating works.

Dental polymers

For many years, dentists have used metal alloys to fill cavities in teeth. Over the last few years new tooth-coloured materials have been developed using polymers. These are mixtures of chemicals that include a monomer plus chemicals to start the polymerisation reaction. The mixture is placed in the cavity in the tooth and a very bright blue light is shone onto the mixture. This starts the polymerisation reaction making a polymer in the tooth.

Packaging materials

Plastics have been used in many ways in recent years for packaging. However, there have been several new developments. For example, there is now food packaging that changes colour if the food starts to go off, making consumers more aware and helping to prevent food poisoning. The addition of antimicrobial chemicals to some packaging prevents bacterial growth and has extended the shelf-life of some foods. There are also some biodegradable plastics used now that decay naturally over time, reducing long-term waste problems.

Wound dressings

Wound dressings are needed to protect wounds while they heal. New polymers have allowed the development of improved dressings that can now include antibacterial barriers, hydrogels and waterproof but breathable films. These help to protect the wound as it heals.

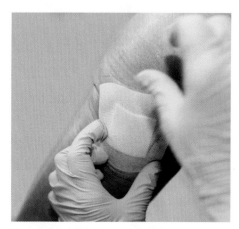

A dentist starts the polymerisation reaction in a new filling.

A wound dressing.

Questions

1 **(a)** What is a smart material? **(b)** What is a shape-memory polymer? **(c)** Give two different uses for smart materials.

2 **(a)** What is a hydrogel? **(b)** Why are hydrogels used in nappies?

3 Why do people prefer to have polymer fillings in front teeth instead of metal fillings?

4 Explain how a cavity in a tooth can be filled with a polymer.

5 Give two recent developments in packaging materials and explain why these are useful developments.

6 **(a)** What advantage does a waterproof coating on a wound dressing have? **(b)** What advantage does an antibacterial coating on a wound dressing have?

7 Modern waterproof coatings for fabrics are now 'breathable'. **(a)** Explain what this means and why this is an improvement on waterproof coatings that were not breathable. **(b)** Explain how breathable coatings work.

8 There have been many developments in the production and uses of polymers in recent years. Choose three separate examples and explain why these developments are helpful to our everyday lives.

A*

Examiner feedback

You will not need to remember all the details about these uses of polymers. However, you may be provided with information about them in an exam question and asked to comment on their uses.

Practical

Nappies contain hydrogels. Plan and carry out an experiment to compare the absorbency of different brands of nappies.

Disposing of polymers

Where does all the rubbish go?

We produce about 5 million tonnes of polymers each year in the UK. What happens to them when we have finished with them?

Waste plastic made from polymers. We produce 20 times more plastic today than we did 50 years ago.

Burial in landfill

Most discarded polymers are buried with domestic and industrial waste in **landfill sites**. This is easy and cheap but can cause many problems. It is becoming difficult to find places to put more landfill sites as we bury more and more rubbish. Also, most polymers are not **biodegradable**. This means that microorganisms cannot break them down, so they will not **decompose**, or rot away, if they are buried. It also means that they will not rot away if dropped as litter.

Landfill sites in the UK are regulated to minimise their impact on the environment.

New polymers are being developed that are broken down by microorganisms, that is, they are biodegradable. Some biodegradable polymers, such as PLA, are being made from cornstarch. Cornstarch is extracted from corn (maize). Some food packaging and shopping bags are made from polymers made from cornstarch. At the moment, these polymers are more expensive to produce than polymers made from chemicals derived from crude oil. However, some companies are using them as they are more environmentally friendly. Their use will increase if their cost becomes more competitive compared with other polymers, if there is more public pressure for their use or if there is government legislation.

Incineration

Polymers burn well and a lot of polymer waste is burned in **incinerators**. However, carbon dioxide (CO_2) is formed when polymers are burned. This is a greenhouse gas and contributes to global warming. In addition, unless the conditions in the incinerator are carefully controlled to ensure there is enough oxygen from the air, toxic gases including carbon monoxide (CO), hydrogen chloride (HCl) and hydrogen cyanide (HCN) can also be produced.

Waste incinerators are more common in countries, such as Japan, where land is a scarce resource.

Modern incinerators are designed to burn waste very efficiently with few harmful emissions except the greenhouse gas carbon dioxide. The heat released can also be used to generate electricity.

Recycling

Most polymers can be recycled. Less crude oil and energy are used in **recycling** polymers than in making them from the raw materials. Also, recycling avoids the problems caused by burying or burning waste polymers.

Polymers are often recycled by chopping up the polymer into pellets that can be melted and moulded into new products. Polymers that can be melted and remoulded are called thermosoftening polymers. New developments allow some polymers to be broken back down into monomers, from which new polymers can then be made.

Polymers must be separated out into their different types to be recycled. Most polymer products have a symbol to show which polymer they are made from. However, the sorting has to be done by hand, which is time-consuming and expensive. New technologies are being developed to sort polymers by machine.

Using products made from crude oil

Polymers are one of several groups of products made from crude oil. Other examples include medicines, solvents and detergents. We also make much use of crude oil for fuels to keep us warm and for transport. Fuels, polymers and other substances made from crude oil have greatly improved our everyday lives. However, the problems of the disposal of some of these substances made from crude oil and the pollutants produced from their use as fuels are problems we have to deal with as a society.

PETE
polyethylene terephthalate

HDPE
high-density poly(ethene)

PVC
poly(chloroethene) (also called polyvinyl chloride, PVC)

LDPE
low-density poly(ethene)

PP
poly(propane)

PS
polystyrene

OTHER
other polymers

Figure 1 Polymers and their recycling symbols.

Questions

1   What are the three ways of disposing of used polymers?

2   How are most polymers disposed of?

3   **(a)** Most polymers are not biodegradable. What does this mean?
    (b) Why is this a problem for burying polymers in landfill?

4   **(a)** Give two disadvantages of burning polymers. **(b)** Give two advantages of burning polymers.

5   **(a)** What must be done to polymers before they can be recycled?
    (b) How is this usually done? **(c)** How are advances in technology helping to solve this problem?

6   **(a)** There are about 60 million people in the UK. At its peak a few years ago, 17.5 thousand million supermarket bags were used per year in the UK. Calculate the average number of bags that were used per person in the UK that year. **(b)** Why has the number of bags used per person started to fall?

7   Draw a table to list the three ways of disposing of polymers. Include columns to show: **(a)** what is done in each method; **(b)** the advantages and disadvantages of each method; **(c)** whether each method has any social, economic or environmental issues.

8   Chemicals made from crude oil have improved modern life, but also bring problems. Discuss some of the advantages and disadvantages of using chemicals made from crude oil.

Taking it further

Polymers made from alkenes are not biodegradable because the electrons in the covalent bonds between the carbon atoms in the polymer chain are shared equally between the atoms, making the bonds very strong. In biodegradable polymers, the electrons in the bonds between different atoms in the chain are not shared equally between atoms, making it easier for other molecules to react with the polymer and break down the chain.

Ethanol production

Ethanol is used to fuel some cars in Brazil.

Practical

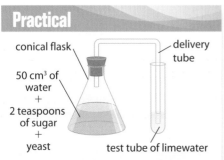

conical flask

delivery tube

50 cm³ of water + 2 teaspoons of sugar + yeast

test tube of limewater

Figure 2 Fermentation in the laboratory.

What is ethanol?
There are many different types of alcohol. The commonest alcohol is ethanol, C_2H_5OH, the alcohol found in alcoholic drinks.

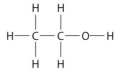

Figure 1 The structure of ethanol.

Uses of ethanol
Ethanol is used as a solvent to make many common substances, such as detergents and medicines, which are also called pharmaceuticals.

Ethanol can also be used as a fuel, as explained in lesson C1 4.5. In Brazil, for example, it is used as fuel for some cars. In the UK, 5% of the mixture sold as petrol at petrol stations is now ethanol. The ethanol used in fuels is made from fermentation of crops and is a biofuel.

Over 330 000 tonnes of ethanol are made in the UK every year. There are two main ways to make ethanol: by fermentation of carbohydrates and by hydration of ethene. This lesson describes and compares these two methods.

Making ethanol by fermentation
Over 90% of the world's ethanol is produced by fermentation from crops that contain a lot of carbohydrates, such as sugar cane, sugar beet, rice and maize. These are **renewable** raw materials because we can grow more to replace those that have been used. The ethanol made by fermentation is not pure; it also contains water. Fractional distillation is used to make pure ethanol from the mixture.

Alcoholic drinks are made by fermentation. Different drinks are made by fermenting different crops. For example, wine is made from grapes and beer from malted barley. Yeast and water are added to the grapes or barley and the mixture left, in the absence of air, for fermentation to produce the drink.

Making ethanol by hydration of ethene
The other main method of producing ethanol is by reaction of ethene with steam. This reaction is called **hydration**. Ethene is made from crude oil. Crude oil is a non-renewable resource (see lesson C1 4.5), which means that it cannot be replaced when we use it. However, the ethanol produced this way is pure.

Table 1 compares the two ways of making ethanol.

Table 1 Comparison of two ways of making ethanol.

	Fermentation of carbohydrates	Reaction of ethene with steam
raw materials	source of carbohydrates (e.g. sugar cane, sugar beet, rice and maize)	crude oil
type of raw materials	renewable	non-renewable

	Fermentation of carbohydrates	Reaction of ethene with steam
reaction	sugar $\longrightarrow$ ethanol + carbon dioxide $C_6H_{12}O_6 \longrightarrow 2C_2H_5OH + 2CO_2$	ethene + steam $\longrightarrow$ ethanol $CH_2{=}CH_2 + H_2O \longrightarrow C_2H_5OH$
temperature	30–40 °C	300 °C
pressure	normal pressure (1 atm)	high pressure (60–70 atm)
catalyst	enzymes in yeast	concentrated phosphoric acid
other essential conditions	aqueous (in water) anaerobic (no oxygen present)	
type of process	batch process (stop–start process, which is labour intensive, i.e. requires a lot of workers)	continuous process (process kept running 24 hours a day, seven days a week, less labour intensive)
comparison of reaction rates (speed)	slow reaction	fast reaction
comparison of ethanol made	impure ethanol (purified by fractional distillation)	pure ethanol
energy use	lower energy use	high energy use for high temperature and pressure
sustainability	raw materials are renewable so sustainable process	raw materials are not renewable so this is not a sustainable process
comparison of economic factors	cheaper process (but the main cost is the energy needed to separate the ethanol by fractional distillation)	more expensive process due to high temperatures and pressures
comparison of environmental factors	uses renewable raw materials and less energy	uses non-renewable raw materials and more energy

Questions

1 Give the formula of ethanol.

2 Give three uses for ethanol.

3 (a) What are the raw materials used to make ethanol by fermentation? (b) What conditions are used to make ethanol by fermentation? (c) How is the impure ethanol that is made purified?

4 (a) What is the raw material used to make ethanol by hydration? (b) What conditions are used to make ethanol by hydration?

5 Explain why fermentation has lower energy costs than hydration.

6 (a) What is the difference between batch and continuous processes? (b) Which process has the highest labour costs and why?

7 Compare the two methods of producing ethanol in terms of rate, purity of ethanol, use of raw materials, type of process and energy costs.

8 Compare the two methods of making ethanol in terms of sustainability and economic and environmental factors.

Vegetable oils and biodiesel

Rapeseed oil is used for cooking and for making biodiesel.

Stored chemical energy from light

Plants make glucose from carbon dioxide and water by photosynthesis. Plants need glucose for respiration, and they may convert it into starch or vegetable oils for storage. These oils provide energy to the plants but we can use them for food and fuel.

Extracting oils

Some plant materials contain enough oil to make extraction worthwhile. These include nuts from hazel bushes, fruit from oil palms and olive trees, and seeds from rapeseed plants and sunflowers. After harvesting, the plant material is sieved to remove stones and other objects that might damage machinery. It is then crushed to break open the oil-containing cells, forming a mixture of oil and broken plant material.

The oil can then be separated from the broken plant material by squashing or **pressing** the mixture. Oil and water are released. They separate into two layers. The water is drained away leaving the oil behind. It may still contain water and other impurities such as plant resins and bacteria, so it is filtered, then heated to drive off the remaining water and kill bacteria.

Vegetable oils may also be separated using a solvent. They dissolve in the solvent to form a solution that is more easily removed from the broken plant material. The solvent is distilled from the mixture, leaving the oil behind. Hexane is a solvent commonly used to dissolve vegetable oils for extraction on industrial scales. It is a hydrocarbon produced from crude oil but it is recycled so that it can be used again.

Practical

Oils that degrade when heated strongly, such as limonene from orange peel, may be separated using steam distillation. Steam is passed through the broken plant material, carrying the oil with it. When the mixture is cooled, a layer of water forms with the oil floating on top.

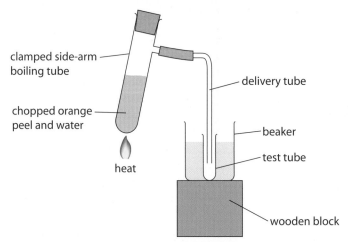

Figure 1 Volatile oils can be separated by steam distillation.

Biodiesel

Fuels for vehicles can be produced from vegetable oils. **Biodiesel** is a biofuel made from vegetable oils such as rapeseed oil. The oil is converted into biodiesel by reacting it with methanol and sodium hydroxide. Biodiesel can be used alone or blended with ordinary diesel. Diesel-engined vehicles can use it without modification.

Unlike diesel from crude oil, biodiesel molecules contain oxygen atoms. A vehicle running on biodiesel produces fewer particulates and less carbon monoxide than it does using ordinary diesel. Particulates increase the risk of respiratory disease and carbon monoxide is toxic. Biodiesel naturally contains very little sulfur, so it releases almost no sulfur dioxide when in use. This helps to reduce production of acid rain.

A **carbon-neutral** fuel has no life-cycle emissions of carbon dioxide. The amount of carbon dioxide released in its production and use is the same as the amount absorbed by the growing plants during photosynthesis. Biodiesel should be a carbon-neutral fuel. However, this is not the case, because fossil fuels are used in its production.

For example, fertilisers and methanol are manufactured from coal or natural gas. Sodium hydroxide is manufactured by passing electricity through sodium chloride solution, and at the moment two-thirds of the world's electricity is generated using fossil fuels. These fuels may also be used by the machinery needed to harvest the plants, process the oil and deliver the biodiesel. Even so, the life-cycle emissions of carbon dioxide from biodiesel are much less than those from ordinary diesel.

Biodiesel is a low-sulfur fuel with lower life-cycle emissions of carbon dioxide.

Questions

1. State three sources of vegetable oils.
2. Suggest why some plant materials may not be useful sources of vegetable oils.
3. Describe how vegetable oils may be extracted using mechanical methods.
4. Suggest a hazard associated with using a solvent such as hexane in the extraction of vegetable oils.
5. Describe two benefits of using biodiesel instead of ordinary diesel.
6. This table shows information about the production of bioethanol. The reduction in greenhouse gas emissions does not include emissions as a result of clearing land, and the **payback time** refers to clearing grassland.

Country	Crop	Greenhouse gas reduction (%)	Payback time/years
UK	wheat	28	20–34
Brazil	sugar cane	71	3–10

   (a) Explain which country's bioethanol is likely to produce the greatest reduction overall in greenhouse gas emissions, assuming that both are made from crops grown on cleared grassland. (b) Suggest why wheat for UK bioethanol is grown on existing farmland or land previously taken out of farming.

7. What is a carbon-neutral fuel? Apart from issues surrounding land use or re-use, explain why biodiesel is not a carbon-neutral fuel.

Examiner feedback

You do not need to memorise how biofuels are manufactured but you may be asked to use information given to you on the topic.

Emulsions

Paints plus

You may have used **emulsion** paint to decorate your bedroom walls. It is a complex mixture of water, coloured pigments and various other chemicals. These stick the pigment to the wall and make the paint easier to use and store. However, there is more to emulsions than paint. Emulsions are mixtures with special properties.

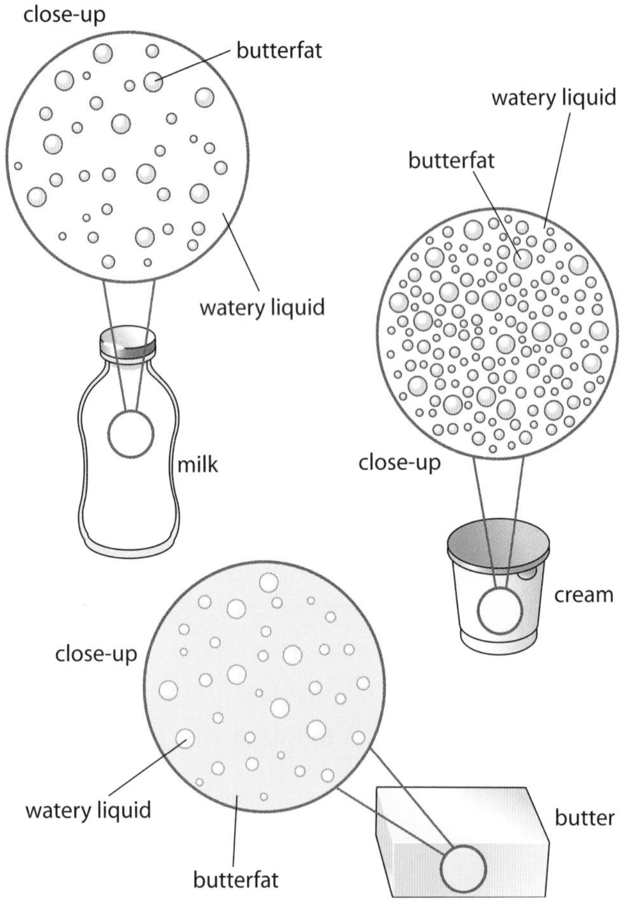

Learning objectives
- describe how emulsions form
- describe the properties of emulsifiers
- explain the uses of emulsions in food, cosmetics and paints.

Making emulsions

Oil and water are **immiscible**. They do not dissolve into one another when they are mixed. You have probably seen how a layer of oil can spread over the top of a puddle of water. When oil and water are shaken vigorously together, tiny oil droplets spread evenly through the water to produce a mixture called an emulsion. Traditional oil-and-vinegar salad dressings are made this way. Milk is an oil-in-water emulsion. It comprises a watery liquid mixed with tiny droplets of butterfat. In full fat milk, the water and butterfat gradually separate, and the butterfat rises to the surface to form a layer of cream. The cream can be processed to make butter, which is a water-in-oil emulsion.

Emulsifiers

Emulsions are not stable mixtures. An oil and water emulsion eventually separates out if it is left to stand. Oil is less dense than water so it floats on top. This happens with oil-and-vinegar salad dressing. Chemicals called **emulsifiers** can be added to make emulsions more stable, extending their shelf-life.

Milk contains proteins that act as emulsifiers. Mayonnaise is made from oil and vinegar, just like a traditional salad dressing, but it also contains a little egg yolk to stop it separating out. Egg yolk contains an emulsifier called lecithin.

Emulsifier molecules have two different properties. One end of the molecule is **hydrophobic**, which means 'water-hating'. It dissolves in the oil in the emulsion. The other end of the molecule is **hydrophilic**, which means 'water-loving'. It dissolves in the water in the emulsion. In an oil-in-water emulsion, for example, the emulsifier molecules surround the tiny droplets of oil. The hydrophobic 'tails' dissolve in the oil, and the hydrophilic 'heads' dissolve in the water. This stops the oil droplets joining together again to form a layer of oil, and so stabilises the emulsion.

Figure 1 Milk, cream and butter are three different emulsions of the same ingredients.

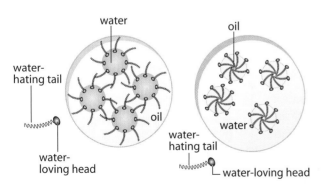

Figure 2 Emulsifier molecules have a hydrophilic 'head' and a hydrophobic 'tail'.

Examiner feedback

The link between the structure of emulsifiers and their properties is the sort of difficult chemistry tested in questions aimed at more able candidates.

Emulsions are very versatile but even with emulsifiers they do eventually separate out.

Mayonnaise without emulsifier quickly seperates into two layers.

Mayonnaise with emulsifier forms a stable emulsion.

Taking it further

Lecithin is a mixture of substances commonly used as an emulsifier in food. Originally, the name was used for a pure substance, now called phosphatidylcholine. This compound is an example of a phospholipid: phospholipids are one of the main components of all cell membranes, which rely on their head-and-tail structure.

Uses of emulsions

Emulsions are thicker, or more viscous, than the oil and water they contain. This special property is important for non-drip emulsion paints, which stay on the brush but spread easily on the walls without running. This thick texture is also important in cosmetics such as skin creams, to make them look and feel better, and in foods for the same reasons. Mayonnaise is thicker than traditional salad dressings. It does not pour and it coats food well. Similarly, cream is thicker than milk. It coats strawberries and other food in an attractive way and has a pleasant texture on the tongue.

Ice cream is a frozen emulsion that contains ice crystals and tiny bubbles of air. Like butter, soft margarines are water-in-oil emulsions. The oils alone would be too runny to make a pleasant spread for your toast. As part of an emulsion, they form a product that does not create an oil slick on your toast but is soft enough to spread straight from the fridge.

Science in action

Cosmetics contain different types of emulsion. Hand creams and shaving creams are usually oil-in-water emulsions because they need relatively little oily material to work. Sun blocks and moisturising creams are usually water-in-oil emulsions. They contain more oily material, so they have a greasy feel and stay on the skin for longer.

Questions

1. When oil and water are mixed and left to stand, why does the oil form a layer on top of the water?

2. What is an emulsion?

3. Compare the viscosity of an emulsion with the viscosity of the oil and water it contains.

4. Describe three different uses for emulsions.

5. In terms of the type of emulsion, what is the difference between milk and margarine?

6. Explain how emulsifiers work.

7. Detergent molecules have a similar structure to emulsifier molecules. Suggest how this helps washing machine detergents remove greasy stains from clothes.

8. Mayonnaise is an emulsion. Explain how it is made and how it is stabilised. To what extent would you agree that an emulsifier is used to extend the shelf-life of the mayonnaise?

A*

Hardening vegetable oils

Route to A*

The link between the melting point of fats and oils and the chemical structure of their molecules is important, and you should aim to understand it.

Animal fats tend to be more saturated than vegetable oils.

Vegetable oils in food

Vegetable oils may be altered chemically to change their properties, making them more suitable for some food uses.

Fats and oils

Many animal fats and some vegetable oils are saturated. The carbon atoms in their chains are joined to each other by single chemical bonds. This makes the chains flexible, so they can line up closely next to each other. As a result, the attractive forces between individual molecules are relatively strong and a lot of energy is needed to overcome them. This means that the melting point of saturated fats tends to be high, making them solid at room temperature.

In contrast, most vegetable oils are unsaturated. Some of their carbon atoms are joined by double bonds instead of single bonds. These C=C bonds can put a rigid bend in the carbon chain. Bent chains cannot line up as closely as unbent chains. As a result, the attractive forces between individual molecules are relatively weak and the molecules are easily moved apart. This means that the melting point of unsaturated oils tends to be low, making them liquid at room temperature.

How unsaturated?

Unsaturated vegetable oils contain C=C bonds, just as alkenes do. The presence of these double bonds can be detected using bromine. Bromine water, an orange solution of bromine, turns colourless when it is mixed with alkenes or with unsaturated vegetable oils.

Like alkanes, completely saturated oils or fats have no double bonds. They cannot decolourise bromine water. The more double bonds present, the greater the volume of bromine water that can be decolourised. Sunflower oil is more unsaturated than olive oil. It can **decolourise** about two-thirds more bromine water than olive oil can.

A **burette** is used to add precise volumes of bromine water to an oil.

Adding hydrogen

Chemists working in the food industry have developed a way to convert cheap unsaturated vegetable oils into solid fats. Hydrogen is used to change carbon–carbon double bonds into single bonds, turning an unsaturated oil into a saturated fat. This process is called **hardening**.

Vegetable oils are hardened by warming them to about 60 °C and bubbling hydrogen gas through them. One of the bonds in a C=C bond breaks, and so does the H—H bond in a hydrogen molecule. Then each of the two carbon atoms makes a new bond with a hydrogen atom. This sort of reaction is called **hydrogenation**. Nickel is used as a catalyst to speed up the reaction. It is not used up in the reaction and is easily separated from the product.

Hydrogenated vegetable oils can be used for cooking in the same way as animal fats, but they are suitable for vegetarians. For example, they can be used in baking to make cakes and pastries. Solid vegetable fats and liquid vegetable oils can be blended together for use in the manufacture of margarine and chocolate.

Figure 1 Hydrogenation converts unsaturated oil into saturated fat at 60 °C in the presence of a nickel catalyst.

Examiner feedback

You may have read about the health risks of eating partially hydrogenated fats, or *trans* fats. You will not be examined on this topic.

Hydrogenated vegetable oils are used to make spreads, cakes and pastries.

Questions

1. In general, what is the physical state of saturated fats at room temperature, and what is the state of unsaturated oils?

2. Which chemical bonds are present in both unsaturated oils and saturated oils?

3. Explain how vegetable oils may be hardened by hydrogenation.

4. State three uses of hydrogenated vegetable oils.

5. What would you see if bromine water were added to sunflower oil? What difference would you see if it were added to olive oil?

6. Describe the main difference in chemical structure between saturated fats and unsaturated oils.

7. **Table 1** Results of experiments to determine the melting points of some vegetable oils, and their amount of unsaturation.

Oil	Melting point/°C	Volume of bromine water reacted/cm³		
		Test 1	Test 2	Test 3
olive	−5	22.6	22.4	22.2
palm	34	14.7	15.3	15.0
sunflower	−16	34.6	34.5	34.7
rapeseed	−11	27.1	27.5	26.7

(a) Calculate the mean volume of bromine water reacted for each vegetable oil. (b) Explain which oil is the most unsaturated. (c) Describe the relationship between the amount of unsaturation of a vegetable oil and its melting point. (d) Coconut oil reacted with 3.2 cm³ of bromine water in a similar experiment. Predict, giving your reasons, the state of this oil at room temperature.

8. Explain the link between the degree of unsaturation of a vegetable oil and its melting point and chemical properties.

Taking it further

Hydrogenation is an example of an addition reaction. The hydrogen atoms are added across the double bond. Alkenes undergo many addition reactions, often producing useful substances. For example, ethene reacts with steam to make ethanol.

Oils and fats in our diet

Food cooks more quickly in oil than it does in water.

Nutritious oils and fats

Oils and fats are an important part of a healthy diet. They are a good source of energy and provide us with **nutrients**. For example, vitamins A, D and E are fat-soluble. They are found in foods such as dairy products, eggs, oily fish and nuts. However, too much oil and fat in the diet is harmful to health.

Cooking with oil

Water boils at 100 °C. This is hot enough to scald you but it limits how quickly food can be cooked by boiling. Food cooks much faster when it is fried. Vegetable oils have higher boiling points than water, so food can be fried at higher temperatures than it can by boiling in water. For example, olive oil can reach around 240 °C before it begins to smoke and decompose. Food cooks more quickly in vegetable oils, and different flavours are produced. Fried or fatty food may have a pleasant taste or texture, which can encourage people to over-eat.

Oils for energy

Fats and oils have a high energy density compared with proteins and carbohydrates. Table 1 shows the typical amounts of energy available to the body from these nutrients. This can be less than the energy released by burning because, for example, not all the products of digestion may be absorbed.

Table 1 Oils for energy.

Nutrient	Energy released in the body / kJ/g	Energy released when burnt / kJ/g
fat	37	39
protein	17	24
carbohydrate	17	17

As oils and fats contain a lot of energy, eating too much fried or fatty food may make you overweight, or even obese.

Too much fatty food can make you obese and cause health problems.

Taking it further

Cholesterol is an important part of cell membranes. It is made by the liver and carried in the bloodstream by substances called lipoproteins. High levels of cholesterol in the blood increase the risk of blocked arteries and heart disease.

Saturated fats can raise the level of cholesterol in the blood. They are found mainly in meat and dairy products. Too much saturated fat in the diet can also make us gain weight.

Unsaturated fats and oils tend to be more healthy options than saturated fats. They are found mainly in vegetables, nuts and fruits, and are less likely to raise cholesterol levels. One type, called omega-3, comes mainly from oily fish such as sardines and mackerel. Omega-3 oils are thought to help prevent heart disease and may even help to improve brain function.

Healthy eating

☐ Reduce the total amount of fat in our diet.

☐ Reduce the amount of saturated fat in our diet.

☐ Raise the proportion of polyunsaturated fats, which
are found in vegetable oils, in our diet.

Figure 1 Typical dietary advice concerning fats and oils.

Science skills

In 2009, American scientists reported the results of a study involving over half a million adults. The volunteers completed questionnaires about their diet, and their medical records were checked over the next six years to see if they later developed cancer of the pancreas. The intake of polyunsaturated fats made no significant difference to cancer rates.

Table 2 A summary of some more results from the study.

	Cases of pancreatic cancer per 100 000 people per year	
	Most fat in the diet	**Least fat in the diet**
Total fat	46.8	33.2
Saturated fat	51.5	33.1
Monounsaturated fat	46.2	32.9
Saturated fat from animals	52.0	32.2

a What type of graph is most suitable to display these results, and why?

b The scientists concluded that saturated fat in the diet, particularly from meat and dairy products, can increase the risk of getting pancreatic cancer. Explain how their results support this conclusion.

Science in action

Bromine water is used to detect the presence of carbon–carbon double bonds. Bromine and iodine are in the same group in the periodic table, so their chemical reactions are similar.

Iodine can also be used to detect the presence of C=C bonds. As iodine is less reactive than bromine, iodine monochloride may be used instead of iodine.

An 'iodine value' is the number of grams of iodine that would react with 100 g of an oil or fat. Sunflower oil has a typical iodine value of about 135 and olive oil about 82. Iodine values are used in the food industry to measure the degree of unsaturation of a fat or oil.

Questions

1 State two sources each of saturated fats and unsaturated oils.

2 Explain why you should include fats and oils in your diet.

3 Outline why people might fry food in vegetable oil rather than boil it in water.

4 Explain why you might have to reduce your intake of saturated fat.

5 Study the data in Table 1. **(a)** Which nutrient has the highest energy density? **(b)** Suggest why fats and carbohydrates are more efficient sources of energy than proteins.

6 Compare the health benefits and problems of different types of fats and oils.

A*

Assess yourself questions

1   Fuel oil is a fraction of crude oil. More fuel oil is produced at oil refineries than can be sold. To solve this problem, some fuel oil is cracked by passing vaporised fuel oil over a hot catalyst. This cracking produces more-useful shorter chain alkanes and alkenes.

(a) Explain in terms of supply and demand, and the production of fuels, such as petrol, why some of the fuel oil produced at an oil refinery is cracked.
(2 marks)

(b) Cracking is a thermal decomposition reaction. What happens in decomposition reactions? *(1 mark)*

(c) What are the alkenes made in cracking used to make? *(1 mark)*

(d) Alkenes are unsaturated molecules. What is meant by the term *unsaturated* in this context? *(1 mark)*

(e) Which of the following molecules are alkenes?

C_3H_6, C_3H_8, C_6H_{14}, C_8H_{18}, $C_{10}H_{20}$ *(1 mark)*

2   Figure 1 shows the cracking of some paraffin that contains the alkane $C_{12}H_{26}$.

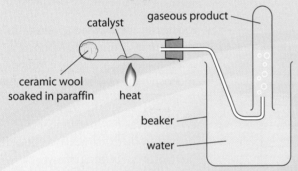

Figure 1 Cracking.

(a) Why was the paraffin soaked in ceramic wool? *(1 mark)*

(b) Why are the first few bubbles of gas not collected? *(1 mark)*

(c) Describe a test that you could do to prove that alkenes have been produced. Give the results of the test. *(2 marks)*

(d) The cracking of $C_{12}H_{26}$ in the paraffin produced ethene, C_2H_4, and another alkane. Write a balanced equation for this reaction. *(1 mark)*

3   (a) The structure of propene is shown in Figure 2.

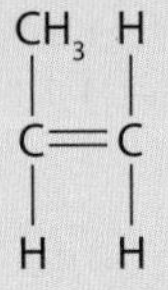

Figure 2 Propene.

Which of the following structures is the correct structure of the polymer made from propene?
(1 mark)

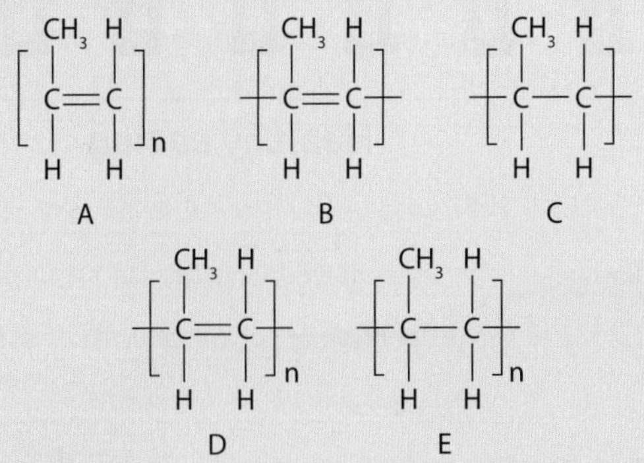

Figure 3

(b) What is the name of the polymer that is made from propene? *(1 mark)*

(c) Draw the structure of the polymer formed from each of the monomers in Figure 4. *(3 marks)*

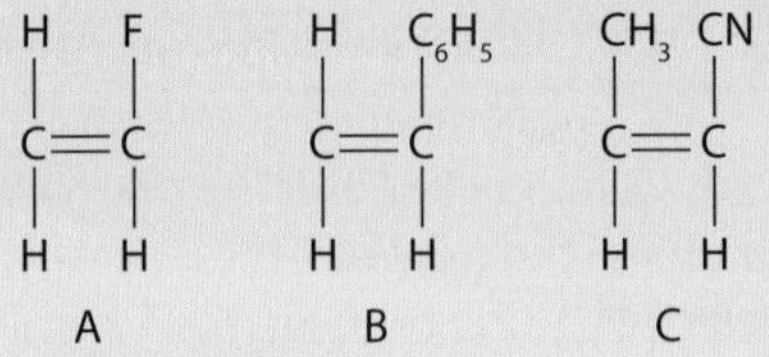

Figure 4 Monomers.

4   Table 1 shows data about waste in the UK over recent years.

Table 1 Data from DEFRA.

	1994	1999	2004	2009
Annual waste per person/kg	445	482	520	473
Annual waste that was recycled or composted per person/kg	15	44	75	178

(a) Describe how the total amount of waste in the UK per person has changed over the years since 1994.
(1 mark)

(b) Draw a bar chart showing how the amount of waste that has been recycled or composted has varied since 1994. *(2 marks)*

(c) (i) Describe how the total amount of waste in the UK that has been recycled or composted per person has changed over the years since 1994. *(1 mark)*

(ii) Suggest a reason why this might have changed since 1994. *(1 mark)*

(d) Many polymers are non-biodegradable. Explain why this is a problem. *(2 marks)*

5   Ethanol is a good fuel that can be used in cars. Petrol sold in the UK contains 5% ethanol made from carbohydrates such as sugar and maize. Ethanol can also be made from ethene. Ethene is made from crude oil.

(a) Ethanol made from carbohydrates is a carbon-neutral fuel. Explain what *carbon neutral* means here. *(2 marks)*

(b) Give an advantage of making ethanol from carbohydrates compared with ethene in terms of the use of raw materials. *(2 marks)*

6 Crude oil is a very important raw material with many uses. Give some social and economic advantages and disadvantages of using products from crude oil as fuels or as raw materials for plastic and other chemicals.

In this question you will be assessed on using good English, organising information clearly and using specialist terms where appropriate. *(6 marks)*

7 Vegetable oils can be extracted from plant materials. Table 2 shows the stages in extracting sunflower oil. Copy the table and write numbers in the boxes to put the stages into the correct order. Two have been done for you. *(4 marks)*

Table 2 The stages in the extraction of sunflower oil.

seeds are harvested	1
seeds are crushed	
the mixture is pressed	
water and other impurities are removed	
water and sunflower oil are obtained	
water and sunflower oil separate into two layers	
water is added to the crushed seeds	
sunflower oil is collected	8

8 **Table 3** The properties of some vegetable oils.

Oil	Melting point/°C	Smoke point/°C	Iodine number	Energy provided / kJ/g
corn oil	−15	240	120	37.1
olive oil	−12	220	60	33.8
rapeseed oil	5	235	100	36.9
sunflower oil	−18	245	130	37.0

The smoke point is the temperature at which the oil begins to give off smoke, risking it setting alight. The higher the iodine number, the more double bonds the oil contains.

(a) Which oil is most likely to become solid in a refrigerator? *(1 mark)*

(b) Which oil is the most likely to ignite? *(1 mark)*

(c) Which oil is the most unsaturated? *(1 mark)*

(d) Which oil provides the least energy? *(1 mark)*

9 Vegetable oils that are unsaturated can be hardened using hydrogen in the presence of nickel at about 60 °C.

(a) What is the purpose of the nickel? *(1 mark)*

(b) Explain what happens to the carbon–carbon double bonds during hardening. *(1 mark)*

Table 4 shows the melting points of four fatty acids, which are components of vegetable oils. Linolenic acid can be converted into stearic acid by hydrogenation.

Table 4 Melting points.

Fatty acid	Number of C=C bonds	Melting point/°C
stearic acid	0	70
oleic acid	1	16
linoleic acid	2	−5
linolenic acid	3	−11

(c) (i) Plot a suitable graph to show the data in the table. *(4 marks)*

(ii) Describe the trend in melting point. *(1 mark)*

(iii) What is the effect of hydrogenation on the melting point of vegetable oils? Use data from the table in your explanation. *(2 marks)*

(d) Describe two food uses of hydrogenated vegetable oils. *(2 marks)*

10 Figure 5 shows information about four different vegetable oils. Use information from it to answer the questions.

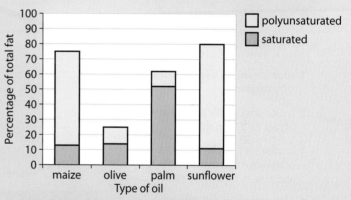

Figure 5 Composition of various vegetable oils.

(a) Which oil contains the most saturated fat? *(1 mark)*

(b) Explain which oil appears to be best for the heart. *(3 marks)*

(c) Studies have shown beneficial health effects from consuming monounsaturated fats. Assuming that the other type of fat in each oil is monounsaturated fat, which is most likely to provide these beneficial health effects and why? *(2 marks)*

(d) Describe two benefits and a drawback of cooking food with vegetable oils rather than with water. *(3 marks)*

11 Describe what emulsifiers are and how they work.

In this question you will be assessed on using good English, organising information clearly and using specialist terms where appropriate. *(6 marks)*

The structure of the Earth

Learning objectives

- describe the structure of the Earth
- describe what tectonic plates are
- explain how convection currents inside the Earth move tectonic plates
- explain where earthquakes and volcanoes are most likely to occur
- explain why scientists cannot accurately predict when earthquakes and volcanic eruptions will occur.

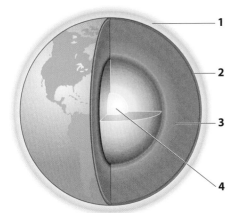

1 **atmosphere** – a layer of gases (100 km thick)

2 **crust** – a relatively thin layer of rock (5–70 km thick)

3 **mantle** – a thick layer of rock (2900 km thick) at over 1000 °C and able to move very slowly

4 **core** – a central ball of iron (3400 km radius) at about 4000 °C

Figure 1 The structure of the Earth.

The structure of the Earth

At the centre of the Earth is the **core**, which is made mostly of molten iron. Next is the **mantle**, which is mainly solid rock but can flow due to some parts that have partially melted. The outer layer of the Earth is called the **crust** and is very thin compared with the mantle and core. Above the crust is the **atmosphere**, which is a layer of gases.

The Earth's crust, the atmosphere and the oceans are our only source of all the minerals and other resources that we use to make the substances that we need for everyday life.

Tectonic plates

The outer part of the Earth is called the **lithosphere** and includes the crust and the upper part of the mantle. It is cracked into a number of huge pieces called **tectonic plates**. These plates are moving at a speed of a few centimetres each year.

The slow movement of tectonic plates is caused by very powerful **convection currents** in the mantle.

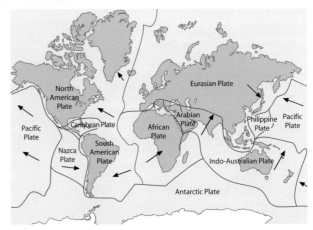

Figure 2 Tectonic plates.

Examiner feedback

Tectonic plates are made up of the crust and the top part of the mantle.

- The currents are caused by heat released inside the Earth from the natural breakdown (decay) of radioactive atoms.
- As rock in the mantle gets hotter it becomes less dense and rises.
- It is pushed to the side by more rock where it cools.
- The cooling means that it becomes more dense and sinks back down.
- It is the sideways movement of the rock that moves the plate above it.

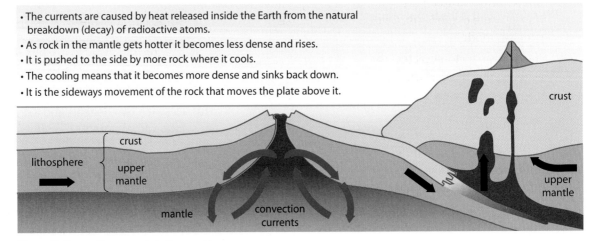

Figure 3 Convection currents in the mantle.

Earthquakes and volcanoes

Earthquakes and **volcanoes** occur at the boundaries between tectonic plates, as shown in Figure 4. As plates move past, over, under or apart from each other, hot magma from the mantle can escape, resulting in a volcano. Friction between the moving plates can make them move in sudden jerks, producing earthquakes.

Scientists know where earthquakes are likely and many buildings in danger zones are built with special foundations to help them withstand earthquakes.

There are some warning signs before an earthquake:

- increased seismic activity: small shocks that may not be detected by people, but are detected by scientific instruments
- water levels in wells fall
- some animals act strangely.

Volcanic eruptions are much easier to predict than earthquakes because we know where volcanoes are and the signs are more definite. Warning signs before an eruption include:

- increasing temperature of the volcano due to magma moving underground
- rising ground level due to the build-up of magma
- more sulfur dioxide (SO_2) gas given out.

When these warning signs appear, people can be moved to safety. However, scientists cannot reliably predict major earthquakes or volcanic eruptions exactly. It is difficult to predict when there will be enough pressure for plates to slide or for magma to burst through the crust. If scientists issue false warnings, people could be moved when not necessary, causing disruption and economic loss, and reducing trust in future warnings.

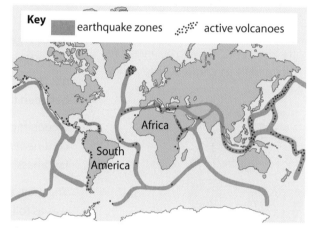

Figure 4 Earthquakes and volcanoes.

Questions

1. What are our three sources of minerals and other resources to make all the substances that we use in modern life?

2. Sketch a diagram of the Earth and label the main layers.

3. A hard-boiled egg is a simple model of the structure of the Earth. Compare the structure of an egg with the structure of the Earth. Give some weaknesses with this model.

4. **(a)** What are tectonic plates? **(b)** How fast do tectonic plates move? **(c)** What causes tectonic plates to move?

5. Why do volcanoes and earthquakes develop at plate boundaries?

6. Why is it important that scientists do not make predictions about earthquakes and volcanic eruptions that do not happen?

7. **Table 1** Data on how much lava has erupted from Mount Etna, Sicily, in recent eruptions.

Year	Number of years since previous eruption	Amount of lava erupted /millions of m³
1794	34	27
1858	64	120
1872	14	20
1906	34	80
1929	23	12
1944	15	25

(a) Use the data in Table 1 to plot a graph with a line of best fit to show how the amount of lava changes with the number of years since the last eruption.
(b) What is the relationship shown by the graph?
(c) Estimate how much lava would erupt if Mount Vesuvius erupted tomorrow.

8. Give some warning signs that earthquakes and volcanic eruptions may be about to happen. Explain why it is important to predict earthquakes and volcanic eruptions but why it is hard to predict exactly when they may happen.

C17.2 Continental drift

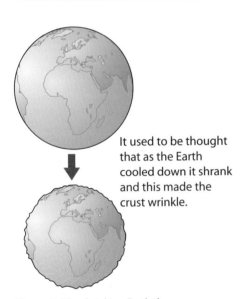

Examiner feedback

Scientific theories become accepted as more observations are made that support the theory. If observations are made that do not support the theory, the theory may have to be revised or replaced by a new theory altogether.

Figure 1 The shrinking Earth theory.

It used to be thought that as the Earth cooled down it shrank and this made the crust wrinkle.

Examiner feedback

It is important that you know the evidence that Alfred Wegener's ideas were based on, but that the main reason his ideas were not accepted at the time was that there was no explanation for how the continents could move.

Shrinking apples

Scientists have wondered for centuries how features on the Earth such as mountains formed. A popular theory for many years was that as the hot, young Earth cooled down, the crust shrank and wrinkled, forming mountains. This wrinkling is similar to the way that apples shrink and the peel wrinkles up as they get older.

We now explain the formation of mountains by rock being forced upwards where tectonic plates collide. However, this theory of plate tectonics is a relatively new theory and was not accepted for some time.

Alfred Wegener's ideas

In 1911, Alfred Wegener read that the fossils of identical creatures had been found both in South America and Africa, and that these were creatures that could not swim. People at the time said that there must have been a piece of land between the continents that was now covered by the Atlantic Ocean.

Wegener came up with the idea of **continental drift**. He believed that the continents were moving around and were once joined together in a big landmass. In 1915, Wegener published a book about his theory.

The main evidence in Wegener's book was as follows:

- The continents appear to fit together like a jigsaw.
- The west coast of Africa and the east coast of South America have the same patterns of rock layers.
- These two coasts have the same types of plant and animal fossils.
- Some of these animals are found only in these parts of the world and their fossils show they could not swim or fly.
- There could not have been a piece of land connecting South America and Africa, which means they must have been joined together.

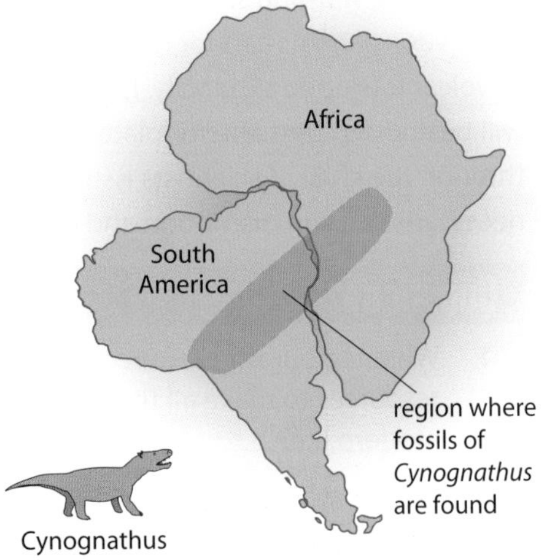

Figure 2 Positions of the continents millions of years ago and the region in which fossils of *Cynognathus* have been found.

Africa

South America

region where fossils of *Cynognathus* are found

Cynognathus

When Wegener died in 1930 his ideas had still not been accepted. The main reason for this was that there was no explanation for how the continents moved. Another reason was that, although he was a scientist, Wegener was known as a meteorologist rather than a geologist. This meant that his ideas were given less credit among geologists.

The acceptance of Wegener's ideas

Wegener's ideas were not accepted until the 1960s, when the Atlantic Ocean floor was surveyed in detail and the Mid-Atlantic Ridge was found. This is a range of underwater mountains and volcanoes in the middle of the Atlantic Ocean.

225 million years ago North Pole

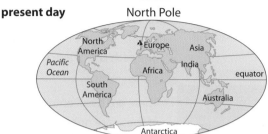

180 million years ago North Pole

65 million years ago North Pole

present day North Pole

Figure 3 The moving continents.

Soon afterwards, it was discovered that the rock in the ocean floor is younger than the rock in the continents. The rock closest to the ridge is youngest as new rock is formed there from magma coming up from inside the Earth. The older rock is pushed away. This new evidence fitted in with the theory of continental drift.

Scientists also discovered that this movement could be caused by very powerful convection currents in the mantle. This prompted the new theory of plate tectonics, which is based on Wegener's theory of continental drift.

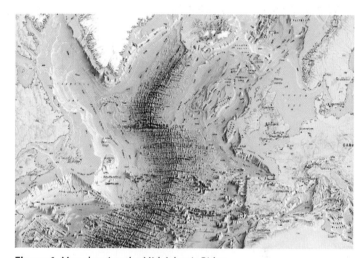

Figure 4 Map showing the Mid-Atlantic Ridge.

Questions

1 **(a)** How did people believe mountains were formed before the theory of plate tectonics? **(b)** How is the formation of mountains explained now with the theory of plate tectonics?

2 What is meant by continental drift?

3 **(a)** How do rock patterns support Wegener's ideas? **(b)** How do fossils of *Cynognathus* support Wegener's ideas? **(c)** What other evidence did Wegener use to support his ideas?

4 A common theory for fossils of creatures that cannot swim or fly, such as *Cynognathus*, on different continents was a piece of land joining continents that is now underwater. What piece of Wegener's ideas did not fit in with this idea?

5 What evidence was discovered that led to Wegener's ideas being accepted?

6 A key reason why Wegener's ideas were not accepted

at the time was that no one could explain what moved the continents. What do scientists now believe is moving the continents?

7 The following data show the age of the rocks on the floor of the Atlantic Ocean between the Mid-Atlantic Ridge and Brazil.

Distance from the Mid-Atlantic Ridge/km	500	1000	1500	2000	2500
Age of rock/millions of years	24	46	71	90	113

(a) Plot a graph to show how the age of rocks on the ocean floor varies with distance from the ridge. Draw a line of best fit. **(b)** Explain how these data support Wegener's theory of continental drift.

8 Explain what the theory of continental drift is and why Wegener's ideas were not accepted when he published them but they are accepted today.

The atmosphere today

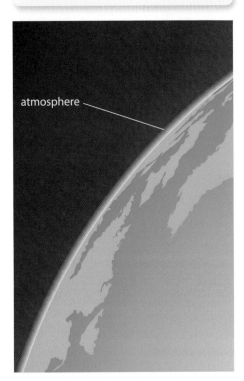

atmosphere

Figure 1 The atmosphere is a very thin layer compared with the diameter of the Earth.

The gases in the atmosphere

The **atmosphere** is a mixture of gases that surround the Earth. The atmosphere gets thinner, that is, there are fewer gas particles, as you go further from the Earth's surface. It is difficult to say exactly where the atmosphere stops as it gets gradually thinner.

Air is the mixture of gases in the lower part of the atmosphere. About 99% of the air is made up of nitrogen and oxygen. About four-fifths of the air is nitrogen and one-fifth is oxygen. This mixture has stayed fairly constant for the last 200 million years.

There are small amounts of other gases, which make up the other 1%. Some of these are noble gases, mainly argon. Noble gases are the unreactive gases in group 0 of the periodic table (see lesson C1 1.4). A small amount of carbon dioxide is also found in air. Water vapour is present in the air as well. The amount of water vapour changes due to changes in the weather and humidity. Because of this, water vapour is not included when giving the composition of air.

Air also contains very small or trace amounts of harmful gases, including sulfur dioxide, nitrogen oxide and carbon monoxide. These gases are formed in a number of ways: some are made by natural processes, such as volcanic activity, or from plants and animals decomposing; some are made by human activities such as burning fossil fuels.

Table 1 Percentage composition of gases in dry air.

Gas	Formula	Percentage in dry air
nitrogen	N_2	78
oxygen	O_2	21
argon	Ar	0.9
carbon dioxide	CO_2	0.04
other gases		traces

The proportion of these gases in the atmosphere has remained much the same for the last 200 million years (see lesson C1 7.5).

other gases (1%)

oxygen (21%)

nitrogen (78%)

Figure 2 The gases in dry air.

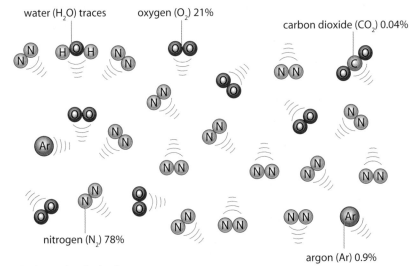

water (H_2O) traces   oxygen (O_2) 21%   carbon dioxide (CO_2) 0.04%

nitrogen (N_2) 78%

argon (Ar) 0.9%

Figure 3 Gas molecules in air.

Separating the gases in air

The gases in air can be separated and used for different purposes. The most abundant gas, nitrogen, is very unreactive. It is used instead of air inside food packaging, such as crisp packets, because the oxygen in air would allow respiring bacteria to make the food go off faster. Oxygen is used to help patients breathe in hospitals. Argon is used as a non-reactive gas when welding and was used to fill filament light bulbs before low-energy light bulbs were introduced.

The gases in air are separated by **fractional distillation**. Air is cooled until it becomes a liquid, at about −200 °C. As it warms up again the separate substances boil at different temperatures and can be collected separately.

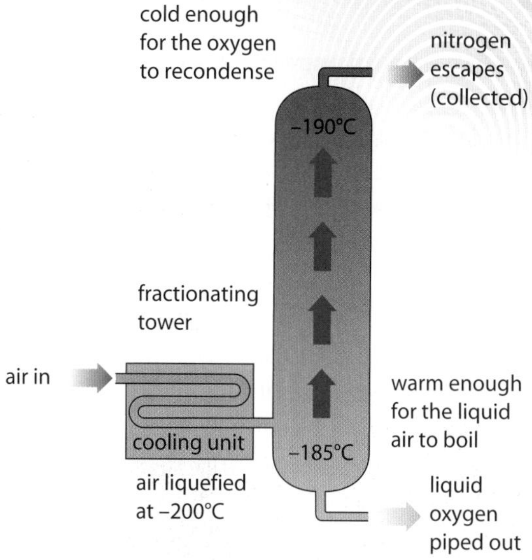

cold enough for the oxygen to recondense

nitrogen escapes (collected)

−190°C

fractionating tower

air in

cooling unit

−185°C

warm enough for the liquid air to boil

air liquefied at −200°C

liquid oxygen piped out

Figure 4 Simplified diagram of fractional distillation of liquefied air.

Practical

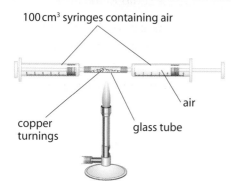

100 cm³ syringes containing air

copper turnings

glass tube

air

When air is passed over heated copper the oxygen in the air reacts with the copper. From this we can find the percentage of oxygen in air.

Figure 5 Apparatus for measuring percentage oxygen in air.

Nitrogen is the gas in crisp packets.

Questions

1 **(a)** Name the main two gases in air and give their proportions. **(b)** Give a use for each of these two gases. **(c)** How long has the atmosphere been like this?

2 **(a)** There are small amounts of noble gases in the air. What are noble gases? **(b)** Name the main noble gas found in the air. **(c)** Give a use for the main noble gas found in air.

3 **(a)** List the main three elements found in air. **(b)** List two compounds found in air.

4 Why is the proportion of gases in air given without any water?

5 Draw a bar chart to show the main gases in air.

6 Nitrogen is used in food packaging. Explain why.

7 There are trace amounts of harmful gases in the air. **(a)** Give one example of a natural process that produces trace amounts of a harmful gas. **(b)** Give one example of an artificial process that produces trace amounts of a harmful gas.

8 Air is a useful mixture of gases. Describe and explain how the gases can be separated.

Examiner feedback

The fractional distillation of air is based upon the same principles as the fractional distillation of crude oil, as both are mixtures containing substances with different boiling points.

The changing atmosphere

Learning objectives

- describe some of the theories scientists have to explain what the Earth's early atmosphere was like, where it came from and how it changed
- describe which gases may have made up the early atmosphere and where they came from
- explain how the atmosphere may have slowly changed to form the one we have today
- explain how the evolution of life affected the atmosphere
- explain that scientists do not know how life began.

The early atmosphere

The Earth is thought to be about 4.5 billion years old. Scientists have evidence that the atmosphere we have today is very different to the one the Earth used to have. However, scientists are uncertain how the early atmosphere formed, which gases were in it, and how it changed to give the atmosphere we have today. They have several theories about the early atmosphere and the changes.

Where did the gases come from?

Some scientists think that the gases that formed the early atmosphere came from inside the Earth. During the first billion years of its existence, the Earth was much hotter and there was a lot of volcanic activity. Since volcanoes release gases into the atmosphere, some scientists believe that the early atmosphere was formed from these gases. However, there are other theories about where the gases in the early atmosphere came from. One theory is that the gases came from comets that collided with the Earth.

Which gases were in the early atmosphere?

Many scientists believe that carbon dioxide, water vapour, ammonia and methane were in the early atmosphere because volcanoes release them today.

The Earth lies between Venus and Mars in the Solar System. There are volcanoes on Venus and Mars and their atmospheres are over 95% carbon dioxide. This has led some scientists to think that Earth's early atmosphere was mainly carbon dioxide. Scientists have evidence that the evolution of life on Earth caused our atmosphere to change. There is no life on Mars or Venus, so their atmospheres have remained the same.

As the hot, young Earth cooled down, the water vapour in the air is thought to have condensed, contributing to the formation of oceans.

There is evidence that leads most scientists to believe that there was little or no oxygen in the early atmosphere. For example, oxygen is not released by volcanoes, and the iron compounds found in the oldest rocks are compounds that could only form in the absence of oxygen.

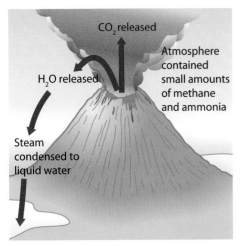

Figure 1 The gases in the early atmosphere came from volcanoes.

Life on Earth

Scientists do not know how life on Earth started, but there are many theories. Experiments by Miller and Urey showed how amino acids, molecules that are essential for life, could have been formed. They fired an electric spark, representing lightning, in a mixture of the gases methane, ammonia and hydrogen, representing some of the possible gases in the early atmosphere, plus water representing the oceans. A mixture of chemicals formed, including amino acids. This is sometimes called a 'primordial soup' meaning a rich mixture of chemicals essential for life. However, these experiments do not show how life itself could have started.

The formation of oxygen

Photosynthesising organisms evolved, including some bacteria and plants. They use up carbon dioxide and make oxygen. The oxygen we have in the atmosphere today is produced by photosynthesis. Over time, the amount

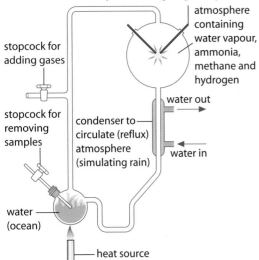

Figure 2 The Miller–Urey 'primordial soup' experiment.

of carbon dioxide decreased and the amount of oxygen increased. Most of the carbon from the carbon dioxide is now in fossil fuels or sedimentary rocks, mainly limestone (see lesson C1 7.5).

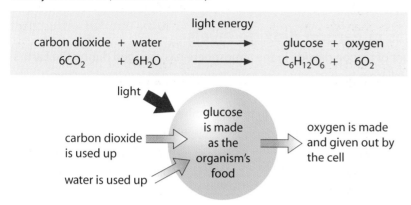

$$\text{carbon dioxide} + \text{water} \xrightarrow{\text{light energy}} \text{glucose} + \text{oxygen}$$
$$6CO_2 + 6H_2O \longrightarrow C_6H_{12}O_6 + 6O_2$$

Figure 3 Photosynthesis carried out in a cell.

These structures are called stromatolites. Some are well over 2 billion years old and contain fossils of bacteria that photosynthesised.

The methane and ammonia in the early atmosphere would have been removed by reaction with the oxygen. The reaction of oxygen with ammonia would have produced some of the nitrogen in the atmosphere. However, there are several theories about where most of the nitrogen came from. Some scientists think it came from volcanoes, some from comets or from bacteria in the soil.

The proportions of the gases in the atmosphere are thought to have remained roughly constant for the last 200 million years (see lesson C1.7.5).

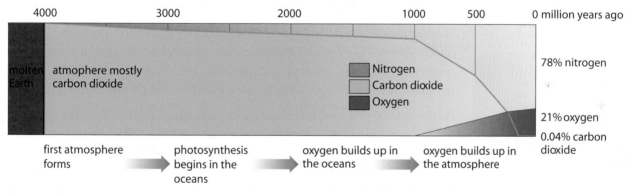

Figure 4 Changes in the Earth's atmosphere.

Questions

1. Give two places that different scientists think the gases that formed the early atmosphere came from.

2. **(a)** Which gases are thought to have made up the early atmosphere? **(b)** Give one reason why many scientists think that the early atmosphere was mainly carbon dioxide.

3. How do some scientists think the oceans formed?

4. Give two reasons why scientists think there was little or no oxygen in the early atmosphere?

5. **(a)** Describe what was done in the Miller–Urey experiment. **(b)** What did this experiment show that was significant? **(c)** Does this experiment explain how life may have started on Earth? Explain your answer.

6. **(a)** What happened on Earth that led to the formation of oxygen? **(b)** Describe how the oxygen in the atmosphere formed. **(c)** What process removed most of the carbon dioxide from the atmosphere?

7. What happened to the ammonia and the methane in the early atmosphere?

8. Oxygen makes up 21% of the air. Carbon dioxide makes up 0.04%. Describe the processes that have resulted in these gases reaching their present levels compared with their levels in the early atmosphere.

Carbon dioxide and global warming

Examiner feedback

Remember that the oceans still act as a reservoir of CO_2, but can no longer absorb as much as humans are producing.

Much of the Earth's carbon is locked up in sedimentary rocks like limestone.

Some of the Earth's carbon is locked up in fossil fuels.

Changes in carbon dioxide levels

The amount of carbon dioxide in the atmosphere has changed during the Earth's history. It fell from high levels in the early atmosphere to low levels, where it had remained for the last 200 million years. However, human activities are now raising the level of carbon dioxide in the atmosphere, and the increase is thought to be causing **global warming**.

Removal of carbon dioxide from the early atmosphere

Many scientists think that when the Earth was young, the main gas in the atmosphere was carbon dioxide. However, there is very little now. As the Earth cooled after its formation, water vapour in the air condensed to form the oceans. About half of the carbon dioxide from the atmosphere at that time is thought to have dissolved in the new oceans.

Some carbon dioxide reacted with substances in sea water, forming insoluble compounds, such as calcium carbonate, that sank to the bottom as sediment. Carbon dioxide also formed soluble compounds, such as calcium hydrogencarbonate, which was used by sea creatures to make calcium carbonate shells. As these creatures died, their shells fell into the sediment. Over time, these sediments formed sedimentary rocks, such as limestone, locking away the carbon in rocks.

Some of the dissolved carbon dioxide was used by algae and plants for photosynthesis. The carbon from the carbon dioxide became part of these organisms. As these organisms died, they decayed to form fossil fuels. The carbon became locked up in coal and as hydrocarbons in crude oil and natural gas.

For the last 200 million years or so, the processes that absorb carbon dioxide have been in balance with the processes that release it, such as volcanic eruptions and the decay of organisms – this is called the carbon cycle. Therefore the amount of carbon dioxide in the atmosphere remained stable at around 0.03% for that period.

Rising levels of carbon dioxide and global warming

In recent years carbon dioxide levels have started to rise, and are now nearer 0.04% than 0.03%. Scientists have evidence that much of this rise is due to burning large amounts of fossil fuels, which produce carbon dioxide. Large-scale deforestation is also thought to be contributing to the increase in carbon dioxide. Some of the extra carbon dioxide is being absorbed by the oceans, but not all of it.

Carbon dioxide is a **greenhouse gas**. This means that it stops some of the Earth's heat escaping into space and thus keeps the Earth warm (see lesson C1 4.4). However, there are signs that the mean temperature of the Earth is rising. Many scientists think that the increase in temperature is linked to the increased levels of carbon dioxide in the atmosphere. This global warming could lead to climate change and to rising sea levels, which could cause flooding. The world is seeking ways to reduce carbon dioxide emissions, with the two main suggestions being to increase energy efficiency and to burn less fossil fuel by using alternative sources of energy.

The effect of carbon dioxide levels on marine life

The oceans are slightly alkaline with a pH of about 8. When carbon dioxide dissolves in the oceans it forms carbonic acid. As the amount of carbon dioxide in the atmosphere changes, the pH of the oceans rises or falls. These changes affect marine life.

As the amount of carbon dioxide in the atmosphere is currently increasing, the pH of the oceans is falling. This lowers the amount of dissolved carbonates that many organisms need to make shells or skeletons. Some creatures may not be able to survive if the pH falls too far.

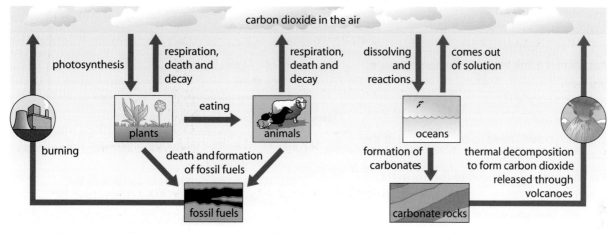

Figure 1 Processes that add and remove carbon dioxide from the air.

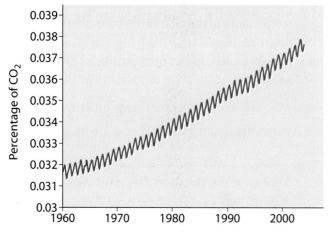

Figure 2 The amount of carbon dioxide in the air has increased over time.

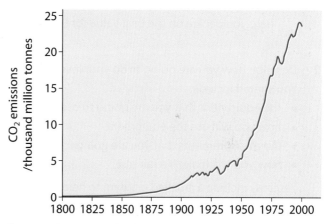

Figure 3 The amount of carbon dioxide released into the atmosphere from burning fossil fuels over time.

Questions

1   **(a)** What was the main gas in the air when the Earth was young? **(b)** Where is most of the carbon from the carbon dioxide now?

2   **(a)** Explain how plants remove carbon dioxide from the air. **(b)** Explain how this carbon ended up in fossil fuels.

3   **(a)** Explain how the oceans removed carbon dioxide from the air. **(b)** Explain how some of this carbon ended up in fossil fuels. **(c)** Explain how some of this carbon ended up in sedimentary rocks.

4   Give four ways in which carbon dioxide is released into the atmosphere.

5   Why has the amount of carbon dioxide in the atmosphere remained constant for the last 200 million years?

6   Carbon dioxide levels in the atmosphere are rising. Explain why.

7   Explain how and why the increasing level of carbon dioxide in the atmosphere is affecting marine life.

8   What effects could rising levels of carbon dioxide be having on the Earth and why? How could we lower levels of carbon dioxide?

ISA practice: the viscosity of oils

There are many different vegetable oils. The properties of these oils, including their **viscosity**, varies. Viscosity is a measure of how easily a liquid flows. The greater the viscosity of a liquid, the slower it flows.

You have been asked to measure the viscosity of a vegetable oil at different temperatures by timing how long drops of oil take to flow down a tile.

Hypothesis

It is suggested that there is a link between the temperature of an oil and its viscosity.

Section 1

1   In this investigation you will need to control some of the variables.
    (a) Name one variable you will need to control in this investigation. *(1 mark)*
    (b) Describe briefly how you would carry out a preliminary investigation to find a suitable value to use for this variable. Explain how the results will help you decide on the best value for this variable. *(2 marks)*

2   Describe how you are going to do your investigation. You should include:
    • the equipment that you are going to use
    • how you will use the equipment
    • the measurements that you are going to make
    • how you will make it a fair test.

    You may include a labelled diagram to help you to explain your method.

    In this question you will be assessed on using good English, organising information clearly and using specialist terms where appropriate. *(6 marks)*

3   Think about the possible hazards in your investigation.
    (a) Describe one hazard that you think may be present in your investigation. *(1 mark)*
    (b) Identify the risk associated with the hazard you have described, and say what control measures you could use to reduce the risk. *(2 marks)*

4   Design a table that will contain all the data that you are going to record during your investigation. *(2 marks)*

Total for Section 1: 14 marks

Section 2

Two students, Study Group 1, carried out an investigation into the hypothesis. Figure 1 shows the results of their investigation.

Time taken for the oil to flow down the tile
10°C: 2 min 5 sec
19°C: 60 sec
31°C: 32 sec
40°C: 21 sec
51°C: 18 sec

Figure 1   Results of Study Group 1's investigation.

5   **(a)** **(i)** What is the independent variable in this investigation?
            (ii) What is the dependent variable in this investigation?
            (iii) Name one control variable in this investigation. *(3 marks)*

    (b) Plot a graph to show the link between the temperature of the oil and the time taken to flow down the tile. *(4 marks)*

    (c) Do the results support the hypothesis? Explain your answer. *(3 marks)*

Below are the results of three other study groups.

Figure 2 shows the results of two other students – Study Group 2.

Time taken for the oil to flow down the tile
10°C: 115 sec
19°C: 50 sec
31°C: 22 sec
40°C: 11 sec
51°C: 8 sec

Figure 2   Study Group 2's results.

Table 1 shows the results from another two students – Study Group 3.

Table 1 Results from Study Group 3.

Temperature of oil/°C	Time for the oil to flow down the tile/s			
	Test 1	Test 2	Test 3	Mean
10	98	95	91	95
19	49	47	48	48
31	18	17	20	18
40	15	27	16	19
51	5	6	5	5

Table 2 gives the results of Study Group 4. Scientists in a lubricating oil laboratory measured the rate of lubricating oil flow in a vehicle engine at different temperatures. They repeated the tests with new oil, oil that had been used for 1000 hours and oil that had been used for 10 000 hours.

Table 2 Results from Study Group 4, scientists in a lubricating oil laboratory.

Temperature of engine/°C	Rate of oil flow/dm³/min		
	New oil	Oil after 500 hours' use	Oil after 1000 hours' use
150	7.4	8.5	12.6
200	9.2	10.4	12.8
250	11.1	12.4	12.4
300	13.7	15.1	12.5
350	16.5	18.0	13.0

6 Describe one way in which the results of Study Group 2 are similar to or different from the original results of Study Group 1, and give one reason for this similarity or difference. *(3 marks)*

7 (a) Draw a sketch graph of the results from Study Group 2. *(3 marks)*

(b) Does the data support the hypothesis being investigated? To gain full marks you should use all of the relevant data from Studies 1, 2 and 3 to explain whether or not the data supports the hypothesis. *(3 marks)*

(c) The data from the other groups only gives a limited amount of information. What other information or data would you need in order to be more certain as to whether or not the hypothesis is correct? Explain the reason for your answer. *(3 marks)*

(d) Use Studies 2, 3 and 4 to answer this question. What is the relationship between the temperature of an oil and its viscosity? How well does the data support your answer? *(3 marks)*

8 Look back at the method of investigation you described in answer to question 2. If you could repeat the investigation, suggest one change that you would make to the method, and give a reason for the change. *(3 marks)*

9 A company makes vehicle engines. How could the results of this investigation help the company decide on the length of time the oil should be used for before replacing it? *(3 marks)*

Total for Section 2: 31 marks
Total for the ISA: 45 marks

Assess yourself questions

1 The properties of some gases in air are shown. Name the gas with the properties given.

(a) This gas is essential for life as it is used for respiration. *(1 mark)*

(b) There are small amounts of this gas in the air but levels are rising and many scientists believe it may be causing global warming. *(1 mark)*

(c) This is the main gas in air. *(1 mark)*

(d) This gas makes up 0.9% of the air and is very unreactive. *(1 mark)*

(e) This gas is thought to have been the main gas in the air when the Earth was young. *(1 mark)*

(f) The gas that there was little or none of when the Earth was young that was produced by photosynthesis. *(1 mark)*

(g) The gas, of which there was a lot when the Earth was young, that was removed from the air by photosynthesis. *(1 mark)*

(h) The amount of this gas in the air depends on the humidity. *(1 mark)*

2 The amount of carbon dioxide in the air has remained constant, until recently, for about the last 200 million years.

(a) State two ways in which carbon dioxide is removed from the atmosphere. *(2 marks)*

(b) State two ways in which carbon dioxide is added to the atmosphere. *(2 marks)*

(c) The amount of carbon dioxide in the air has been increasing in recent years. Explain why. *(1 mark)*

(d) The blue line on the graph in Figure 1 shows how the amount of carbon dioxide in the air has changed in recent years. The red line on the graph shows how the Earth's temperature has changed.

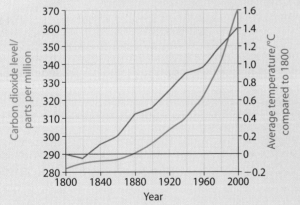

Figure 1 Graph showing changes in temperature and the amount of carbon dioxide in the air.

How strong a piece of evidence is this that increasing levels of carbon dioxide are causing global warming? *(2 marks)*

3 Table 1 shows the boiling points of the main gases in air.

Table 1 Boiling points of the main gases in air.

Gas	nitrogen	argon	oxygen
Boiling point/°C	−196	−186	−183

The gases in air are separated by fractional distillation of liquefied air. Which gas will boil first as the liquefied air is allowed to warm? *(1 mark)*

4 Figure 2 shows the structure of the Earth. Name each part shown. *(3 marks)*

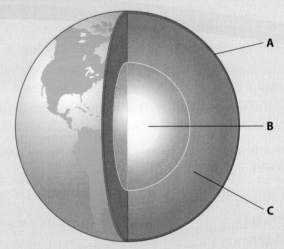

Figure 2 The structure of the Earth.

5 Figure 3 shows the tectonic plates on the Earth's surface.

(a) What are tectonic plates? *(2 marks)*

(b) Give the letters of two places where volcanoes and earthquakes are likely. *(1 mark)*

(c) Explain why volcanoes are not found in the UK today. *(1 mark)*

(d) What is happening to the distance between Africa and South America? Explain your answer. *(2 marks)*

(e) The Andes mountains are near D on the map.

(i) Explain why mountains have formed in this area according to the theory of plate tectonics. *(2 marks)*

(ii) Describe an older theory that explained how mountains formed as the Earth cooled. *(2 marks)*

(f) Scientists think that the movement of the plates is caused by convection currents.

(i) Explain how these convection currents arise. *(3 marks)*

(ii) About how far are the plates moving each year? *(1 mark)*

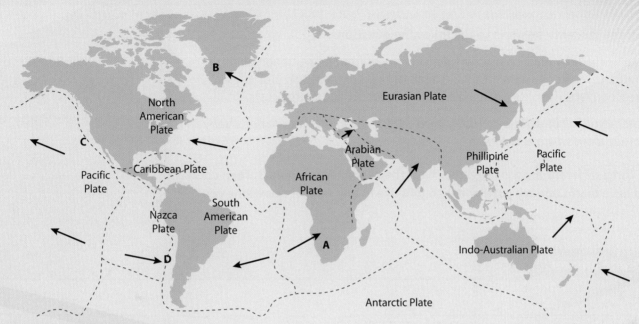

Figure 3 Tectonic plates

6 **(a)** Alfred Wegener proposed the theory of continental drift in 1915. Which one of the following ideas does not support his theory?

   A Fossils of fish are found in different parts of the world.

   B The shape of continents appear to fit together like a jigsaw.

   C Rocks near the centre of the Atlantic Ocean are younger than those nearer the continents.

   D Volcanoes and earthquakes appear in zones and are not spread evenly around the world. *(1 mark)*

   (b) Fossils of the land reptile *lystrosaurus* have been found in Africa, India and Antarctica. Explain how this supports Wegener's theory of continental drift. *(2 marks)*

   (c) Why were Wegener's ideas not accepted when he first put them forward? *(1 mark)*

7 Changes in water levels underground are a very strong indicator of earthquakes. There was a major earthquake in China in 1976 that killed about 250 000 people. Table 2 gives information about the water levels in a mine in the week before the earthquake. Water is pumped out of the mine each day and the more water pumped out, the higher the water level in the ground is.

Table 2 Water measurements.

Days before earthquake	7	6	5	4	3	2	1	0
Rate of water pumping out of the mine / m³/s	45	40	35	30	25	25	50	75

   (a) Plot a graph to show how the pumping rate changed in the week before the earthquake. *(4 marks)*

   (b) Describe the changes in water level in the week before the earthquake. *(2 marks)*

   (c) Why is it important to monitor underground water levels in earthquake zones? *(2 marks)*

8 Carbon dioxide dissolves in the sea and then reacts to form some soluble compounds, such as calcium hydrogencarbonate, and some insoluble compounds, such as calcium carbonate. These compounds can all become part of sedimentary rocks, locking away carbon dioxide.

   (a) Outline how insoluble compounds can become part of sedimentary rocks. *(2 marks)*

   (b) Outline how soluble compounds can be used by marine organisms and become part of sedimentary rocks. *(3 marks)*

9 Explain and evaluate the effects of human activities on the atmosphere.

   In this question you will be assessed on using good English, organising information clearly and using specialist terms where appropriate. *(6 marks)*

GradeStudio Route to A*

Here are three students' answers to the following question:

Ethanol can be made by reaction of steam with ethene or from fermentation of carbohydrates. Compare the advantages and disadvantages of these two processes in terms of reaction rate, use of raw materials, purity of product and energy costs.

In this question you will be assessed on using good English, organising information clearly and using specialist terms where appropriate. (6 marks)

Read the three different answers together with the examiner comments. Then check what you have learnt and try putting it into practice in any further questions you answer.

 Grade answer

Student 1

The answer does not compare the two processes.

Making ethanol from ethene is fast and makes pure ethanol. Fermentation uses renewable raw materials.

The answer does not mention energy costs.

Examiner comment

The information the student has given is all correct but would miss many of the marks. The student has not compared the two processes for any of the four areas asked about. For example, the student writes that production from ethene is fast but has not indicated if this is faster or slower than fermentation. Also, the student has not answered the whole question, only covering three of the four areas asked for, missing out the part about energy costs. The student has not indicated what raw materials are used.

 Grade answer

Student 2

The answer does not compare the purity of ethanol produced by the two processes.

The production of ethanol from ethene is faster and makes pure ethanol. Fermentation uses renewable raw materials while ethene uses non-renewable raw materials. Fermentation has lower energy costs.

The answer does not mention what the raw materials are.

Examiner comment

The student has compared the two processes in terms of reaction rate, use of raw materials and energy costs. For example, the student writes that production from ethene is 'faster'. However, there is no comparison about purity of product as the student has not stated if the ethanol made by fermentation is pure or not. The student has also not described what the raw materials are.

Grade answer

Student 3

The answer compares the two processes in all four areas.

The student has explained the difference in energy costs.

> The rate of reaction to produce ethanol from ethene is faster than from fermentation. It also produces purer ethanol. However, the production of ethanol from fermentation has lower energy costs because lower temperatures and pressures are used. Fermentation uses renewable raw materials using carbohydrates like sugar cane. By comparison, ethene is made from crude oil, which is non-renewable.

The identity and type of raw materials are given for both processes.

Examiner comment

This answer has covered all four areas asked for in the question. These are: reaction rate, use of raw materials, purity of product and energy costs. It provides a comparison between the two methods for each of these four areas. The answer goes into sufficient depth, providing an explanation of the difference in energy costs and including the identity of the raw materials for both processes, as well as whether they are renewable or non-renewable. The answer is structured in a logical sequence dealing with each of the four areas separately, one at a time. Clear sentences are used and spelling, punctuation and grammar are good.

- Read the question more than once. Read it the first time to get a general idea of what you are being asked, and then again to make sure you understand exactly what you are being asked to do.
- In questions that ask for several things, ensure that each part is answered. You could highlight each thing you are asked to do and tick them off as you cover them.
- In questions that ask for a comparison, make sure that you make relative comments that actually compare the things asked about.
- Present your answer in a clear, structured way. Think about the points you want to make to answer each part of the question and then answer them in turn.
- Do your best to use good spelling, punctuation and grammar throughout your answers.
- Try to use the correct scientific terminology.
- Avoid using words like 'it' and 'they'. Always say what you are referring to.

Examination-style questions

1 Here is a simplified periodic table showing the first 20 elements.

1	2	3	4	5	6	7	0
H hydrogen 1							**He** helium 2
Li lithium 3	**Be** berylium 4	**B** boron 5	**C** carbon 6	**N** nitrogen 7	**O** oxygen 8	**F** fluorine 9	**Ne** neon 10
Na sodium 11	**Mg** magnesium 12	**Al** aluminium 13	**Si** silicon 14	**P** phosphorus 15	**S** sulfur 16	**Cl** chlorine 17	**Ar** argon 18
K potassium 19	**Ca** calcium 20						

(a) (i) How many electrons do the elements neon and argon have in their outer shells? *(1 mark)*

   (ii) What key property can you tell about fluorine from its position in the periodic table? *(1 mark)*

(b) Give the name, group number and period number for the element with electronic structure 2, 8, 4. *(3 marks)*

(c) What type of bonding would you expect to find in the following compounds? Explain your answer in each case.

   (i) ammonia (NH_3) *(1 mark)*

   (ii) sodium sulfide (Na_2S). *(1 mark)*

2 Dolomite (magnesian limestone) is a double carbonate of calcium and magnesium: $CaMg(CO_3)_2$.

(a) When heated strongly, carbon dioxide is driven off.

   (i) What name is given to this type of reaction? *(1 mark)*

   (ii) How could you show that the gas is carbon dioxide? *(1 mark)*

   (iii) Complete and balance the equation for this reaction:

   $$CaMg(CO_3)_2 \longrightarrow \text{_____} + MgO + CO_2$$ *(2 marks)*

(b) 2 g of pure dolomite, when heated to complete reaction, gives off 0.96 g of carbon dioxide. In a class experiment heating 2 g of dolomite chips each, four students ended up with the following amounts of mixed oxide residue:

   student **A** 0.90 g, student **B** 1.06 g, student **C** 1.10 g, student **D** 1.4 g.

   Comment on these results: what do they tell you about these four experiments? *(4 marks)*

3 Cobalt is a hard, silver-gray transition metal that is just a little less reactive than iron. It is used with iron to make hard-wearing steel alloys.

(a) Cobalt occurs in a natural mineral called cobaltite – a compound of cobalt, arsenic and sulfur. Metal ores are often converted to their oxides by roasting in air before the metal is extracted. What products would be formed in this way and why would it not be safe to do this in the science laboratory? *(3 marks)*

(b) Do you think that cobalt metal is extracted from its oxide by electrolysis or carbon reduction? Explain your answer. *(2 marks)*

(c) Why are metals such as iron and aluminium rarely used in their pure form? *(1 mark)*

4 Oil produced from plants can be refined and used to replace diesel for motor vehicles. What are the advantages and disadvantages of using these biofuels instead of fossil fuels? *(4 marks)*

5 Polymers can be made from unsaturated hydrocarbons called alkenes.

(a) Which two of the following five hydrocarbons are alkenes? *(1 mark)*

$$C_3H_8, C_2H_4, C_4H_{10}, C_2H_6, C_4H_8$$

(b) What are hydrocarbons? *(1 mark)*

(c) What is meant by the term *unsaturated* in this context? *(1 mark)*

(d) Bromine water can be used in a test to show that a compound is unsaturated. Describe what you would see in the reaction between bromine water and an unsaturated compound. *(1 mark)*

(e) Alkenes are made from the thermal decomposition of alkanes in a process called cracking. In this process, the alkanes are vaporised and passed over a hot catalyst. Balance this equation for the cracking of decane.

$$C_{10}H_{22} \longrightarrow C_6H_{14} + C_2H_4 \qquad \textit{(1 mark)}$$

(f) The polymer poly(propene) can be made by the polymerisation of propene. The structure of propene is shown.

$$
\begin{array}{ccc}
CH_3 & & H \\
| & & | \\
C & = & C \\
| & & | \\
H & & H
\end{array}
$$

Draw the structure of poly(propene). *(1 mark)*

(g) Many plastic bottles are made from poly(propene). The amount of plastic bottles recycled has risen steadily over recent years. Some data are shown in the table below.

Year	1994	1996	1998	2000	2002	2004
Tonnes of plastic bottles recycled	2000	5000	9000	11 000	18 000	38 000

Plot a graph showing how the mass of plastic bottles recycled has changed in recent years. *(3 marks)*

(h) Some plastic bottles are recycled, some are burned in incinerators and some are buried in landfill. Describe some advantages and disadvantages of the different methods of disposal of plastic bottles.

In this question you will be assessed on using good English, organising information clearly and using specialist terms where appropriate. *(6 marks)*

6 (a) Vegetable oils are extracted from plants and have many uses. Rapeseed oil is a common vegetable oil used in the UK.

    (i) From which part of plants are vegetable oils extracted? *(1 mark)*

    (ii) Name one method, other than pressing, by which oil can be separated from the crushed plant material. *(1 mark)*

    (iii) For use in food manufacture, plant oils can be hardened in a reaction with heat and a nickel catalyst. Which chemical do the plant oils react with? *(1 mark)*

6 (a) (iv) Plant oils can also be made into a fuel. What is the name of the fuel? *(1 mark)*

(b) Many foods are cooked in vegetable oil rather than water. Explain the advantage of cooking foods in vegetable oil rather than water. *(1 mark)*

(c) Vegetable oils are unsaturated. The amount of unsaturation can be measured using the iodine number. The higher the iodine number, the more unsaturated the molecule.

The table below shows the iodine number and melting point of some vegetable oils.

Vegetable oil	Iodine number	Melting point/°C
Coconut	10	25
Palm kernel	37	24
Olive	81	−6
Sunflower	125	−17
Linseed	178	−24

    (i) Plot a scattergraph with melting point on the vertical axis against iodine number on the horizontal axis. *(2 marks)*

    (ii) Describe the relationship between iodine number and melting point. *(1 mark)*

(d) Vegetable oils do not dissolve in water. However, emulsions of water and vegetable oils can be made by adding an emulsifier such as lecithin from egg yolk.

    (i) Give one example of a food that is an emulsion. *(1 mark)*

    (ii) Give one advantage of an emulsion of vegetable oil and water over the separate oil or water. *(1 mark)*

    (iii) Describe key features of an emulsifier molecule. *(1 mark)*

7 (a) The outer part of the Earth is the atmosphere, which is a mixture of gases.
Match the gases below to their percentage in the atmosphere. *(1 mark)*

argon	oxygen	nitrogen

98%	78%	21%	1%

(b) The diagram below shows the way in which scientists believe the continents were arranged just over 200 million years ago. Alfred Wegener suggested this arrangement in 1915 but his ideas were not accepted for many years. Give some evidence that Alfred Wegener used to support his idea of continental drift and the main reason his ideas were not accepted at the time.

In this question you will be assessed on using good English, organising information clearly and using specialist terms where appropriate.   *(6 marks)*

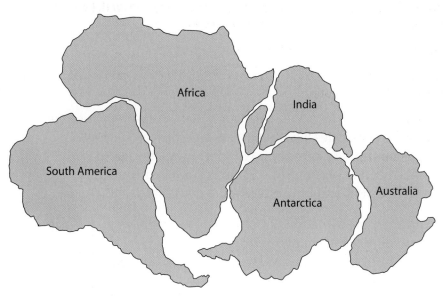

(c) The Earth is thought to be made up of three main layers: the core, the mantle and the crust. The upper mantle and crust are broken up into huge pieces called tectonic plates that are slowly moving. What is thought to be causing the plates to move?   *(2 marks)*

Energy

The astronaut in the photograph is wearing a spacesuit carefully designed to keep her body at a comfortable temperature while she is working in space. In the first part of this unit you will learn about the different ways in which energy can be transferred by heating, and how objects can be designed to increase or reduce the transfer of energy.

The backpack worn by the astronaut includes a battery to provide power for radios and life support systems. These systems are designed to waste as little energy as possible. In the second part of this section you will learn about different kinds of energy transfers, and how efficiency is calculated.

The astronaut is working on an array of solar cells that produce electricity for the space station. In the third part of this unit you will look at why electricity is such a useful way of transferring energy. The final part looks at different energy resources that can be used to generate electricity, including renewable and non-renewable resources, and their advantages and disadvantages.

Test yourself

1 a Describe the different properties solids, liquids and gases.

   b Use the idea that everything is made of particles to explain these differences.

2 List six different forms of energy, and give an example of each.

3 Suggest some ways of reducing the amount of energy we use.

4 a Explain the difference between renewable and non-renewable energy resources.

   b Give three examples of each.

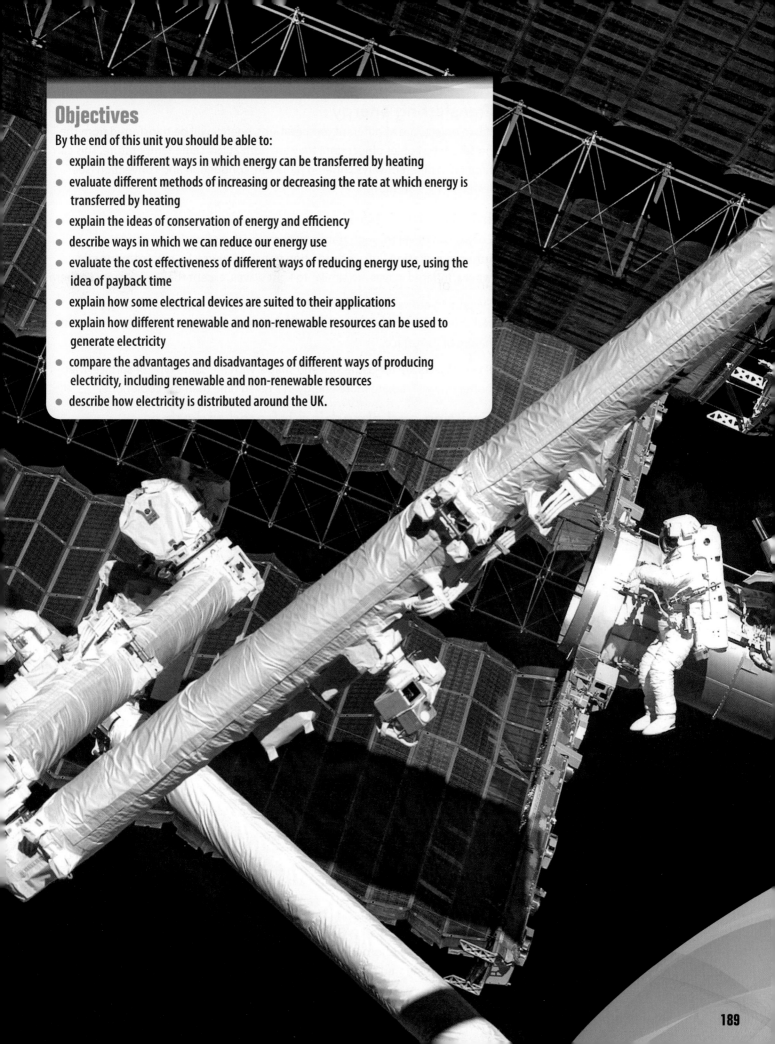

Objectives

By the end of this unit you should be able to:

- explain the different ways in which energy can be transferred by heating
- evaluate different methods of increasing or decreasing the rate at which energy is transferred by heating
- explain the ideas of conservation of energy and efficiency
- describe ways in which we can reduce our energy use
- evaluate the cost effectiveness of different ways of reducing energy use, using the idea of payback time
- explain how some electrical devices are suited to their applications
- explain how different renewable and non-renewable resources can be used to generate electricity
- compare the advantages and disadvantages of different ways of producing electricity, including renewable and non-renewable resources
- describe how electricity is distributed around the UK.

Infrared radiation

Learning objectives

- explain what infrared radiation is
- describe the factors that affect the amount of infrared radiation emitted or absorbed by an object
- explain how infrared radiation can be used.

Transferring energy

If two objects are at different temperatures, energy will be transferred from the hotter to the cooler object until they are both at the same temperature. This can happen in different ways: infrared radiation, conduction and convection (see lessons P1 1.3 and 1.4).

Infrared radiation

Energy can travel through transparent materials or through a vacuum as **infrared radiation**. Infrared radiation transfers energy by **electromagnetic waves**. Infrared waves are similar to light waves, except that we cannot see them.

Everything **emits** and **absorbs** infrared radiation. The amount of infrared radiation absorbed or emitted by a body depends on its temperature and on the nature of its surface.

If two objects are the same size and shape, with the same type of surface, the hotter one will radiate more energy in a given time than the cooler one.

Emitting and absorbing infrared radiation

A surface will reflect some of the infrared radiation that reaches it, and absorb the rest. Light-coloured, shiny surfaces are good at **reflecting** radiation, so they are poor at absorbing it. Dark, matt surfaces are good at absorbing radiation.

Surfaces that are good at absorbing radiation are also good at emitting it. Dark, matt surfaces are good emitters of radiation, and light, shiny surfaces are poor emitters.

The coffee is hotter than its surroundings. The cola is colder than its surroundings.

A thermal image of a photographer. The colours show the amount of infrared radiation emitted by different parts of his body and the surroundings. White represents the most radiation, and blue and black represent the least.

Using infrared radiation for heating

Infrared radiation from the Sun is used in many countries to heat water for washing up and bathing. Water in pipes on the roof absorbs infrared radiation from the Sun.

Heaters or lamps that emit infrared radiation can be used for heating buildings. They are also used in hair salons and for physiotherapy.

Sensing using infrared radiation

The image of the photographer was made using a **thermal imaging camera** that detects infrared radiation instead of visible light. The police use thermal

Route to A*

A thermal image of a military airfield can show which aeroplanes have recently been refuelled, and can also show whether some aeroplanes have recently left the airfield. Can you explain how a thermal image can show these things?

Figure 1 shows an investigation into how surfaces absorb and emit infrared radiation. Three identical containers with equal volumes of cold water were covered in different materials and allowed to stand in the Sun. The temperature of the water was measured at regular intervals. Graph A shows the results. The same three containers were then filled with equal volumes of hot water and allowed to cool down. Graph B shows the results of this second experiment.

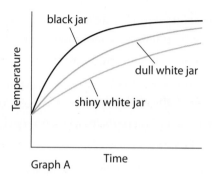

Graph A

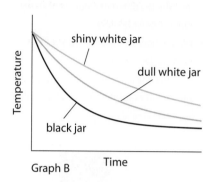

Graph B

Figure 1 Investigating absorption and emission.

a List all the variables, and say if they are continuous or categoric.

b Which one is the independent variable?

c What is the dependent variable?

d Explain why this is a fair test.

imaging cameras to track criminals at night. The fire service uses thermal imaging cameras to help to find people trapped in collapsed buildings.

Many burglar alarms rely on sensors that detect the infrared radiation emitted by the human body. These are called **passive infrared devices**, or PIRs. The 'passive' part of the name indicates that they only detect radiation; they do not emit it.

Questions

1 Describe two uses for devices that: **(a)** emit infrared radiation; **(b)** detect infrared radiation.

2 Explain what will happen over time to the temperatures of the drinks in the photograph on page 190.

3 Which will emit more infrared radiation, a glass of milk taken from the fridge or a cup of tea? Explain your answer.

4 You can buy insulated mugs to keep hot drinks hot. Explain what would be the best colour for an insulated mug.

5 Cars of many different colours are parked in the sun. Which cars will be the hottest inside? Explain your answer.

6 Which will emit more infrared radiation over a period of 5 minutes, a white mug full of hot tea or a white mug full of lukewarm tea?

7 Look at the experimental results in Figure 1 Graph B. **(a)** Explain why the graph for the black jar becomes horizontal. **(b)** Why are the graphs curved?

8 Look at the second photograph on these pages. Explain how the image was made and how you can use the image to determine whether the person is wearing thick or thin clothing.

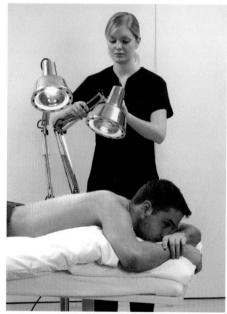

A physiotherapist uses infrared radiation for pain relief after a sports injury.

Passive infrared sensor in a home.

Kinetic theory

Kinetic theory

The **kinetic theory** states that everything is made of tiny particles, and the arrangement and movement of the particles determines the properties of solids, liquids and gases.

In solids, particles are held closely together by strong bonds (forces). They can vibrate but they cannot move around. This explains why solids keep their shape and usually can't be compressed.

In liquids, the bonds between the particles are not quite as strong and the particles can move past each other. Liquids can flow and take the shape of their container. The particles are still very close together, so liquids usually can't be compressed.

In a gas, the particles are far apart and moving around quickly. Gases are compressible, and expand to fill their container.

Changing state

When a solid melts the particles break away from their fixed positions and move around. They have more **kinetic energy**. A solid takes in energy while it is melting but because this energy is being used to break the bonds between the particles the temperature does not change. Figure 2 shows how the temperature changes as a substance is heated.

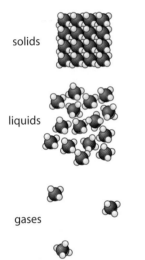

solids

liquids

gases

Figure 1 The arrangements of particles in solids, liquids and gases.

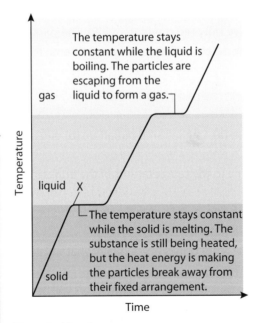

The temperature stays constant while the liquid is boiling. The particles are escaping from the liquid to form a gas.

The temperature stays constant while the solid is melting. The substance is still being heated, but the heat energy is making the particles break away from their fixed arrangement.

Figure 2 A heating curve.

Cooling by evaporation

The particles in a liquid or gas have a range of different energies. The temperature of a substance is determined by the average kinetic energy of its particles.

192

Some of the particles in a liquid will have enough energy to escape the liquid and become a gas. When these particles leave the liquid the average energy of the remaining particles is less, so the liquid is colder. Evaporation has transferred energy away from the liquid.

Sweating helps us to cool down. The liquid absorbs energy from the body to evaporate.

Condensation and scalds

When a gas condenses to form a liquid, energy is released as the particles become closer together and form strong bonds. This is why a scald from steam is so painful. The steam is hot, which is painful enough. However, it releases more energy when it condenses on your skin. Energy is also released when a liquid freezes.

Factors affecting evaporation and condensation

Evaporation will happen faster if:
- the temperature is higher
- there is more surface area from which particles can escape
- air is moving over the surface of the liquid – this carries away any evaporated particles so they cannot condense back into the liquid again.

If the air over a liquid is not moving it will eventually become **saturated**, when the number of particles evaporating each second is the same as the number condensing. Evaporation and condensation are still happening but the overall amount of gas in the air does not change.

Condensation happens when a gas cools down. This often happens when it comes into contact with a cold surface, such as a mirror or window in a bathroom or kitchen. Condensation happens faster if the temperature is colder.

Questions

1 Why can gases be compressed, but not solids or liquids?
2 Explain the best weather for hanging washing out to dry.
3 Look at Figure 2. At X the substance is still being heated, but the temperature has stopped rising. Explain what is happening to the energy going into the substance.
4 Explain how sweating helps to keep you cool.
5 Look at the photograph. What effect would water have on their body temperature if the hikers got wet? Explain your answer.
6 Alcohol has a lower boiling point than water. Explain why a drop of alcohol on your skin feels colder than a drop of water.
7 Sketch a graph similar to Figure 2 to show the change in temperature as the same substance is allowed to cool.
8 Explain in detail the shape of the graph you drew for question 7.

These hikers are trying to keep dry.

Examiner feedback

Evaporation from a liquid can happen at any temperature. When a liquid boils, evaporation is happening throughout the liquid and bubbles of gas form in the liquid. These are bubbles of the substance that is boiling, *not* bubbles of air.

Science skills

A student recorded the temperature every minute while a liquid substance cooled.

a Draw a graph to show these results.

b Draw a curve of best fit, ignoring any anomalous results.

c Explain the shape of the curve.

d Explain why a line graph is the best way of showing these results.

Time/min	Temperature/°C
0	90.0
1	76.0
2	65.0
3	56.0
4	55.0
5	54.5
6	48.0
7	42.5
8	48.0
9	34.0
10	31.0

Conduction

Conduction

Heat travels through solids by **conduction**. Some solids conduct heat better than others. The frying pan in the photograph is made from metal because metal is a good **conductor** of heat. Energy will be transferred quickly from the burning gas to the food in the pan. The spoon is made of wood because wood is a good **insulator**. The handle of the spoon will not get hot.

When a solid is heated the particles gain more energy. They cannot move around but they vibrate more. The higher the temperature the more the particles vibrate. When one end of a solid is heated the particles in the heated end start to vibrate more. These particles bump into nearby particles and make them vibrate more, and so on. The energy is conducted through the solid.

Learning objectives

- describe how energy is transferred in solids by heating
- explain why some solids are conductors of heat and some are insulators.

The metal frying pan is a good conductor and the wooden spoon is a good insulator.

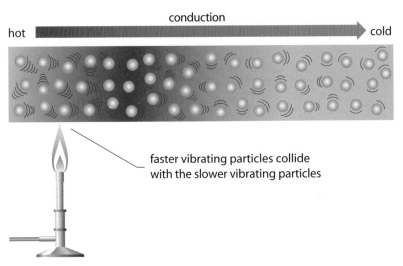

faster vibrating particles collide with the slower vibrating particles

Figure 1 Heating a solid.

Examiner feedback

It is not true to say that insulating materials do not get hot. A ceramic mug is made of an insulating material, but energy from a hot drink will eventually be conducted through the mug and make the outside of the mug hot to touch. Insulating materials reduce the speed at which energy is conducted by heating.

Science skills

A student took rods made of four different metals and put a blob of wax at one end of each rod. She heated the other end and measured how long it took for the wax to start melting. The table shows the results.

a Suggest some possible sources of error in this investigation.

b How could the student improve the accuracy and reliability of the results?

Metal	Time for wax to start melting/s
copper	17
aluminium	31
brass	56
stainless steel	98

Taking it further

Thermal conductivity is a measure of how well a material transfers energy by heating. It is the energy transferred per second per degree of temperature difference along a metre of material with a cross-sectional area of 1 m^2. Its units are W/K/m.

Conductors and insulators

Metals are good thermal conductors because they have **free electrons**, i.e. electrons that can move through the material. This is why metals are also good electrical conductors. The electrons move faster when the metal is heated. They collide with other particles and transfer energy.

Solids such as wood and plastic do not have free electrons, so they are poor conductors of heat, or good insulators. Most liquids and gases are poor conductors, as the particles can move about freely and do not pass on energy from one to another very easily.

Because gases are poor conductors of heat, the insulating properties of a material can be improved if it includes pockets of trapped air. The photographs show materials that are very good insulators.

Science in action

The best insulator known to humans is aerogel. This is a solid made from a silica or carbon framework with air trapped inside it. Aerogel is 99.8% air, and so it also has an extremely low density. It was used by NASA as insulation for Mars rovers.

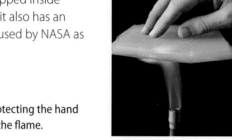

The aerogel is protecting the hand from the heat of the flame.

Animals and insulation

Many animals are adapted to live in cold conditions. Mammals and birds that live in cold climates have insulation to help to reduce the transfer of energy from their bodies to the surroundings. Feathers, fat and fur are all good insulating materials. Humans also use fat as an insulator, but we rely more on clothing to keep us warm.

These insulating materials all contain trapped air.

Questions

1. How is energy transferred by conduction?
2. Why are liquids and gases poor conductors?
3. Explain why materials that are good electrical conductors are usually also good at conducting by heating.
4. Look at the insulating materials in the photographs above right. Which one do you think is the best thermal insulator? Explain your answer.
5. Small birds often look bigger when the weather is cold, because they spread their feathers out. Suggest why they do this.
6. Many houses have double-glazed windows. These have two sheets of glass with an air gap between them. Why does double glazing provide better insulation than single glazing?
7. First aiders will often cover someone who has been injured outdoors with a very thin blanket made from shiny metal foil. Suggest some of the advantages and disadvantages of using foil instead of a normal blanket.
8. Look at the pan in the first photograph. Explain why it is made of metal and why a chef uses a cloth when picking it up. Include the role of free electrons in your answer.

Examiner feedback

It is very important to understand why insulation works and why some forms of insulation are more effective than others.

Penguins have a layer of fat beneath their skin that keeps them warm in the water. Their feathers trap air.

Convection

Convection currents

Fluids (liquids and gases) are poor conductors, which is why insulating materials such as polystyrene foam contain pockets of trapped air. However, air and other fluids can transfer energy if they are free to move. This process is called **convection**.

When a fluid is heated the particles move around faster and take up more space. This makes the fluid less **dense**, so it rises up past the colder fluid around it. This sets up a flow called a convection current. Figure 1 explains how a heater on the side of a fish tank can cause heating of all of the water in the tank.

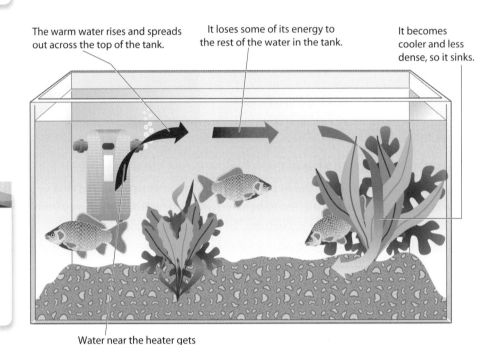

The warm water rises and spreads out across the top of the tank.

It loses some of its energy to the rest of the water in the tank.

It becomes cooler and less dense, so it sinks.

Water near the heater gets warmer and less dense.

Figure 1 Convection in a fluid.

Convection currents can form around any object that is warmer or cooler than its surroundings. For example, energy from a mug of hot tea will be transferred to the air around it, and this air will warm up and rise. Cooler air flows in to take its place, and this makes the tea cool faster. Convection currents can also form around cold objects. Energy is transferred from the air to the cold object so the air cools down. The air becomes more dense and sinks. Warmer air takes the place of the sinking air.

Using convection

Domestic hot water systems make use of convection, as shown in Figure 2. A boiler heats cold water, which then becomes less dense and rises. Hot water is stored in the hot water tank until it is needed.

Most rooms in homes are heated by radiators or fires, as shown in Figure 3.

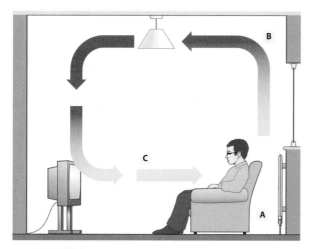

Figure 3 Heating a room using convection.

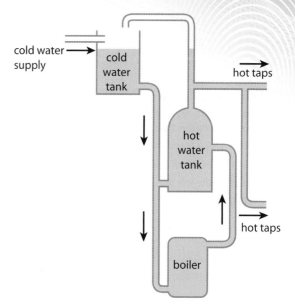

Figure 2 A hot water system.

This conservatory is being cooled by a convection current.

The radiator heats the air near it (A). The particles move faster and so this air becomes less dense and rises. At B it cannot rise any further, and is pushed along the ceiling by more warm air rising beneath it. As the air moves away it gradually transfers heat to the air around it. It descends when it reaches the far wall, and moves across the room to replace the air rising at A.

The photograph shows how a room can be also cooled by a convection current.

Questions

1 What is convection? Explain in as much detail as you can.

2 Why doesn't convection happen in solids?

3 If the heating is turned off on a day in winter, why is the coldest place in a room likely to be under a window?

4 **(a)** Explain why the cooling element in a freezer is usually at the top. **(b)** Explain why the coldest part of a fridge is usually at the bottom.

5 Explain why smoke detectors are usually fitted to ceilings rather than walls.

6 Mercury is a metal that is liquid at room temperature. **(a)** Why might mercury be a good conductor?

(b) Why might it be difficult to measure the conducting properties of mercury?

7 Look at Figure 2. **(a)** Why does the pipe for the hot water taps come out of the top of the hot water tank, not the bottom? **(b)** The hot water tank also has an electric immersion heater. Explain where this should be positioned in the tank.

8 Look at the photograph of the conservatory. Write a paragraph for a marketing brochure to explain how opening a roof vent near the top can help to cool the whole space. Use ideas from lessons P1 1.1 and P1 1.3 in your answer.

How fast can energy be transferred by heating?

Science in action

Polythene is normally a very good insulator. In 2010 scientists working in the USA stretched polythene into very thin fibres only tens of nanometres thick. These fibres are better conductors than iron, because stretching the polythene gives the molecules a more ordered structure. The new material could be used to make lighter radiators for cars.

Examiner feedback

It will be useful to remember that 1 nanometre is 1×10^{-9} m or one millionth of a millimetre.

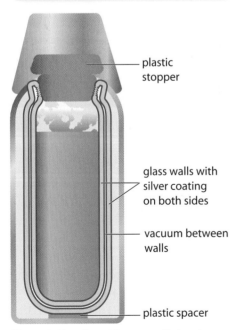

plastic stopper

glass walls with silver coating on both sides

vacuum between walls

plastic spacer

Figure 1 How does this vacuum flask reduce energy transfers?

Factors affecting energy transfer by heating

Energy is transferred from hotter objects to cooler ones. The greater the temperature difference, the greater the rate at which energy is transferred.

A thick metal bar will conduct energy along its length more quickly than a thin wire, because there are more particles to pass on vibrations. The material from which the bar is made also affects the rate of transfer. Some materials are better conductors than others.

There are other factors that affect the rate at which an object transfers energy to its surroundings. The motorbike engine in the photograph has metal fins on the outside. These help to cool the engine by providing a large surface area of hot metal in contact with the cooler surrounding air.

The surrounding material also makes a difference. If the motorbike has its engine running while it is not moving, the air near the engine will heat up very quickly. This will reduce the temperature difference between the fins and the air, and the rate of energy transfer will go down. If the motorbike is moving, or if there is a breeze, the temperature difference will remain high.

Fins on a motorbike engine help to transfer heat to the surroundings.

It takes more energy to heat up water by 1 °C than it takes to heat up air by 1 °C (you will learn more about this in lesson P1 1.7). If a hot object is put into water, it can transfer more energy to the water before the temperature difference gets less and reduces the rate of energy transfer.

Evaluating designs

A vacuum flask is designed to keep hot drinks hot, or to keep cold drinks cold. It has several features that are designed to reduce the transfer of energy between the contents of the flask and its surroundings.

Vacuum flasks are designed to reduce all energy transfers as much as possible. However, the solar panel shown in Figure 2 is designed to reduce energy transfers in some places and increase it in others.

Solar hot water panels are a technological development that can help us to reduce our energy bills.

a Suggest what scientific knowledge was used by the engineers designing the panel.

b What factors would a householder consider before installing a solar panel?

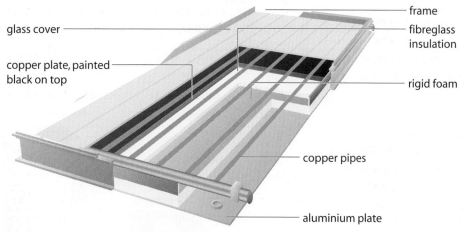

glass cover

copper plate, painted black on top

frame

fibreglass insulation

rigid foam

copper pipes

aluminium plate

Figure 2 A solar panel for heating water.

Animal adaptations

Animals that are adapted to live in hot or cold climates often have adaptations to their body shape or size. The photographs show an Arctic fox and a fennec, or desert fox. The large ears of the desert fox help it to keep cool.

Animals that live in cold climates are often larger than related species that live in warmer areas. Their large size means they have a smaller surface area in comparison to their total volume and thus transfer less energy to their surroundings than animals in hot climates.

The Arctic fox (top) is adapted to live in cold climates. The desert fox (bottom) is adapted to live in hot conditions.

Questions

1 Look at Figure 1. Explain which features of the flask reduce energy transfer by: **(a)** radiation; **(b)** conduction; **(c)** convection.

2 Many vacuum flasks have steel walls instead of glass.
(a) How would this affect how fast hot coffee in the flask cools? Explain your answer. **(b)** Why do you think steel is used instead of glass?

3 Would the flask keep a cold drink cold on a hot day? Explain your answer.

4 Look at Figure 2. Explain the design of the parts of the solar panel that are intended to: **(a)** let infrared radiation go through; **(b)** absorb infrared radiation; **(c)** reflect infrared radiation.

5 Explain why the desert fox's large ears help to keep it cool.

6 Describe two adaptations the Arctic fox has for living in a cold climate.

7 Explain why air moving over an object can increase its rate of cooling.

8 Explain how and why parts of the solar panel are designed to reduce heat transfer by convection, conduction and radiation.

Heating buildings

Examiner feedback

Don't get solar panels and **solar cells** mixed up. Solar panels are used for heating water, and solar cells are used to produce electricity using energy from the Sun.

Reducing heating bills

The cost of heating a house can be up to £1000 per year. Some of this money is wasted if energy escapes from the house. The amount of energy lost can be reduced by insulating the house.

Heating bills can also be reduced by installing alternative sources of energy. One example of this is using solar panels to heat water. This water can be used to heat the building, or can be used to provide hot water for washing and bathing.

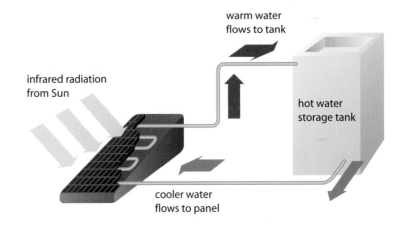

Figure 1 Heating water using infrared radiation from the Sun.

Table 1 Various methods of reducing energy bills.

Energy-saving measure	Typical cost / £	Savings per year / £
solar panels	3500	70
loft insulation	150	150
double glazing	3500	200
cavity wall insulation	350	100
insulating the hot water tank	60	15
draught-proofing doors and windows	50	15

However, it costs money to install extra insulation or solar panels, and so a homeowner would need to look at the **payback time** for different insulation methods before choosing which to use. The payback time is the length of time it takes to save the amount of money that the improvement cost. For example, if it costs £60 to insulate a hot water tank and this saves £15 per year in energy bills, the payback time is four years. The shorter the payback time, the more **cost effective** the insulation method.

Energy from the Sun can also be used to heat houses directly. The house shown in Figure 3 is heated by the Sun as the conservatory along the front allows radiated energy in and traps it. Conservatories used for heating have to be carefully designed as part of the house; a conservatory added later is not likely to contribute much to heating the house.

Designing better houses

There are many government building regulations that specify how buildings should be designed and the materials that can be used. These are intended to make sure homes are safe to live in and do not waste too much energy.

Part of the regulations defines the **U-values** for roofs, walls and floors. The U-value shows how good a material or a building component is as an insulator. The lower the U-value, the less energy the material transfers. Table 2 shows some typical U-values.

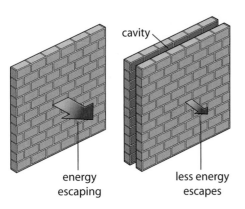

Figure 2 A solid brick wall and a cavity wall.

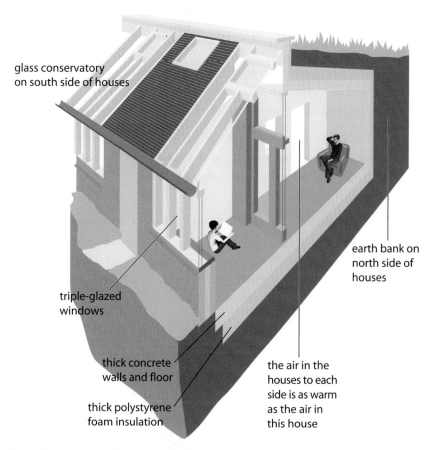

glass conservatory
on south side of houses

triple-glazed
windows

thick concrete
walls and floor

thick polystyrene
foam insulation

earth bank on
north side of
houses

the air in the
houses to each
side is as warm
as the air in
this house

Figure 3 An energy-efficient house.

The design of the home can make a big difference, as well as the materials from which it is made. Figure 3 shows the structure of a row of low-energy houses at the Hockerton Housing Project, near Nottingham.

Questions

1. How can solar panels help to reduce heating bills?

2. Look at Table 1. Which method will save the most energy? Explain your answer.

3. How can someone work out which type of insulation would be the most cost effective?

4. **(a)** Work out the payback times for all the energy-saving methods shown in Table 1. **(b)** Which method has the shortest payback time?

5. Why might someone decide to insulate their hot-water tank first, even though it does not have the shortest payback time?

6. Modern houses usually have cavity walls. Explain why they are now built with a layer of insulation between the two parts of the wall.

7. **(a)** In Table 2, which type of window transfers the least thermal energy? Explain how you worked out your answer. **(b)** Explain why this type of window transfers the least energy.

8. Explain why the house shown in Figure 3 uses hardly any energy for heating.

A*

Examiner feedback

You do not need to remember the values in Table 1 or Table 2.

Table 2 U-values of some building materials and components.

Component	U-value W/m² °C
solid brick wall	2.2
cavity brick wall, no insulation	1.0
cavity brick wall with insulation	0.6
single-glazed window, metal frame	5.8
single-glazed window, wood or uPVC (plastic) frame	5.0
double-glazed window, wood or uPVC (plastic) frame	2.9

Science skills

Different building materials are tested in laboratories using standard procedures. Standard procedures are set ways of testing things, and allow different laboratories to get the same results if they are testing the same materials. Results that are the same when measured by different people are said to be reproducible.

a Why do building materials need to be tested?

b Why do testing laboratories follow standard procedures?

c How could a laboratory make sure its results are reliable?

d How could the laboratory use the range of its results to determine how accurate they are?

Specific heat capacities

- explain what specific heat capacity is
- use the equation for specific heat capacity
- evaluate the use of materials according to their specific heat capacities.

Storing energy

The amount of energy stored in an object depends on the mass of the object, its temperature and on the material it is made from. For a particular object, the greater its mass, and the higher its temperature, the more energy is stored.

The same mass of different materials at the same temperature store different amounts of energy. The energy needed to raise the temperature of 1 kg of a material by 1 °C is called its **specific heat capacity**.

$$E = m \times c \times \theta$$

heat transferred = mass × specific heat capacity × temperature change
(joules, J)   (kilograms, kg)   (J/kg °C)   (degrees Celsius, °C)

Example 1

How much energy does a kettle transfer when it heats 1 kg of water from 10 °C to 100 °C? The specific heat capacity of water is 4200 J/kg °C.

$$E = m \times c \times \theta$$

heat transferred = mass × specific heat capacity × temperature change
$$= 1\,kg \times 4200\,J/kg\,°C \times 90\,°C$$
$$= 378\,000\,J,\ or\ 378\,kJ$$

Example 2

It takes 4500 J of energy to heat a 1 kg block of iron by 10 °C. What is the specific heat capacity of iron?

$$\text{specific heat capacity} = \frac{\text{heat transferred}}{\text{mass} \times \text{temperature change}}$$
$$= \frac{4500\,J}{1\,kg \times 10\,°C}$$
$$= 450\,J/kg\,°C$$

How much energy does a kettle transfer?

In an exam you will be expected to be able to re-arrange equations to put the quantity you need to calculate on the left.

Figure 1 shows apparatus used to find the specific heat capacity of a metal. The energy supplied by the electric immersion heater can be measured accurately.

a Explain why the results using this method might show a systematic error.

b What effect will this have on the value of specific heat capacity worked out from the results?

c Suggest how the size of this systematic error could be reduced or eliminated.

Figure 1 Apparatus for measuring specific heat capacity.

Heat sinks

The components inside computers are cooled using a block of metal, called a **heat sink**, attached to the component. The large mass of the heat sink compared with the component means that a lot of energy can be transferred to it without raising its temperature much. The heat sink then transfers the energy to the surrounding air.

Radiators and storage heaters

Central heating systems use water to transfer heat energy from a boiler to the radiators around the home. Water has a very high specific heat capacity, and so it can store a lot of energy. The energy is transferred to the rooms in the home as the hot water passes through radiators.

Some homes use electricity for heating. Storage heaters heat up using cheaper electricity available at night (you will learn more about this in lesson P1 4.6). Figure 3 shows how storage heaters work. Concrete has quite a high specific heat capacity, and the mass of concrete used in each heater is large, so each storage heater can store a lot of energy. This heat is released gradually during the day to keep the home warm.

Oil-filled radiators are portable electric heaters. Once the oil inside them is hot the electricity can be switched off. They will continue to heat the room for some time after the electricity is switched off.

Table 1 The specific heat capacities of some materials.

Material	Specific heat capacity J/kg °C
air	100
aluminium	899
concrete	900
copper	390
iron	450
lead	130
oil	540
water	4200

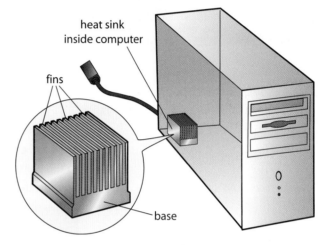

Figure 2 A heat sink in a computer.

Questions

1 A student heats a 1 kg block of aluminium and a 1 kg block of copper to 50 °C. Explain which block will be storing the most energy.

2 Why does it take longer to boil a kettle full of water than one only half full?

3 Explain why stand-alone radiators are filled with oil, instead of being filled with air.

4 How much energy does it take to heat up 500 g of lead by 30 °C?

5 A washing machine heats 10 kg of water for each wash cycle. How much energy is saved by washing clothes at 30 °C instead of 50 °C?

6 A storage heater contains 100 kg of concrete. 1800 kJ of energy is transferred to it. What is the temperature change of the concrete?

7 A student heats up a 500 g block of iron from 18 °C to 46 °C, using 6280 J of energy. **(a)** Calculate the specific heat capacity of iron using these results. **(b)** Suggest why your answer is different to the value in Table 1.

8 Explain why the heat sink in Figure 2 has fins, and why the metal used to make it should have a high specific heat capacity and be a very good thermal conductor.

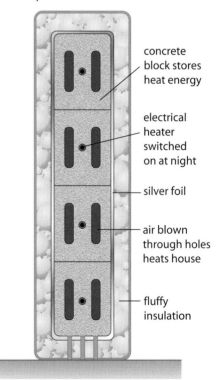

Figure 3 How a storage heater works.

Energy transfers

The bent bow is storing elastic potential energy.

Forms of energy

Energy is needed to keep us working, and to operate all the machines around us. Different forms of energy include light, sound, electrical, potential and **kinetic energy**.

Energy can also be stored. **Nuclear energy** is stored inside atoms. Food, fuels and electrical batteries are all stores of **chemical energy**. Anything that is squashed, stretched or twisted stores **elastic potential energy**. It takes energy to move an object upwards against the force of gravity. Any object in a high position stores this energy as **gravitational potential energy**.

Energy transfers

Machines transfer energy between different forms. For example, an mp3 player transfers stored chemical energy into electrical energy and then sound.

Sometimes more than one energy transfer is involved. The engine in a car transfers chemical energy in the petrol into kinetic energy, which is useful. However, some of the energy is transferred by heating and sound. These forms of energy are not useful, so we call them wasted energy.

Sometimes one form of energy can be both useful and wasted. A boiler uses the chemical energy stored in gas or oil to heat water. The energy that is transferred to the water being heated is useful energy. However, the boiler itself will also get hot and this energy is wasted energy.

The rollercoaster carriages are transferring gravitational potential energy into kinetic energy as they fall. The kinetic energy will be transferred back into gravitational potential energy as the carriages go up the next rise. The next rise cannot be as high, as friction will cause some of the energy to be wasted in frictional heating.

Conservation of energy

Energy cannot be created or destroyed; it can only be transferred usefully, stored or dissipated (wasted). The total amount of energy does not change. This is called the **principle of conservation of energy**.

If you could measure the total energy stored in the petrol used by a car, it would be exactly the same as the total energy produced by the engine.

Spreading out

If you look at an energy transfer it can often seem as if some energy has 'disappeared'. A cup on the table has gravitational potential energy, but what eventually happens to this if you knock the cup to the floor? The falling cup transfers gravitational potential energy to kinetic energy, and when it hits the floor this is transferred to sound energy and to increased energy in some of the particles in the floor. All of this energy ends up spreading out – dissipating – into the surroundings, which become warmer.

A car uses chemical energy stored in its fuel. The fuel stores a lot of energy in a small space. This chemical energy is eventually transferred by heating into the surroundings, which become warmer. This dissipated energy is very difficult to use for further energy transfers.

The light bulb transfers energy by heating and light. In this case the energy transferred by heating is wasted energy, but for a heater, it would be the useful form of energy.

Science skills

The idea that energy is conserved was originally a hypothesis that was tested by gathering experimental data.

a Suggest some of the difficulties in confirming this hypothesis using a rollercoaster and explain why more precise results could be obtained under laboratory conditions.

Questions

1 What are the energy transfers in a torch?

2 You are running a race. What forms of energy are you transferring that are: **(a)** useful? **(b)** wasted?

3 A car uses a litre of petrol when it is driven to the shops and back. What happens to the chemical energy that was stored in the petrol?

4 What are the forms of wasted energy produced by a Bunsen burner?

5 What happens to the elastic potential energy in the bow in the first photograph?

6 If energy cannot be destroyed, how can we 'waste' energy?

7 Draw a flow chart to show all the energy transfers in a wind-up torch, starting with food. Show how energy is wasted at each stage.

8 The rollercoaster carriages in the photograph are moved to the top of the first rise on the track by electric motors. Once they start falling for the first time, there is no more energy input.

Explain why the rollercoasters can go up other rises on the track without the need for motors, and what happens to the energy originally transferred to the carriages by these electric motors.

Efficiency and Sankey diagrams

Efficiency

All energy transfers produce some forms of wasted energy. The **efficiency** of a device is a measure of the amount of energy that is usefully transferred. The higher the efficiency, the more of the input energy is transferred into useful forms of energy.

The energy transfers in a device can be represented using a **Sankey diagram.** Figure 1 shows a Sankey diagram for a light bulb. The widths of the arrows are proportional to the amounts of energy they represent.

Calculating efficiency

Efficiency can be calculated using the energy or the **power** transferred by a device. Power is the energy transferred each second, and is measured in **watts (W)** or **kilowatts (kW)**.

$$\text{efficiency} = \frac{\text{useful energy out}}{\text{total energy in}} (\times 100\%)$$

$$\text{efficiency} = \frac{\text{useful power out}}{\text{total power in}} (\times 100\%)$$

You can use joules or kilojoules in the energy version of the equation, as long as you use the same units for both numbers. You can use watts or kilowatts in the power version, as long as you use the same units for both numbers.

The efficiency can be quoted as a decimal number less than one, or as a percentage if you multiply your answer by 100%.

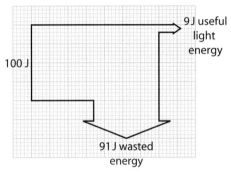

Figure 1 A Sankey diagram for a light bulb, showing the energy transferred each second.

9 J useful light energy
100 J
91 J wasted energy

Example 1

What is the efficiency of an electric kettle if it uses 500 kJ of electrical energy and transfers only 400 kJ of energy to the water in the kettle?

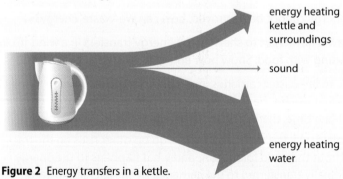

energy heating kettle and surroundings

sound

energy heating water

Figure 2 Energy transfers in a kettle.

$$\text{efficiency} = \frac{\text{useful energy out}}{\text{total energy in}} (\times 100\%)$$

$$= \frac{400 \text{ kJ}}{500 \text{ kJ}}$$

$$= 80\%$$

So the kettle only wastes 20% of the energy that is transferred to it.

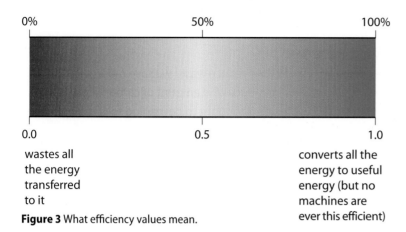

0%	50%	100%
0.0	0.5	1.0

wastes all
the energy
transferred
to it

converts all the
energy to useful
energy (but no
machines are
ever this efficient)

Figure 3 What efficiency values mean.

Science skills

The diagram shows an investigation to find the efficiencies of different bouncing balls. Some of the kinetic energy in the ball is transferred to heat energy as it bounces. This means that a ball never bounces to the same height from which it was dropped. The height of the ball is a measure of the gravitational potential energy stored in it. The higher the ball at the top of its bounce, the more efficient it is. The table shows the results for two different balls.

Drop	Bounce height/cm		
	Ball 1	**Ball 2**	**Ball 3**
1	59.0	38.0	49.5
2	60.5	35.5	47.0
3	58.0	38.5	47.5
4	60.0	37.0	48.0
5	57.5	31.5	49.0

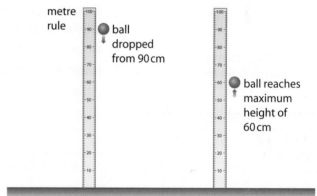

Figure 4 Bouncing balls.

a Find the mean and range of each set of data, ignoring any anomalous results.

b Suggest why there is a range of results for each ball.

c What was done in the investigation to improve reliability?

d For which ball are the results most precise? Explain your answer.

Questions

1 Look at the Sankey diagram in Figure 2. How could the kettle be made more efficient?

2 An electric immersion heater uses 50 kJ of electrical energy and transfers 45 kJ of heat to the water.
(a) How efficient is it? **(b)** What forms of energy are wasted?

3 Draw a Sankey diagram to represent the immersion heater in question 2.

4 How efficient is the light bulb in Figure 1?

5 Your muscles waste about 75 J of energy for every 25 J they convert into movement. How efficient are your muscles?

6 An electric fan has an efficiency of 80%. If it produces 120 W of useful kinetic energy in the air, how much power is it using?

7 **(a)** What is the efficiency of the bouncing ball shown in Figure 4? **(b)** How high would you expect its second bounce to be? **(c)** What assumptions have you made in working out your answers?

8 Compare light bulbs and kettles in terms of energy transfers and efficiency and illustrate your answers with diagrams.

Reducing energy consumption

Learning objectives

- describe some ways of reducing energy consumption
- evaluate the effectiveness and cost effectiveness of some of these.

Figure 1 Switching off unused equipment can reduce wasted energy.

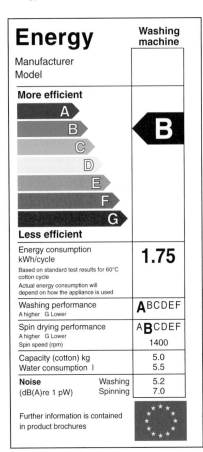

Figure 2 An energy efficiency label for a washing machine.

Reducing wasted energy

We all pay for the energy we use, so if we reduce waste we save money. Reducing the amount of fossil fuels we use also reduces the amount of carbon dioxide that enters the atmosphere. Carbon dioxide is thought to be leading to climate change.

One very easy way of reducing wasted energy is to keep our homes cooler and wear more clothes.

We should also switch off all appliances and lights that are not being used. All the energy transferred by a light bulb in an empty room is wasted energy. Appliances such as TVs or computers that are left on standby also waste energy.

Waste can also be reduced by using more efficient appliances. Modern low-energy light bulbs and LED lights are more efficient than old fashioned light bulbs. They cost more than normal bulbs. However, they also last longer so they will save more money in electricity bills and replacement costs than they cost to buy. They are cost effective.

All new appliances have an energy label that shows how efficient they are – see Figure 2. However, more efficient appliances are usually more expensive than less efficient ones. It is not usually cost effective to replace an old appliance that is still working with a new, more efficient one.

Science skills

Not only may buying a new, more efficient appliance cost more money, but throwing away an old appliance that still works may also result in more energy being used overall.

a Why might replacing an old appliance with a new one not always result in reducing overall energy consumption and carbon dioxide emissions?

Transport and energy

Figure 3 shows how much energy it takes to move one passenger one kilometre using different forms of transport. Less energy would be used for transport if more people took the bus or train instead of using a car. Even more energy would be saved if more people walked or used a bicycle for short journeys; they would also be healthier.

Modern cars are usually more efficient than older ones, which means they can go further on a litre of fuel than older cars. Buying a new, more efficient car can save on fuel costs, but it may not be cost effective. It costs a lot to buy a new car, and it also takes a lot of energy to make a new car.

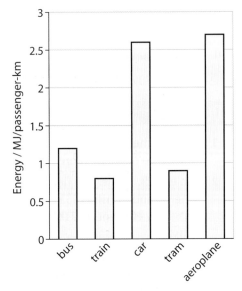

Figure 3 Different types of transport need different amounts of energy. These figures assume an average number of people in each form of transport.

Which of these ways of saving energy are decided by individuals, which are decided by the government, and which are a combination of both?

b Banning the sale of old-fashioned inefficient light bulbs.

c Explaining to people why it is important to reduce their energy use.

d Giving a grant for replacing an inefficient boiler with a new, efficient one.

Using wasted energy

Sometimes wasted energy can be reused. In many factories, large fans extract air from the building to remove fumes or smells, and to ensure a supply of fresh air. The removed air transfers energy with it, which is wasted as it spreads out and warms the surroundings. If the waste air is passed through a **heat exchanger**, some of the energy can be transferred to heat the air coming into the building and warm it.

Questions

1 Give two reasons why we should try to reduce wasted energy.

2 How will keeping our homes cooler reduce wasted energy?

3 What information would you need to allow you to work out whether buying a more expensive LED light instead of a normal bulb would save you money overall?

4 Jenny lives on her own and uses her tumble dryer once a week. Sam has three young children and uses her tumble dryer every day. Explain who is more likely to benefit from buying a new, more efficient tumble dryer.

5 The energy per passenger-km for cars in Figure 3 was calculated assuming each car carried two people. How would the energy change if:
(a) all cars carried four people? **(b)** all cars had only one person in them?

6 Which of the values in question 5 would be more likely to be used by:
(a) a car manufacturer selling cars? **(b)** a train company trying to persuade people to use the train? **(c)** Explain your answers.

7 How does fitting a heat exchanger to the air circulation system in a factory help to save money and help the environment?

8 What does 'cost-effective' mean? Explain some of the factors you would consider in deciding whether replacing a central heating boiler will be cost-effective.

Assess yourself questions

1 Figure 1 shows an insulated box used to keep food hot.

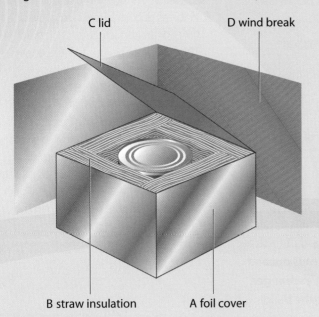

Figure 1 Insulated box.

Choose the correct parts, A–D, to answer the questions below:

(a) What stops the box emitting infrared radiation?

(b) What helps to stop heat being transferred by convection?

(c) What helps to stop heat being transferred by conduction?

(d) What stops the wind moving warmed air away from the box? *(4 marks)*

2 A student was testing different ways of insulating a food box. She carried out four different tests, each using materials in different ways. Look at tests (a)–(c) and decide which kind of variable was being used. Choose your answers from the box.

(a) Foam of different thicknesses.

(b) Foam, foil or bubble wrap.

(c) One, two or three layers of foam. *(3 marks)*

categoric	continuous

3 **(a)** Describe how a convection current will form in the air near a lit candle. Draw a diagram to illustrate your answer. *(4 marks)*

(b) Sketch the convection current that would be formed by an ice cube floating in a glass of water. *(1 mark)*

(c) Explain why the two convection currents are different. *(4 marks)*

4 **(a)** Explain what the terms 'payback time' and 'cost-effective' mean. *(2 marks)*

(b) Describe how you would decide which type of insulation to add to a house. *(3 marks)*

5 Look at the house in Figure 2.

Figure 2 House with cooling features.

Explain how each of the labelled features helps the house to keep cool. *(3 marks)*

6 Animal adaptations to maintaining the correct body temperature can involve their shape, the materials their body is made from, or their behaviour. Explain how these adaptations of elephants help to keep them cool.

(a) Large ears. *(2 marks)*

(b) No fur. *(2 marks)*

(c) They often stand in the shade of trees. *(2 marks)*

(d) They suck up water in their trunks and spray it over their bodies. *(3 marks)*

7 A 150 W fan produces 130 W of useful kinetic energy in the air.

(a) How is the remaining 20 W of energy transferred? *(2 marks)*

(b) Draw a Sankey diagram to represent the energy transfers in the fan. Draw your diagram on graph paper. *(2 marks)*

(c) Calculate the efficiency of the fan. *(3 marks)*

8 Explain how putting a lid on a cup of soup will help to keep it hot. *(5 marks)*

9 A storage heater contains 10 kg of concrete, with a specific heat capacity of 900 J/kg·°C. At the end of its overnight heating period, the temperature of the concrete is 60 °C.

How much energy has been stored in the concrete? State any assumptions you had to make in working out your answer. *(5 marks)*

10 The apparatus shown in Figure 3 was used to investigate how well different-coloured materials absorb and emit infrared radiation. Table 1 shows the results of the investigation.

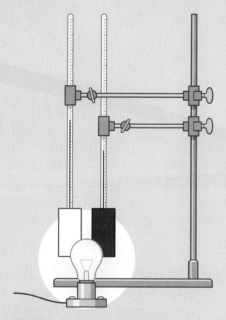

Figure 3 Experimental apparatus.

Table 1 Results of experiment.

| Time/ | Temperature/°C | |
min	Black	White
0	18	18
2	21	19
4	24	21
6	26	23
8	30	25
10	32	27
12	30	26
14	28	25
16	27	24
18	26	23
20	25	22

(a) Plot a graph to show these results. *(4 marks)*

(b) At what point do you think the bulb was switched off? Explain your answer. *(2 marks)*

(c) Write a conclusion for this investigation. *(4 marks)*

11 A school hall has a very high ceiling, and it gets very hot in the summer. Explain why cooling will be most effective if windows near the ceiling are opened as well as opening windows or doors at ground level. *(4 marks)*

12 A 1.5 kg block of aluminium is heated up using an immersion heater. 13 kJ of energy is transferred to the block. The specific heat capacity of aluminium is 899 J/kg/°C.

(a) Calculate the temperature rise (to the nearest degree) in the aluminium block. *(3 marks)*

(b) Explain why the temperature rise would actually be less than this. *(1 mark)*

13 A student takes a beaker full of crushed ice and heats it.

(a) Sketch a graph to show how the temperature of the ice changes as the ice melts and as the student continues to heat the water formed. Include significant temperatures on the graph. *(3 marks)*

(b) Explain the shape of your graph using kinetic theory. *(4 marks)*

14 A wine cooler consists of a container made from porous pottery. When it is used, the pot is soaked in water and a wine bottle is placed inside it. Explain how the wine cooler works. *(5 marks)*

15 A coolbox is used to keep food or drinks cold for picnics. Explain why the coolbox has the following features.

(a) A plastic rather than a metal outer case. *(2 marks)*

(b) Foam between the inner and outer cases. *(2 marks)*

(c) A white inner case. *(2 marks)*

16 Blocks of ice are put inside the coolbox to help to keep the contents cold.

(a) How does the ice help to keep the contents cold? *(1 mark)*

(b) Explain two ways (other than weight) in which ice is a better material to use for this purpose than a block of metal cooled to the same initial temperature. *(4 marks)*

17 How could you test a selection of coolboxes to find out which is the most effective at keeping food cool? Describe what you would do, and how you would make your test fair.

In this question you will be assessed on using good English, organising information clearly and using specialist terms where appropriate *(6 marks)*

Electrical energy

Energy transfers in electrical appliances

Electricity is a very useful way of transferring energy, as electrical devices can be designed to bring about many different energy transfers. The photograph shows some appliances that transfer electrical energy into light, heat, sound and kinetic energy.

A lamp, an electric oven, headphones and the Segway. The Segway contains electric motors and moves forwards when you lean forwards. Can you work out the energy transfers in each case?

Science skills

a Explain what form of chart you would use to display this data.

b What advantages would this type of display have compared with the table?

Look at the data in Table 1.

c Suggest why no-one owned microwave ovens or telephone chargers in 1970.

d What economic factors might a person take into account when deciding to buy a new appliance?

e What environmental factors might they take into account?

f How might the factors in **d** and **e** depend on the type of appliance?

Table 1 The number (in 1000s) of different appliances owned in the UK, 1970 and 2000.

Year	1970	2000
fridges & freezers	10837	37006
washing machine	11728	19379
tumble dryer	134	8635
dish washer	221	6009
telephone chargers	–	3710
oven	7683	14428
hob	7615	11538
microwave	–	20144
kettle	10259	24117
toaster	4540	19623

The number of some types of electrical appliances owned (in thousands) in 1970 and 2010.

Energy and power

The amount of electrical energy a device uses depends on its **power** and how long it is switched on for. Energy is measured in joules (J). The power of an appliance is the rate at which it transforms energy, and is measured in **watts** (W). 1 watt = 1 joule of energy transferred each second.

$$E \qquad = \quad P \quad \times \quad t$$
energy transferred = power × time
(joules, J) (watts, W) (seconds, s)

Examiner feedback

Make sure that the units you use in these calculations are always the correct ones. In the formula to work out the energy transferred, if energy is in joules, power must be in watts. If you are given a value in kilowatts, convert it to watts by multiplying by 1000. The time must be in seconds. If you are given a time in minutes convert it to seconds by multiplying by 60. If you are given a time in hours, multiply by 3600.

Example 1

A 20 W light bulb is switched on for 5 hours. How much energy does it transfer?

5 hours = 5 × 3600 seconds
= 18 000 seconds

$E = P \times t$
energy = power × time
= 20 W × 18 000 seconds
= 360 000 J (or 360 kJ)

Example 2

A 3 kW heater uses 8000 kJ of energy. For how many minutes was it switched on?

$E = P \times t$
energy = power × time
$$\text{time} = \frac{\text{energy}}{\text{power}}$$
$$= \frac{8\,000\,000\,\text{J}}{3000\,\text{W}}$$
= 2667 seconds
= 44.4 minutes or 44 minutes 24 seconds

Examiner feedback

In example 2, you could have left the energy in kJ and the power in kW and you would have got the same answer. However unless you are very confident with maths and equations, it is safest in an exam to always convert the values to the standard units (joules and watts, in this case) before putting the numbers into the equation.

Questions

1. What energy transfers are the following devices designed to bring about? **(a)** electric drill **(b)** fan heater **(c)** television.

2. How is energy wasted in the devices in question 1?

3. Name two electrical devices (other than those in question 1) that are designed to transfer electrical energy into: **(a)** heating; **(b)** light; **(c)** sound; **(d)** movement.

4. A 50 W radio is switched on for 3 hours. How much energy does it use?

5. A tumble dryer uses 2700 kJ of electrical energy when it is used for half an hour. What power is the tumble dryer?

6. A computer uses 2400 kJ of energy. Its power is 65 W. How long was it switched on for? Give your answer in hours, minutes and seconds to the nearest second.

7. An electric oven has a power of 3 kW. A cake takes 40 minutes to bake. **(a)** What is the maximum amount of energy the oven will use to bake the cake? **(b)** Explain why this is a maximum amount. (*Hint*: think about what the thermostat in an oven does.)

8. 'The increasing ownership of toasters could help to reduce the amount of electricity used.' Explain this statement. (*Hint*: think about how you would make toast if you did not have a toaster.)

Paying for electricity

This hair straightener iron has a power rating of 40 W.

The power of appliances

We use electricity for a lot of different things but it all has to be paid for. Electricity bills are worked out from the amount of energy used.

Many household devices transfer a lot of energy, and their power is usually measured in kilowatts (kW), where 1 kW = 1000 W. The **power rating** of an appliance is shown on a label.

Calculating the cost

A joule is quite a small amount of energy. It is impractical to quote energy use in thousands of kilojoules, so electricity companies use the **kilowatt-hour (kWh)**. This is the amount of energy that is transferred by a 1 kW device in one hour. It is sometimes called a **Unit** of electricity.

$$E \quad = \quad P \quad \times \quad t$$
energy transferred $=$ power $\times$ time
(kilowatt-hours, kWh) (kilowatts, kW) (hours, h)

Example 1

A 10 kW electric shower is used for a total of 90 minutes during a week. How many kilowatt-hours of energy does it transfer in one week?

energy = power × time
= 10 kW × 1.5 h
= 15 kWh

Electricity companies usually give their prices in pence per kWh. You can work out the cost of electricity by multiplying the energy by the cost per kWh.

total cost = number of kilowatt-hours × cost per kilowatt-hour
(in pence, p)   (in kWh or Units)   (in pence, p)

Example 2

An electric heater has a power rating of 2 kW. What is the cost of using the heater for three hours if one kWh of electricity costs 5p?

Energy in kWh = 2 kW × 3 h = 6 kWh

Cost in pence = 6 kWh × 5p = 30p

Example 3

It costs £2.62 to use a 3.5 kW tumble dryer. The unit price was 15p. How long was it used for? First calculate the energy used.

$$\text{number of kilowatt hours} = \frac{\text{total cost}}{\text{cost per kilowatt hour}}$$
$$= \frac{262p}{15p}$$
$$= 17.47 \text{ kWh}$$

Then calculate the time:

$$\text{time} = \frac{\text{energy}}{\text{power}}$$
$$= \frac{17.47 \text{ kWh}}{3.5 \text{ kW}}$$
$$= 4.99 \text{ hours}$$

Electricity meters and bills

Each home has an electricity meter that records the amount of electricity used. Each electricity bill is based on the number of units used since the previous bill.

AQALec ELECTRICITY BILL

Previous reading	Current reading	Units used	Cost per unit	Total cost
45100	45500	400	7 pence	£28.00

Figure 1 An electricity bill.

A type of electricity meter fitted in many older homes.

Science skills

The electricity meter in the photograph on the right is a 'smart' meter. It can show the customer how much electricity is being used at different times of day, and how the electricity use compares with the previous day, week or month. This should help consumers to reduce the amount of electricity they use. The meter can send readings directly to the electricity company, so they do not need to employ people to read the meters.

a In what way does the electricity company benefit if its customers have smart meters?

b How could smart meters be a disadvantage for the electricity company?

c The government have said that all homes should have smart meters by 2020. Suggest why.

Questions

1 Explain why there are two different units for measuring energy used.

2 What is a Unit of electricity?

3 An electricity bill says the current reading is 11 654 Units, and the previous one was 10 763 Units. What will the electricity bill be if electricity costs 14 p per Unit?

4 A 3 kW electrical heater transfers 15 kWh of energy. How long was it switched on for?

5 How much energy is transferred to a 100 W bulb left on for 2 hours 15 minutes?

6 An electric lawnmower has a power rating of 1.2 kW. It takes 30 minutes to mow a lawn and costs 9 p. What is the price of electricity?

7 The cost of running an aquarium pump continuously is 8 p per week. If the price per kWh is 12 p, what is the power of the pump (to the nearest watt)?

8 Explain how electricity is charged for, and how to calculate the energy used by an appliance and the cost of the electricity.

Taking it further

Can you work out how many joules there are in a kilowatt-hour of electrical energy?

Using different devices

Learning objectives

- discuss the advantages and disadvantages of using different electrical appliances for a particular application
- consider situations where electricity or specific devices are not available.

Choosing a device

There are many different uses for electricity, and for each application there are often several different types of device that can be used. Some devices are more powerful than others. The photograph shows a low-power tubular heater. This is an alternative to using a 1 or 2 kW electric fire or fan heater.

Sometimes you can choose between completely different types of equipment. For example, many homes have both a conventional oven and a microwave oven. Microwave ovens heat food in a different way to conventional ovens, which means the food cooks much more quickly. Because the microwave oven itself does not get hot, less energy is wasted in heating the surroundings. A microwave oven has an efficiency of nearly 0.6, whereas a conventional oven has an efficiency of only about 0.15 (see lesson P1 2.2).

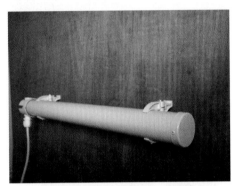

This tubular heater has a power of 120 W. It is being used to make sure the temperature in a conservatory does not fall below freezing point.

The cake on the left was cooked in a conventional oven. The one on the right was cooked in a microwave oven.

Working away from the mains supply

Sometimes electrical devices are needed where there is no mains electricity supply. If electricity is available nearby, **rechargeable batteries** can be used to power some types of equipment. If there are no facilities for recharging then **disposable batteries** can be used. However, disposable batteries are only suitable for low-power devices such as torches and radios.

In some parts of the world, disposable batteries are not available or are too expensive. In 1994 Trevor Bayliss invented a clockwork radio to be sold in Africa. The radio would work for about 15 minutes after being wound for two minutes. The clockwork radio allowed people to listen to educational and news broadcasts without having to buy batteries. Today there are also wind-up torches on sale, as well as radios and other devices powered by **solar cells**.

This worker is using a battery-powered drill, as there is no electricity supply on the construction site.

Science skills Clockwork torches and radios are sold all over the world.

How might a clockwork radio be useful to:

a a person living in the UK?

b someone living in a remote part of Africa?

This fan is powered by electricity made in a solar cell.

A mains-powered fan.

Questions

1. The tubular heater in the first photograph can be left on overnight. **(a)** How much will it cost to leave it on for eight hours, if electricity costs 15p per kWh? **(b)** How much would it cost to run a 2 kW electric fan heater for the same time?

2. What are some of the advantages and disadvantages of using a tubular heater instead of a fan heater?

3. **(a)** Give two reasons why a microwave oven would use much less energy than a conventional oven to cook a piece of food. **(b)** Suggest why people still use conventional ovens for cooking. Give as many reasons as you can.

4. An electrician is putting new wiring into an old house. Why might she need to use a battery-powered drill?

5. **(a)** Look at the photographs of the fans above. What are the advantages and disadvantages of the different types? **(b)** What are the advantages and disadvantages of a hand-held fan that you move yourself?

6. It takes 1.5 hours to cook jacket potatoes in a 2 kW conventional oven. It takes 20 minutes to cook the same-sized potatoes in an 850 W microwave oven. What is the difference in cost if electricity costs 16p per kWh?

7. You can buy refrigerators that work using bottled gas. These are more expensive than mains-powered fridges of a similar size. Suggest who might buy these fridges.

8. A woman has a battery-powered radio that she listens to when she is gardening. She has a clockwork radio that she takes on camping holidays. Suggest why she uses both kinds of radio, and whether or not a solar-powered radio might be better for one or both uses.

Power stations

Learning objectives

- describe how power stations work
- describe the different energy resources that can be used by power stations.

Inside a power station

Electricity is not a source of energy because it has to be generated using other forms of energy. Most of the electricity we use in the UK is generated in power stations. Energy stored in fuel is used to heat water and turn it into steam. The steam turns a turbine, and the turbine makes the generator turn. Figure 1 shows what happens inside a power station.

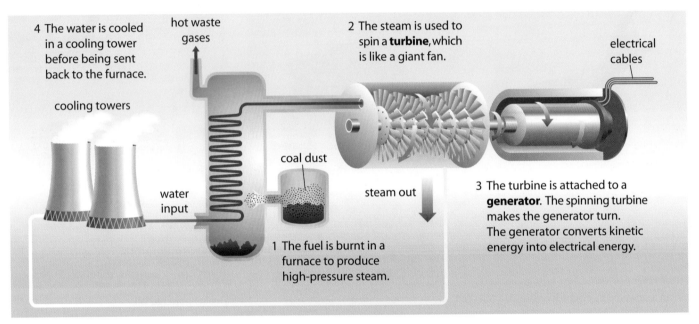

4 The water is cooled in a cooling tower before being sent back to the furnace.

cooling towers

hot waste gases

water input

coal dust

2 The steam is used to spin a **turbine**, which is like a giant fan.

electrical cables

steam out

3 The turbine is attached to a **generator**. The spinning turbine makes the generator turn. The generator converts kinetic energy into electrical energy.

1 The fuel is burnt in a furnace to produce high-pressure steam.

Figure 1 A coal-fired power station.

In some power stations that use natural gas as the energy source, the hot waste gases from burning are at a high pressure and are used to drive the turbine directly. These are called **gas turbine** power stations.

water vapour from cooling towers

waste gases from burning fuel emitted from this chimney

A coal-fired power station.

Energy resources for power stations

Most of the power stations in the UK use **fossil fuels**. Fossil fuels are being formed underground continuously but very slowly. It takes millions of years for these fuels to form, and we are using them up much faster than they are being formed. These fuels are called **non-renewable** resources, because once we have used up the ones that exist at the moment there will be no more left.

Nuclear fuels

Nuclear power stations generate electricity in a similar way to a fossil-fuelled power station but they use **uranium** or **plutonium** as fuel. These elements are **radioactive**. They do not burn in a chemical reaction like fossil fuels do. Instead, the atoms themselves split up to make new elements, releasing energy which is used to make steam. This kind of reaction is called **nuclear fission**. Fission produces a lot of energy from a small amount of fuel, so a nuclear power station has lower fuel costs than a fossil-fuelled one. Supplies of nuclear fuel are likely to last much longer than supplies of fossil fuels.

Biofuels

Biomass is biological material obtained from living things, or from things that have recently died. Biomass includes wood and other plant material and animal waste. Biomass is a **renewable resource** because new plants can be grown to replace the ones used.

Biofuels are fuels made using biomass. Biofuels include:

- straw, nutshells, woodchips and other waste materials
- plants such as willow or *Miscanthus* grass grown for use as biofuel
- ethanol, made from **fermented** plant material such as sugar cane
- biodiesel, made from various plant oils
- methane, made by the fermentation of animal wastes in **sludge digesters**.

Some power stations in the UK can burn biofuels together with fossil fuels.

Questions

1. Explain why electricity is not a source of energy.
2. Explain why fossil fuels are referred to as non-renewable fuels.
3. Why are biofuels referred to as renewable fuels?
4. **(a)** Name two nuclear fuels. **(b)** Describe two differences between a fossil-fuelled and a nuclear power station.
5. All the power stations on these pages use stored energy to make steam. Which kinds of stored energy are used?
6. Draw a flow chart to show all the stages in a coal-fired power station.
7. Look at Figure 2. Suggest how and why a similar chart for 2050 might differ from Figure 2.
8. Describe three different ways in which natural gas can be used in power stations, and explain which is the most efficient.

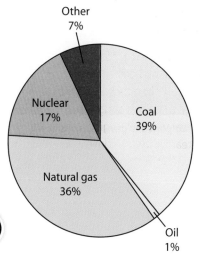

Figure 2 Energy sources for generating electricity in the UK in 2007. Coal, oil and natural gas are all fossil fuels. 'Other' includes hydroelectricity, wind power and other fuels such as biomass.

Comparing power stations

Problems with fossil fuels

There are several different fuels that can be used in power stations. Each type of fuel has advantages and disadvantages. Table 1 shows some of the pollution caused by coal-fired power stations.

Table 1 Pollution problems with coal-fired power stations.

Waste entering atmosphere	What problems does it cause?	What can be done?
carbon dioxide	contributes to global warming	capture it and store it so it does not go into the atmosphere
sulfur dioxide	causes acid rain	remove it from the waste gases, or remove sulfur from the coal before it is burnt
nitrogen oxides	cause acid rain	use furnaces that reduce the amount produced
smoke and dust	can be harmful to health	remove from the waste gases

Natural gas is cleaner and more efficient than coal as it does not contain sulfur. Power stations that burn natural gas emit less carbon dioxide for each kilowatt hour of electricity they produce.

Most of the measures in the last column of Table 1 are used in UK power stations, except for capturing the carbon dioxide emissions. Several companies are developing **carbon capture and storage** schemes. One possible type of storage is under the North Sea, where oil and gas have been extracted.

Biofuels

Crops take in carbon dioxide from the atmosphere when they grow. If the crop is burnt, the same amount of carbon dioxide gets put back into the atmosphere. This means that in using biofuels, the total amount of carbon dioxide in the atmosphere has not changed overall.

That is not the whole story, however. Energy is needed to make fertiliser and to plant, harvest and transport the crops. Most of this energy is obtained by burning fossil fuels. So some carbon dioxide *is* added to the atmosphere, although not as much as if the same energy had been released from burning fossil fuels directly.

At present coal is cheaper than biofuel for power stations in the UK.

Nuclear power

Nuclear power stations do not emit any carbon dioxide or other gases. However, there are other potential problems with nuclear power stations. The waste they produce is radioactive, and some of it will be hazardous for thousands of years. The waste must be sealed into concrete or glass and buried safely so the radioactivity cannot damage the environment. A nuclear power station also needs to be carefully **decommissioned** (dismantled safely) at the end of its life so that no radioactivity escapes into the environment. It costs a lot more to build and to decommission a nuclear power station than a fossil-fuelled one.

Coal is transported to power stations by rail.

There are not many accidents in nuclear power stations, and the power stations are designed to contain any radioactive leaks. However, if a major accident occurs it can have very serious consequences.

An accident at the Chernobyl nuclear reactor in the Ukraine contaminated land for miles around. Radioactive dust even reached the UK.

Questions

1 List the ways in which coal-fired power stations can cause pollution.

2 Describe how pollution from fossil-fuelled power stations is currently being dealt with in the UK.

3 Describe two advantages of using natural gas instead of coal to generate electricity.

4 Explain some advantages and disadvantages of nuclear power.

5 **(a)** Suggest why a nuclear power station costs more to build than a fossil-fuelled power station.

 (b) Why is decommissioning it properly very important?

6 How can a nuclear accident affect people in parts of the world very distant from where it occurred?

7 Power companies were required by law to take the measures shown in Table 1 to reduce pollution from coal-fired power stations. Suggest why it was necessary to make such laws.

8 Biofuels are often described as 'carbon neutral'. Suggest what this means, and why it is not actually correct.

Electricity from renewable resources

Learning objectives

- describe the different ways in which renewable resources can be used to generate electricity.

Wind and water

Wind and water can be used to generate electricity by turning turbines directly. Wind turbines can be built on land or at sea but need to be placed in windy locations. They only produce electricity when the wind is blowing.

Water can be used to turn turbines in different ways. The spinning turbine turns a generator to produce electricity.

- **Hydroelectricity** can be produced by building dams in hilly areas to trap water in reservoirs. The water flows downhill and turns turbines at the bottom.
- **Tidal power** involves building a **barrage** across a river estuary. The water turns turbines as it flows in and out. **Tidal stream turbines** are a bit like underwater wind turbines. They are placed where strong tidal currents flow. This technology is still being developed. Tidal power is not available all the time but it is available at predictable times.
- **Wave power** uses the motion of waves to generate electricity. One way of doing this is to make the waves force air through a tube built on the coast. The moving air makes a turbine spin. Wave power is only available when there are high waves. The photograph on the left shows a different type of wave power generator, which is anchored out at sea. It floats on the surface and bends as waves pass beneath it.

The Pelamis Wave Energy Converter being tested in Scotland. These wave energy machines can be anchored out at sea.

Solar power

Solar cells contain chemicals that convert light energy into electrical energy. They produce electricity directly from the Sun's radiation. At present solar cells are expensive and not very efficient. New materials are being developed all the time that should improve efficiency.

Solar cells are very useful for producing electricity in remote locations. The solar cells on this buoy charge a battery. Electricity from the battery is then used at night to power a light on the buoy.

Solar power can also be used to turn turbines. One way of doing this is to use an array of mirrors to focus energy from the Sun on a furnace at the top of a high tower. The concentrated energy heats water to make steam.

Examiner feedback

Some students think that solar cells will only be widely used when their efficiency is nearly 100%. This is not correct. There are many reasons why solar cells are not in widespread use today, but cost is likely to be the most important reason.

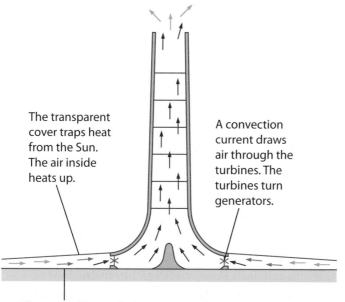

The transparent cover traps heat from the Sun. The air inside heats up.

A convection current draws air through the turbines. The turbines turn generators.

The ground beneath the cover gets hot. The energy it stores is released at night, so the tower can still generate electricity at night.

Figure 1 A solar tower uses convection currents to turn turbines.

A solar power station in Spain. The mirrors concentrate sunlight on the furnace at the top of the tower, where water is heated to make steam.

Solar towers can also be built to use energy from the Sun to create convection currents. These currents then turn air turbines. Figure 1 shows how this type of solar tower works.

Geothermal energy

Hot rocks can also be used to generate electricity. In some volcanic areas hot water and steam rise to the surface, or pipes can be drilled into the ground to allow the steam to rise. The steam can be used to drive turbines, which drive generators. This is known as **geothermal energy**. Hot water produced in volcanic areas can also be piped to nearby houses to heat them directly.

Route to A*

Geothermal energy is not renewable in the same sense as the other sources on these pages, as eventually the hot rocks will cool down. However the supply of heat will last much longer than supplies of fossil fuels so geothermal energy is often included when talking about renewables.

Questions

1   How can electricity be produced using the wind?

2   How can electricity be produced directly using the Sun's radiation?

3   Describe four different ways in which water can be used to generate electricity.

4   Look at all the renewable resources on this page. Which ones can generate electricity: **(a)** all the time? **(b)** only some of the time?

5   **(a)** Which resources can produce electricity at predicable times? **(b)** Why is this important?

6   Describe two different ways in which solar towers can be used to generate electricity.

7   Why are solar towers not likely to be used in the UK?

8   Describe how a geothermal power station works and compare it with a fossil-fuelled power station.

Renewables and the environment

People often think of renewable energy resources as 'clean' sources of energy, because most of them do not add polluting gases to the atmosphere. However, they can affect the environment in other ways.

Visual and noise pollution

One objection that many people have to wind turbines is that they cause visual pollution (they spoil the view). Fossil-fuelled power stations are not pretty, but people have got used to them, and they are usually built in areas that already have industrial buildings. Wind farms are often built in places where people go to enjoy the countryside, because the winds are usually stronger and steadier there. Some people also complain about the noise they make.

Wildlife

The flooding of land for reservoirs for hydroelectric power stations destroys wildlife habitats. Growing crops for biofuels could also damage habitats if previously unfarmed land is ploughed up or rainforests are cleared.

Tidal barrages are huge dams that change the flow of rivers. This may affect birds and other wildlife that live or feed on tidal mudflats, and may affect the migration of fish. The first, and only large, tidal power station is built across the estuary of the Rance River, in France. It has been operating since 1966.

Some people object to wind farms because some birds are killed. This problem can be reduced by not siting wind farms on bird migration routes.

Do these **wind turbines** spoil the view?

Dunlin feed on animals that live in the mud. These may not survive if the flow of water in the estuary is changed.

Building a dam across a river can prevent the migration of fish such as salmon. A fish ladder can help them to get past the dam.

Land use

Biofuels can be used to generate electricity, and they can also be used as fuel for vehicles. Growing biofuels uses land. Some of this land could otherwise be used for growing food so food prices could be affected. If food prices rose, this would particularly affect the developing world.

This is also true of hydroelectricity, as the reservoirs flood large areas of land. Unlike biofuel crops, a new reservoir could provide habitats for different kinds of wildlife, and a valuable leisure amenity.

Wind farms do not have such a great effect on the land, as farming can still take place around them.

Waste gases

The main problem with fossil-fuelled power stations is that they emit carbon dioxide into the atmosphere. In geothermal power stations, the hot water rising from the depths of the Earth often contains some dissolved gases, such as carbon dioxide and methane. These gases can escape into the atmosphere and contribute to global warming. However, a geothermal power station only produces about one-tenth as much carbon dioxide as a coal-fired power station for the same amount of electricity generated.

The reservoirs created for hydroelectric power stations can also pollute the atmosphere. Carbon dioxide and methane are released for a while after the land is first flooded, as plants die and rot.

Science skills New wind farms or other renewable resources need planning permission. Which of the possible objections on these pages are likely to be based on:

a Scientific evidence?

b Opinion?

Questions

1 Why are some people more concerned about the visual impact of wind turbines than power stations?

2 Some wind farms are built in the sea. What problems could this cause?

3 What effects might wind turbines on land have on: **(a)** wildlife? **(b)** farming?

4 What effects could the growing of biofuel crops have on the environment?

5 What effects might a tidal barrage have on scenery, shipping and wildlife?

6 Suggest how a wave power generator (see the photograph in P1 4.3) might affect the environment.

7 Tidal power could be obtained using tidal stream turbines or by building a barrage across an estuary. Explain which option will: **(a)** have the greatest effect on wildlife; **(b)** be the most expensive to build; **(c)** be the most expensive to maintain.

8 Hydroelectric power stations can be built next to dams on rivers, or a dam can be built in the hills to make a new reservoir. Compare the advantages and disadvantages of these two options.

Route to A*

If you are asked to compare different ways of doing things, such as in question 8, try to consider all the possible factors. For example, large rivers may already have roads nearby, whereas building a new dam in the hills might also involve building access roads so that construction and maintenance machinery and materials can be taken to the dam.

Electricity distribution and voltage

The National Grid

All power stations and almost all users of electricity are connected by a system of wires and cables called the **National Grid**. This allows electricity to be distributed to most parts of the UK.

Electricity passing through a wire will heat it up. The warming of the **transmission lines** in the National Grid is wasted energy. If the **voltage** of the electricity is increased, the current will be lower so less energy is wasted. Figure 1 shows the different voltages used in the National Grid.

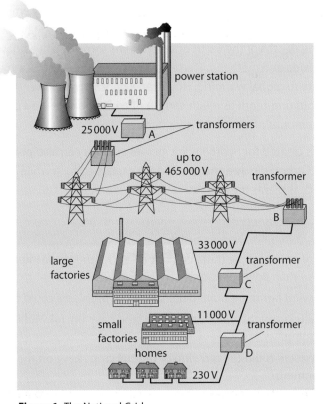

Figure 1 The National Grid.

Science skills

A student used a **resistor** as a model of transmission lines. The table shows the results of an experiment to measure the energy transferred in the resistor with different currents.

Current/A	Power/W
0.0	0.0
0.2	0.2
0.4	0.8
0.6	1.8
0.8	3.2
1.0	5.0
1.2	7.2
1.4	9.8
1.6	12.8
1.8	16.2
2.0	20.0

a Plot a graph to show this data.

b Write a conclusion for the investigation.

Transformers

Voltage is changed using **transformers**. A **step-up transformer** increases the voltage and reduces the current. A **step-down transformer** makes the voltage lower but increases the current.

The relationship between power, voltage and current is given by the equation below.

$$P = V \times I$$

power	=	voltage	×	current
(watts, W)		(volts, V)		(amps, A)

If a transformer doubles the voltage, the current is halved.
This means that the power stays the same, as long as no energy is wasted in the transformer.

Renewable resources and the National Grid

The National Grid allows electricity to be distributed to most places in the UK. It was set up when most of our electricity was generated in a relatively small number of big power stations. Today there are a lot more, smaller sources of electricity, such as wind farms and hydroelectric power stations. These all need to be connected to the National Grid if they are to be useful. However, sometimes this can cost more than it is worth for the amount of electricity produced.

Overground or underground?

Most of the transmission lines in the National Grid are suspended from pylons. These wires do not have to be insulated. They can be damaged by lightning, high winds or icy weather. However, it is easy to find and repair damaged sections of power line.

Underground cables can be used in scenic areas, where rows of pylons would spoil the view. Underground cables are less easily damaged by severe weather. However they need to be well insulated, they are more expensive to install, and finding and repairing faults is more difficult and takes longer.

This house has its own small hydroelectricity supply from a nearby river. However, it would cost too much to connect it to the National Grid, so the owner cannot sell any spare electricity.

Science skills

New wind farms are being built in the north west of Scotland, and the transmission lines shown in the photograph need to be upgraded. The plan is to replace the pylons with much bigger ones. These pylons are very close to the Cairngorms National Park. Protesters say that the new transmission lines should be buried.

c Who should make the decision about what sort of new power lines are installed?

d Who should pay the extra cost if underground cables are installed?

The pylons in this photograph carry electricity south from power stations in the north of Scotland.

Questions

1 Why is the voltage increased before electricity is sent through the National Grid?

2 Why is the voltage then reduced before electricity is supplied to homes?

3 Look at Figure 1. The transformers are labelled A–D. For each transformer, say whether it is a step-up or step-down transformer.

4 Which of these electricity supplies provides the most power: 2 A at 230 V or 18 A at 20 V? Explain your answer.

5 A step-down transformer halves the voltages of the electricity supplies in question 4. What will the new currents be?

6 An advert for solar cells claims that any electricity that the homeowner does not use can be sold to the National Grid. Explain why this claim is not entirely correct.

7 What are the advantages and disadvantages of burying power cables underground?

8 Explain why the following statement is partly correct and partly incorrect: 'A step-up transformer increases the energy provided by the electricity supply.' Use data from Figure 1 to support your answer.

Meeting the demand

The demand for electricity

The demand for electricity changes during the day and also during the year. Figure 1 shows some typical examples.

The demand also changes from minute to minute. If there is a popular programme on TV, millions of people sit down to watch it and the overall demand for electricity falls. At half-time in a football match, or when the adverts come on, thousands (or even millions) of people get up and switch on lights or kettles, and the demand can shoot up by over 2 MW within a minute or two. This sudden change is called a **TV pick-up**.

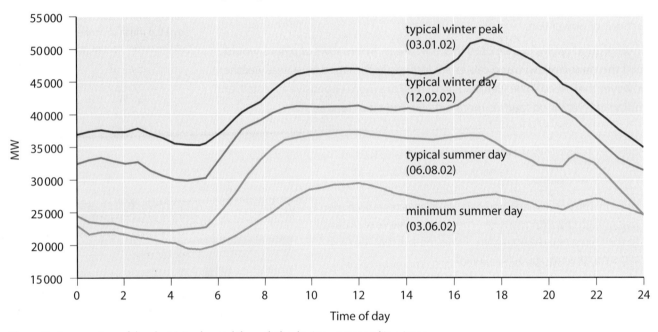

Figure 1 A comparison of the electricity demand through the day in summer and in winter.

Power engineers need to predict these changes because it is not easy to suddenly increase the amount of energy generated. It can take hours to start up a power station from cold, although gas-fired power stations can start up more quickly than coal-fired ones. Power stations are often kept running below their full generating capacity. This can waste some energy but it means that the amount of electricity generated can be increased within minutes instead of hours.

Hydroelectric power stations are very useful because they can start producing their maximum amount of electricity within a minute. Supplying enough electricity will be even more complicated when more renewable resources are used. Many sources of renewable energy are not **reliable**. This means they are only available some of the time, and we cannot always predict when they will be available.

Pumped storage

Power stations run more efficiently when they are generating their maximum amount of electricity, so sometimes more electricity is being generated than is needed. Some of this energy can be stored using a pumped-storage power station (see Figure 2).

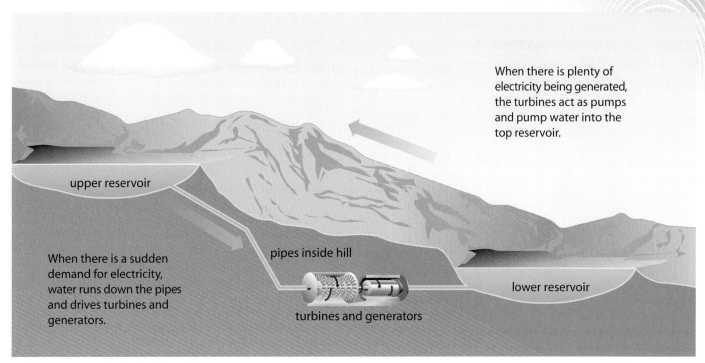

When there is plenty of electricity being generated, the turbines act as pumps and pump water into the top reservoir.

upper reservoir

pipes inside hill

When there is a sudden demand for electricity, water runs down the pipes and drives turbines and generators.

lower reservoir

turbines and generators

Figure 2 A pumped-storage power station.

Electricity tariffs

An electricity **tariff** is the amount that customers pay for electricity. Electricity companies try to reduce the demand for electricity during the day by increasing the price. Customers on tariffs such as 'Economy 7' pay a lower price for electricity used during seven hours overnight. Storage heaters (see lesson P1 1.7) heat up during the night because this is when cheap electricity is available.

Recharging an electric car at home could almost double the amount of electricity a home uses. Electricity companies are developing 'smart' controllers that only let electric cars recharge when there is enough supply available.

Electric cars will be recharged from the mains supply.

Questions

1 Look at Figure 1. Explain the demand for electricity on a typical winter day.

2 **(a)** Why is there a peak in demand in the early evening in winter but not in summer? **(b)** Why is there more demand for electricity in winter than in summer?

3 **(a)** Why do power engineers need to know what weather is forecast for the next few hours? **(b)** Why do they sometimes need to know what the TV schedules are?

4 Why can't power engineers just use hydroelectricity to meet sudden demands? (*Hint:* you may need to look back at Lesson P1 4.1.)

5 Other than hydroelectricity, which renewable resources are available at predictable times?

6 When might wind power be available but not solar power?

7 Look at Figure 1. Explain when a pumped-storage power station would be: **(a)** pumping water up to the top reservoir; **(b)** generating electricity.

8 Explain why electricity is often cheaper to use from about 11 pm to 6 am.

ISA practice: keeping drinks hot

Hot drinks are placed in many different types of containers. You have been asked to investigate the best type of container to keep drinks hot.

The four different drinks containers: a glass, a ceramic mug, an insulated mug and a plastic mug.

Your task is to investigate four different cups to find out which one keeps a drink hot for longest.

Hypothesis

It is suggested that there is a link between the material used in the cup and the time it takes for a drink to cool.

Section 1

1 In this investigation you will need to control some of the variables.

 (a) Name one variable you will need to control in this investigation. *(1 mark)*

 (b) Describe briefly how you would carry out a preliminary investigation to find a suitable value to use for this variable. Explain how the results will help you decide on the best value for this variable. *(2 marks)*

2 Describe how you would carry out the investigation. You should include:
- the equipment that you would use
- how you would use the equipment
- the measurements that you would make
- how you would make it a fair test.

You may include a labelled diagram to help you to explain your method.

In this question you will be assessed on using good English, organising information clearly and using specialist terms where appropriate. *(6 marks)*

3 Think about the possible hazards in the investigation.
 (a) Describe one hazard that you think may be present in the investigation. *(1 mark)*
 (b) Identify the risk associated with the hazard you described in (a), and say what control measures you could use to reduce the risk. *(2 marks)*

4 Design a table that will contain all the data that you would record during the investigation. *(2 marks)*

Total for Section 1: 14 marks

Section 2

A group of students, Study Group 1, carried out an investigation into the hypothesis. The students used the same volume of hot water in each container. They only had time to test the glass and the ceramic mug when they started their investigation. They tested the other mugs the next day.

Figure 1 shows the results they obtained.

Time (min)	Glass container temp (°C)	Ceramic mug temp (°C)	Metal mug temp (°C)	Plastic foam mug temp (°C)
0	85	85	85	85
1	83	81	81	82
2	82	79	79	80
3	80	76	76	78
4	78	74	74	77
5	76	72	71	75
6	75	70	69	73
7	73	69	67	72
8	72	66	65	71
9	71	65	64	69
10	69	63	60	67

Figure 1 Results for Study Group 1.

5 (a) (i) What is the independent variable in this investigation?
 (ii) What is the dependent variable in this investigation?
 (iii) Name one control variable this investigation. *(3 marks)*
 (b) Plot a graph to show the link between the type of cup and the temperature loss. *(4 marks)*
 (c) Do the results support the hypothesis? Explain your answer. *(3 marks)*

Below are the results from three other study groups. Table 1 shows the results from another group of students, Study Group 2.

Table 1 Results from Study Group 2.

Type of cup	Temperature/°C		Change of temperature/°C
	At the start	After ten minutes	
glass	80	64	16
ceramic	80	58	22
metal	80	56	24
plastic foam	80	63	17

Table 2 shows the results of a third group of students, Study Group 3. Figure 2 is a graph produced by Study Group 4, a group of scientists in a research laboratory. The scientists used metal mugs of four different sizes and investigated how long each mug took to cool down after being filled with hot water.

Table 2 Results from Study Group 3.

Type of cup	Change of temperature after 15 minutes/°C			
	Test 1	Test 2	Test 3	Mean
glass	22	23	20	22
ceramic	31	30	29	30
metal	34	35	32	34
plastic foam	22	31	20	24

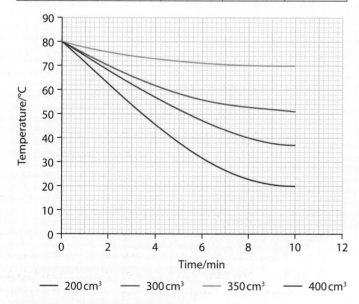

Figure 2 Study Group 4's results.

6 Describe one way in which the results of Study Group 2 are similar to or different from those of Study Group 1, and give one reason why the results are similar or different.

(3 marks)

7 (a) Draw a sketch graph or chart of the results from Study Group 2. *(3 marks)*

(b) Does the data support the hypothesis being investigated? To gain full marks you should use all of the relevant data from Study Groups 1, 2 and 3 to explain whether or not the data supports the hypothesis. *(3 marks)*

(c) The data from the other groups only gives a limited amount of information. What other information or data would you need in order to be more certain as to whether or not the hypothesis is correct? Explain the reason for your answer. *(3 marks)*

(d) Use the results of Study Groups 2, 3 and 4 to answer this question. What is the relationship between the material of the drinks container and the length of time the drink remains hot?
How well does the data support your answer?

(3 marks)

8 Look back at the investigation method used by Study Group 1. If you could repeat the investigation, suggest one change that you would make to the method, and explain the reason for the change. *(3 marks)*

9 A company wants to make drinks containers that will lose no more than 20 °C in 10 minutes. How could the results of this investigation help the company to decide on the best size and material for the drinks container?

(3 marks)

Total for Section 2: 31 marks
Total for the ISA: 45 marks

Assess yourself questions

1 Which of these statements apply to using biofuels to generate electricity? Select two answers. *(2 marks)*

A They can be burnt in power stations in a similar way to fossil fuels.

B They do not produce any carbon dioxide when they burn.

C Burning biofuels adds less carbon dioxide to the air overall than burning fossil fuels.

D Burning biofuels in a power station does not add any carbon dioxide to the air overall.

E The carbon contained in biofuels was taken out of the atmosphere by respiration when the plants grew.

2 A TV uses 90 W of power when it is switched on. Electricity costs 16.5p per Unit.

(a) What is 90 W in kW? *(1 mark)*

(b) How much energy (in kWh) does the TV use in six hours? *(2 marks)*

(c) How much does this electricity cost? *(1 mark)*

(d) Why should you switch a TV off when it is not being used, instead of putting it on standby? *(1 mark)*

3 **(a)** Write down two disadvantages of using energy from uranium to generate electricity. *(2 marks)*

(b) Write down two advantages of using uranium. *(2 marks)*

4 **(a)** What is a TV pick-up? *(2 marks)*

(b) Why do power engineers need to use weather forecasts? *(2 marks)*

(c) Which kind of power station can start generating in the shortest time if there is an increase in demand? *(1 mark)*

5 Write down one energy resource that matches each of these descriptions.

(a) Available at any time. *(1 mark)*

(b) Produces carbon dioxide. *(1 mark)*

(c) Availability depends on the weather. *(1 mark)*

(d) Available at predictable times, but not all the time. *(1 mark)*

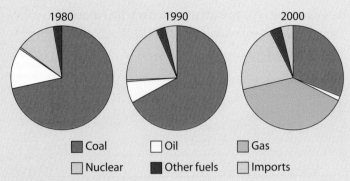

Figure 1 Pie charts of energy resources used to generate electricity.

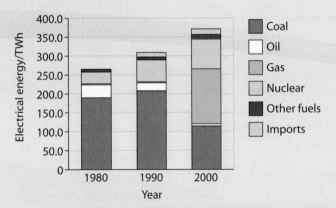

Figure 2 Bar charts of energy resources used to generate electricity.

6 Figures 1 and 2 use two types of chart to show the different energy resources used to generate electricity in the UK in three separate years.

(a) What information does Figure 2 provide that Figure 1 does not? *(1 mark)*

(b) Describe three changes between the energy resources used in 1980 and in 2000. *(3 marks)*

(c) Suggest reasons for these changes. *(3 marks)*

7 Eilean Dubh is a small island off the coast of Scotland, with no mains electricity supply. There are only a few houses on the island, and their total energy use averages 30 000 kWh per year.

The islanders currently use a diesel generator to provide their electricity. This costs 20p for every kilowatt hour of electricity generated.

They are considering investing in a renewable source of energy. Some details about two alternative energy sources are shown in the table below.

	Capital cost	Maximum output/kW
wind turbine	£25 000	6.0
solar cells	£40 000	7.5

(a) What is the maximum possible output of the wind turbine over one year in kWh? *(3 marks)*

(b) The wind turbines are likely to produce only about one-third of this amount. Why is this? *(2 marks)*

(c) If the solar cells generate about 7000 kWh per year, and last for 20 years, how much will each Unit of electricity cost? *(5 marks)*

(d) The electricity from the wind turbine is likely to cost about 13p per unit. Other than cost, suggest what advantage the wind turbine has over the solar cells. *(1 mark)*

(e) If the islanders could get all their electricity from the wind turbine, what would be the payback time for installing the turbine? *(4 marks)*

8 (a) Give two reasons why using a microwave oven instead of a conventional oven can help to reduce the amount of energy used. *(2 marks)*

(b) How can homeowners make sure they buy the most efficient appliances? *(1 mark)*

9 A ready meal takes an hour to cook in a 3 kW conventional oven. The same meal can be cooked in 15 minutes in a microwave oven. The oven uses 850 W to cook food.

(a) Electricity costs 14p per unit. How much does it cost to cook the meal in the conventional oven? *(3 marks)*

(b) How much money does a homeowner save if he uses the microwave oven to cook the same meal? *(3 marks)*

(c) A cheap microwave oven costs £50. The homeowner has meals like this about twice a week. What is the payback time for the microwave oven? *(2 marks)*

10 Here are some opinions about hydroelectricity.

A   Hydroelectric power stations do not contribute to global warming.

B   Hydroelectric power stations are useful because they can start and stop quickly.

C   Pumped storage power stations can store electricity.

(a) (i) Suggest why most people would think that statement A is correct. *(1 mark)*

(ii) Explain why it is not quite correct. *(1 mark)*

(b) (i) How does the start-up time of a hydroelectric power station compare to that of a gas-fired and a coal-fired power station? *(1 mark)*

(ii) Why is it useful to have some power stations that can start up quickly? *(2 marks)*

(c) Describe two differences between a pumped storage power station and a normal hydroelectric power station. *(2 marks)*

(d) In what form is energy stored in a hydroelectric power station? *(1 mark)*

(e) At what time of day is a pumped storage power station usually storing energy? Explain your answer *(4 marks)*

(f) Explain why opinion C is not correct. *(1 mark)*

11 (a) What does a transformer do? *(1 mark)*

(b) Explain the difference between a step-up and a step-down transformer. *(1 mark)*

(c) What is the National Grid? *(1 mark)*

(d) Explain why the National Grid is needed, instead of just connecting each town only to its nearest power station. *(3 marks)*

(e) Why is electricity transmitted around the country at very high voltages? *(1 mark)*

12 It costs £9000 to install a set of solar cells in the roof of a house. The suppliers of the solar cells say that the owners should be able to sell approximately £630 of electricity to the grid each year. What is the payback time for the solar cells? *(3 marks)*

13 Renewable energy resources can have environmental effects. Give one possible environmental effect of each of the following resources.

(a) Hydroelectricity. *(1 mark)*

(b) Wind power. *(1 mark)*

(c) Tidal power. *(1 mark)*

(d) Biofuels. *(1 mark)*

14 Many people think that biofuels do not add carbon dioxide to the atmosphere.

(a) Explain why they think this. *(2 marks)*

(b) Explain why this idea is not usually correct. *(3 marks)*

15 Carbon dioxide and sulfur dioxide can both be emitted when fossil fuels are burnt.

(a) Name one environmental effect of each of these pollutants. *(2 marks)*

(b) Describe how the emissions of these pollutants can be reduced. *(2 marks)*

16 Most people who own gardens use a powered mower to cut their lawns.

(a) Suggest two advantages of a petrol-engined mower compared to a mower with an electric motor. *(2 marks)*

(b) Suggest two disadvantages. *(2 marks)*

GradeStudio Route to A*

B Grade answer

Student 1

> A solar-powered plane uses energy from the Sun. It doesn't carry fuel. It weighs less than a normal passenger plane. The solar cells power the engines and recharge the batteries. No gases are given off.

It is better to say 'carbon dioxide'.

The correct scientific word is 'emitted'.

Examiner comment

This candidate has lifted information from the question but has not really developed it. They have outlined one or two advantages but have given no disadvantages. They have not stated that a renewable energy source is used. The significance of a 26-hour flight has been missed.

A Grade answer

Student 2

A better answer would explain the advantages of this fact.

> The solar-powered plane uses a renewable energy source. In flight no carbon dioxide is emitted. Although the plane has a small mass, it only carries one person, but the Airbus has a crew and lots of passengers. The Solar Impulse has a lower speed than the Airbus.

A better answer would point out that journey times are therefore longer.

Examiner comment

This candidate has mentioned that the energy source is renewable. They have also mentioned that the polluting gas is carbon dioxide. Disadvantages of the solar plane are included, as the question requires. Two points are mentioned that could be developed further for a better answer. This candidate has also failed to mention the significance of a 26-hour flight.

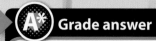 **Grade answer**

Answer includes the environmental consequence of using aviation fuel.

> The solar-powered plane uses energy from the Sun, which is a renewable energy source. The Airbus uses a fossil fuel, which, when ignited, emits carbon dioxide – a greenhouse gas that contributes to global warming.

The candidate has picked up on the significance of a 26-hour flight.

> The solar cells use energy from the Sun to power the engines and to charge the batteries so that the batteries can be used to power the plane when it is dark. Solar cells are inefficient, so Solar Impulse needs 12 000 of them. The plane only carries one person so imagine the number of solar cells that would be needed to power a plane carrying hundreds of passengers.

A good summarising sentence.

> Solar Impulse is much slower than an Airbus, so journey times would be longer, which would not be good for the passengers. Although Solar Impulse is more environmentally friendly than Airbus and wouldn't use up non-renewable fossil fuel, it is not a practical option for carrying large numbers of passengers.

Examiner comment

This candidate has covered the main advantages and disadvantages of the solar-powered plane over an Airbus 340. They recognise that the energy source is renewable and that flying the plane does not contribute to global warming. They realise the significance of a 26-hour flight and that the batteries need to be charged during daylight hours so that they can power the plane during darkness. They have recognised the practical difficulties: the need for vast numbers of solar cells to make a plane carrying hundreds of passengers airborne, and the longer journey times because of a lower speed. The answer is completed with a succinct summary.

 MOVING UP THE GRADES

- Read the information in the question very carefully.
- Make sure you know what you are being asked to do.
- The question is worth 6 marks and your use of language and grammar is important, so remember to check your spelling.
- Jot down the points as they occur to you.
- BUT organise the points into a logical order before starting your answer.

P1 Waves and the Universe

Information reaches our eyes and ears through light and sound, and both of these behave as waves. In chapter 5 you will find out about wave behaviour. Not just water waves, although they are useful because they are easy to see, but also different waves including light, other electromagnetic waves, and sound.

As well as using sound waves to communicate with those close to us, we can use electromagnetic waves for TV, radio and mobile phones. This allows us to communicate with people everywhere, including on the other side of the world or even in space. Different electromagnetic waves have different properties, and you will find out about some of these and how these properties make them suitable, or unsuitable, for communications.

In 1835, a French philosopher, Auguste Comte, said that the stars were so far away that we would never be able to find out what they were made of. Yet less than half a century later, scientists had discovered that the light and other electromagnetic waves from the stars carry information about their chemical composition. The waves also carry information about how the galaxies are moving and how far away they are. In chapter 6 you will find out how this information is carried, and the theories scientists now have, as a result of this evidence, about the beginning of the Universe.

Test yourself

1   How are sounds made?
2   Draw a diagram of a lamp and an eye. Draw rays to show how light from the lamp reaches the eye.
3   What do we call materials that (a) transmit light? (b) absorb light?
4   What colours are in the spectrum of white light?
5   Explain which of these are stars: (a) Venus; (b) the Sun; (c) Halley's comet; (d) Pluto; (e) the Pole Star.

Objectives

By the end of this unit you should be able to:

- explain how transverse and longitudinal waves behave
- explain, and draw diagrams showing, reflection, refraction and diffraction
- interpret wavelength and frequency data to identify types of electromagnetic waves
- explain how radio waves, microwaves, infrared and visible light are used for communications
- explain the Doppler effect and red shift
- explain the Big Bang theory of the Universe.

What is a wave?

Describing a wave

An **oscillation** is a repeated pattern of movement, which could be backwards and forwards, side to side, or up and down. A **wave** is an oscillation that travels from one place to another. Most waves travel through some material, called the **medium.** The medium does not move but the oscillations pass through it. For example, a cork bobbing up and down on the waves is not carried along by the waves – it just goes up and down. Energy is transferred by the wave and if the oscillations are bigger, or faster, more energy will usually be transferred. The energy of the water waves in the photograph is enough to erode the rocks.

Longitudinal and transverse waves

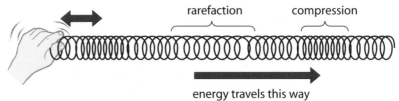

Figure 1a Waves in a spring can be longitudinal…

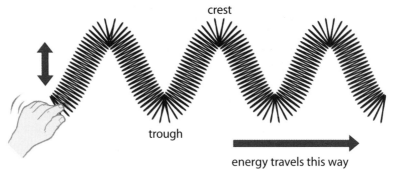

Figure 1b …or transverse.

Storm waves pounding rocks.

Figure 1 shows how waves can be sent along a slinky spring in two different ways. In Figure 1a the spring has been pushed forward and pulled back and pulses are travelling along it so that the coils squash together, in a **compression**, and spread out, in a **rarefaction**. This type of wave is called a **longitudinal wave**. The oscillations are parallel to the direction of energy transfer.

In Figure 1b the spring has been moved to one side and then the other, causing a **crest** and a **trough** to travel along the spring. This type of wave is called a **transverse wave**. The oscillations are perpendicular to the direction of energy transfer.

Examples of mechanical waves

The waves in the spring are examples of **mechanical waves**, which can be transverse or longitudinal and travel through solids, liquids or gases. Water waves and the waves in the rope in Figure 2 are transverse waves.

A **shock wave** is caused by an explosion or similar event like an earthquake. They transfer a lot of energy and move very fast. Shock waves through the air are longitudinal. However, those that travel through the solid Earth can be transverse or longitudinal.

Sound waves

Sound waves are always longitudinal waves. They need a medium to travel through and so cannot travel through a vacuum, or we would hear the Sun. Sound can travel through solids, liquids and gases.

Electromagnetic waves

Electromagnetic waves include visible light and range from **radio waves**, which have the least energy, to **gamma rays** with the most. They can all travel in a **vacuum** and through space. Scientists spent many years trying to decide how light travelled through a vacuum. Now they know that all electromagnetic waves behave as transverse waves – oscillations of an electric and a magnetic field.

Figure 2 Moving your hand up and down sends waves along the rope.

energy travels this way

Science skills

The table shows the speed of longitudinal shock waves through some different rocks.

Rock	Wave speed m/s
granite	5700
basalt	6400
limestone	6000
sandstone	2900
sand	1500
clay	1800

a Which variable is the independent variable?

b What type of variable is:

i the rock type?

ii the wave speed?

c What is the range of wave speeds in these rocks?

d Plot a graph of this data.

e What is the mean value of the wave speed?

Science in action

The seismometer

The seismometer is a sensitive instrument used to detect shock waves travelling through the Earth. Early seismometers looked like the one above. It is placed in the basement of a building, on solid ground, away from traffic and other vibrations. It picks up transverse and longitudinal waves caused by explosions or earthquakes. The longitudinal waves travel faster and arrive first. The further away the earthquake, the longer the delay before the transverse waves arrive. The delay is used to calculate the distance to the earthquake. Using distances from three seismometers in different locations scientists can work out the exact position of the earthquake.

Questions

1 Give an example of: **(a)** a longitudinal wave; **(b)** a transverse wave.

2 How are transverse and longitudinal waves different?

3 Explain what is meant by the words 'compression' and 'rarefaction'.

4 Explain what is meant by the words 'crest' and 'trough'.

5 After an explosion all the windows in a nearby building are broken. How did this happen?

6 Describe and explain the similarities and differences between sound waves and light waves.

A*

Measuring waves

Wavelength

Figure 1 shows a transverse wave. You can see that the pattern repeats. One complete wave is called a **cycle**. The length of one complete wave is called the **wavelength**. It is the distance from any point on the wave to the place where the pattern repeats. The same is true for a longitudinal wave, as shown in Figure 2.

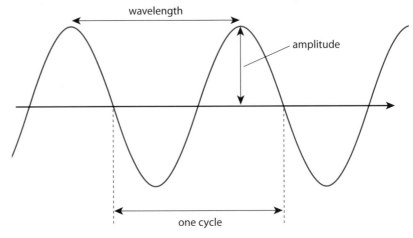

Figure 1 A transverse wave.

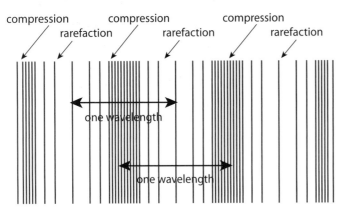

Figure 2 A longitudinal wave.

Amplitude

The **amplitude** is the maximum displacement (the height of a crest or the depth of a trough) that a point moves away from its position when there is no wave.

Frequency

Frequency is the number of cycles passing a point in one second. This depends on the source of the waves. If you are making waves in a spring, moving your hand faster increases the frequency of the waves. The unit 'one cycle per second' is called one **hertz**, Hz.

Wave speed

The wave speed depends on the medium. For example, light travels faster in a vacuum than it does through glass. In Figure 3 waves are being sent along a rope. The girl can't make the waves go faster by waving her hand faster – she just makes more, smaller waves.

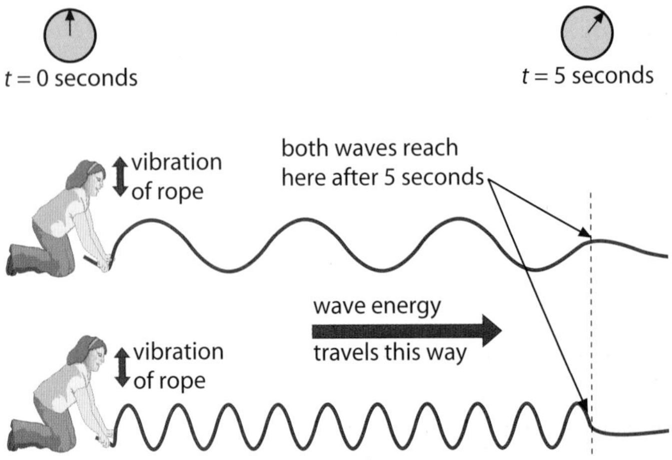

$t = 0$ seconds

$t = 5$ seconds

vibration of rope

both waves reach here after 5 seconds

wave energy travels this way

vibration of rope

Figure 3 Wave speed doesn't change when frequency is increased.

The wave equation

For all waves, there is a relationship between the frequency, the wavelength and the wave speed.

$$v = f \times \lambda$$

wave speed	=	frequency	×	wavelength
(metres per second, m/s)		(hertz, Hz)		(metres, m)

As the frequency is increased more waves travel away from the source, but if the medium is the same, the speed is unchanged, so the wavelength is shorter.

Science skills

To find out how the speed of water waves changes with the depth of the water, some scientists measured the speed of waves in a tank of water. They changed the depth by adding more water. They made the waves by dipping a metal bar in the water at a regular rate of 2 Hz.

a In this experiment what is:
 i the dependent variable
 ii the independent variable
 iii a variable that is kept the same?

b Plot a graph to show how the wave speed changes with the depth of water.

c Are there any anomalous points? If so, which points are anomalous?

d A student says: 'The speed of waves is proportional to the depth of the water.' Explain whether you agree.

e Suggest how the students could have measured:
 i the depth
 ii the speed.

Depth of water/cm	Speed of waves / cm/s
0	0
1	30
2	45
3	55
4	62
5	63
6	77
8	89
10	99

Examiner feedback

In calculations you may have to rearrange the equation, and change units from, for example, centimetres to metres. Take care and read the question carefully.

Example 1

A radio wave has a frequency of 200 000 Hz and a wavelength of 1500 m.
What is its speed?

speed = frequency × wavelength

speed = 200 000 Hz × 1500 m

speed = 300 000 000 m/s.

Example 2

Water waves are travelling at 10 m/s and one reaches the beach every five seconds. What is their wavelength?

1 wave in 5 s = 1 ÷ 5 waves in 1 s

frequency = $\frac{1}{5}$ s = 0.2 Hz

wavelength = $\frac{\text{wave speed}}{\text{frequency}}$

wavelength = $\frac{10 \text{ m/s}}{0.2 \text{ Hz}}$

wavelength = 50 m.

Questions

1 Ten waves pass a point on a rope in 4 s. What is their frequency?

2 Five waves measure 25 cm and pass a point in 1 s. What is: **(a)** the wavelength? **(b)** the frequency?

3 Waves in a spring have a frequency of 8 Hz and a travel at a speed of 4 m/s. What is their wavelength?

4 Light waves have a wavelength of 0.0000005 m and a frequency of 600 000 000 000 000 Hz. What is the speed of light?

5 Water waves with wavelength 1.5 cm travel across a tank at 0.021 m/s. What is their frequency?

6 If the frequency of waves is doubled what happens to: **(a)** the wave speed? **(b)** the wavelength?

7 Longitudinal waves travel through steel at 6000 m/s. If the frequency is 2000 Hz what is the distance between the centre of a compression and the centre of a rarefaction?

8 Draw a diagram of a transverse wave and use it to explain what is meant by the wavelength, amplitude, frequency and wave speed of a wave, and the units each of these are measured in.

A*

Wave behaviour

Studying waves

When waves are **transmitted**, for example light passing through glass, they are travelling through a medium. In some materials the energy of some waves is **absorbed** so the waves die away. For example, sound waves are not transmitted through thick foam. The energy is transferred to the foam which heats up slightly.

All waves can be **reflected, refracted** and **diffracted**. These different kinds of wave behaviour are easy to see with water waves.

Science skills

A **ripple tank** is a shallow tank of water with a glass bottom and a light over the top. This casts shadows of the waves on the screen under the tank. To prevent waves from reflecting off the sides they are gently sloping and made of a material that absorbs energy. A small dipper oscillates to make the waves. You can experiment with one or two wave sources making circular waves, or a long flat dipper to make plane waves.

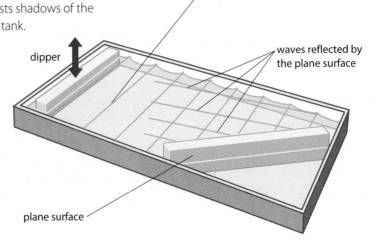

Figure 1 A ripple tank used to produce plane waves.

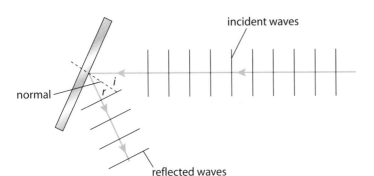

Figure 2 Water waves reflected by a barrier.

Reflection

When waves strike an interface (boundary) between materials, instead of being absorbed or transmitted, they may be **reflected**. Figure 2 shows plane (flat) waves being reflected by a barrier. Three lines are drawn to show what happens to the direction of the wave. The first is a perpendicular line, called the **normal**, crossing the barrier. The other two (arrowed lines) show the direction of the waves and are perpendicular to the **incident** and the reflected plane waves. When waves are reflected the **angle of incidence i = the angle of reflection r**.

Refraction

When waves cross an interface between two materials they may change direction. This is called **refraction**. Figure 3 shows water waves being refracted towards the normal as they pass from deep to shallow water. Waves travelling along the normal are not refracted. If the direction of the water waves is reversed they follow the same path, and are refracted away from the normal as they cross the interface from shallow to deep water.

Examiner feedback

Make sure you don't confuse diffraction and refraction. Diffraction is spreading out of waves, and only happens to waves. Refraction is a change of direction of waves. Reflection and refraction may also happen to a stream of particles.

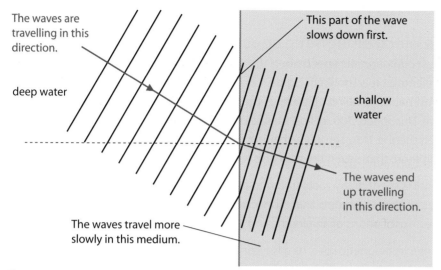

The waves are travelling in this direction.

This part of the wave slows down first.

deep water

shallow water

The waves end up travelling in this direction.

The waves travel more slowly in this medium.

Figure 3 Water waves refracted by a change to shallow water.

The atmosphere

The atmosphere is not uniform. It has parts that have different temperatures and parts that may contain dust, water vapour or droplets. As waves are transmitted, some may be absorbed, and at interfaces between the different layers some may be refracted. For example, light is absorbed by clouds but radio waves are not. Mirages are caused by hot layers of air refracting light from the sky so that it appears to come from the ground and looks like a reflection from water.

Diffraction

Diffraction is the spreading out of waves when they pass an edge, as in Figure 4(a), or through a gap, as in Figure 4(b), 4(c) and 4 (d). Diffraction is greatest when the gap is the same size as the wavelength of the wave, as shown in Figure 4(d). The wavelength of light is very small, about half a millionth of a metre, so light doesn't spread round corners unless the hole is very tiny.

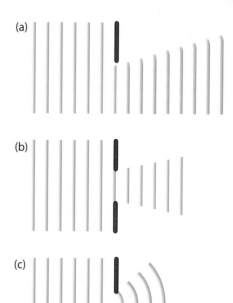

(a)

(b)

(c)

(d)

Figure 4 Diffraction of waves.

Questions

1 Draw a diagram and explain what happens when water waves hit a straight barrier at an angle.

2 Waves are refracted at an interface. What does 'refraction' mean?

3 How would you show that an unknown radiation was a wave and not a stream of particles?

4 Draw diagrams and use them to explain how diffraction depends on wavelength.

5 Light from the stars twinkles because it is refracted as it passes through the atmosphere. Explain what this means, and why it happens.

6 Figure 5 shows how scientists investigate layers of rock by detonating an explosion and detecting the reflections. Explain how the depth of an interface between two rock layers can be worked out.

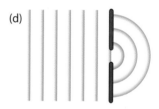

explosion   detectors

Figure 5

7 The waves on many beaches always seem to arrive parallel to the shore. This is because waves are refracted towards the normal as they enter shallower water. Draw a diagram to explain this effect.

8 Sir Isaac Newton said that light was not a wave because shadows had sharp edges. Explain why waves do not give shadows with sharp edges, and why scientists today say that light is a wave.

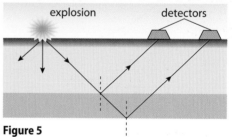

Electromagnetic waves

Learning objectives

- list the types of waves in the electromagnetic spectrum, in order of energy, frequency and wavelength.
- Calculate frequencies and wavelengths of electromagnetic waves.
- Explain that radio waves, microwaves, infrared and visible light are used for communication.

The electromagnetic spectrum

The electromagnetic **spectrum** is the complete range of electromagnetic wavelengths. It is shown in Figure 1 in order of increasing energy. Electromagnetic waves all travel at the same speed in a vacuum and through space. This speed, 300 million metres per second, or 3×10^8 m/s, is the fastest speed there is. If an aeroplane could go at this speed it would go around the world more than seven times in one second.

Scientists spent many years trying to decide how light travelled through a vacuum. Now they know that all electromagnetic waves behave as transverse waves – oscillations of an electric and a magnetic field.

The electromagnetic spectrum is a continuous range of wavelengths, there are no gaps. As the energy increases, the frequency of the waves increases and the wavelength decreases, as shown in Figure 2. Electromagnetic waves with different wavelengths have some very different properties. For example, long wavelength radio waves are transmitted through brick and stone, but light is not. This is why different parts have different names, but there is no sharp division between the different parts of the spectrum. Table 1 shows some typical wavelengths. You can work out frequency from the wavelength and the speed of 300 000 000 m/s using the wave equation.

Table 1 Typical wavelengths in the electromagnetic spectrum.

Electromagnetic waves	Typical wavelengths
radio waves	1 m, 3 km
microwaves	1 cm, 10 cm
infrared (IR)	1 mm, 1 millionth of a metre
visible light: red, orange, yellow, green blue, indigo, violet	from about 7×10^{-7} m to 4×10^{-7} m 0.51 millionths of a metre

Science skills Figure 2 shows how the wavelength of electromagnetic waves changes as the frequency changes.

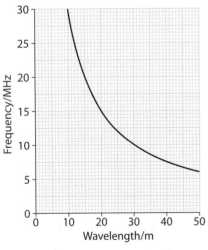

Figure 2 Change of wavelength with frequency.

a What is the wavelength when the frequency is 20 MHz?

b What happens to the wavelength when the frequency doubles?

c Use a pair of values from the graph to calculate the speed of the waves.

All electromagnetic waves travel at the speed of light in a vacuum.

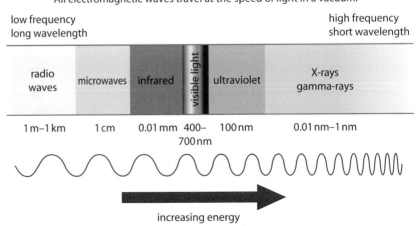

Figure 1 The spectrum of electromagnetic waves.

Are electromagnetic waves safe?

All electromagnetic waves have a heating effect when absorbed, and this is greater if the waves are carrying more energy. The **intensity** of a wave is a measure of the energy arriving on a unit area per second. For example, light is all around us and is normally quite safe. However, the more intense light from the Sun, or a laser, can damage eyes. Laser users wear eye protection.

Transmission through the atmosphere

- Radio waves pass through the atmosphere, and long waves are not absorbed by walls, so we use radio waves for broadcasting radio programmes and other information.

- Microwaves do not spread out like radio waves, they are very directional and there has to be a line-of-sight between transmitter and receiver. Some wavelengths are absorbed by water, so they are not so suitable for transmitting information.

- A lot of infrared radiation is absorbed by water vapour and gases in the atmosphere, so infrared is only used for very short distances.

- Light is transmitted through the atmosphere, but some is reflected from particles and if there are a lot of water droplets in the air, such as in clouds or fog, then the light is reflected so much a signal will not get through.

- Ultraviolet, X rays and gamma rays are absorbed by the atmosphere.

Questions

1 Which waves are more suitable for broadcasting a signal over a wide area?

2 Infrared waves from a remote control have a frequency of 3.19×10^{14} Hz. What is the wavelength?

3 Sodium lights give out yellow light with wavelength 0.000 000 59 m. What is the frequency?

4 Sun screens are all rated using the same test to see how much UV is prevented from reaching the skin. Why is it important to use the same test?

5 What electromagnetic waves have a typical frequency of about:
(a) 100 million million Hz? **(b)** 1 000 million million Hz?

6 Look at Figure 3.

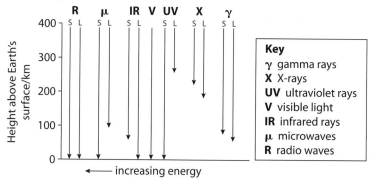

Figure 3 Schematic representation of absorption of short (S) and long (L) wave types of electromagnetic radiation by the atmosphere.

(a) Which waves are absorbed by the atmosphere? **(b)** For which waves is this an advantage? Explain your answer.

7 Describe the electromagnetic spectrum.

Route to A*

The speed of light can be written as 300 000 000 m/s or in standard form as 3×10^8 m/s, but also as 3×10^5 km/s, so take care with the units in questions. Changing all the numbers to standard form is a useful way to avoid unit problems. To calculate the frequency of infrared radiation with a wavelength of 1 mm:

Wavelength $= 1 \times 10^{-3}$ m

Speed of light $= 3 \times 10^8$ m/s

Use the wave equation: $v = f\lambda$.

Rearranging, frequency $f = \dfrac{v}{\lambda}$.

$f = \dfrac{v}{\lambda} = \dfrac{3 \times 10^8}{1 \times 10^{-3}}$.

Therefore frequency $= 3 \times 10^{11}$ Hz

This is an acceptable answer, but you could also write 300 000 000 000 Hz.

Radio waves and microwaves

Learning objectives

- describe how microwaves and radio waves are used in communications
- explain why microwaves are used to communicate with satellites
- explain the dangers of powerful microwave and radio transmissions
- evaluate the use of different types of waves for communication.

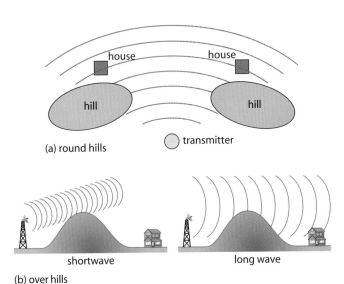

Figure 1 Radio waves can be received because of diffraction.

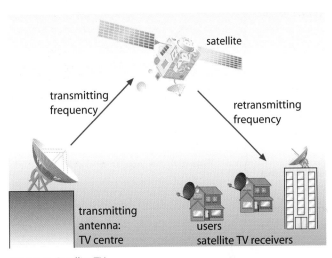

Figure 2 Satellite TV.

Radio communications

Radio waves are used to broadcast radio and television signals from transmitters.

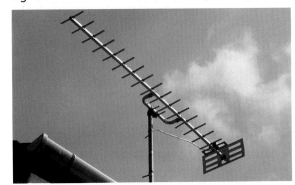

Radio waves are received by TV aerials.

The information, for example sound or pictures, is converted to an electrical signal and then added to the radio waves that are transmitted in all directions. For a receiver to pick up radio waves, the aerial must be made of metal so it absorbs the waves. When it does so, the radio waves produce an alternating current in the aerial with a frequency which is the same as the radio wave itself. The original electric signal is recovered and used to reproduce the information; for example, it can be changed into the sound that comes from a loudspeaker. Each TV channel and radio programme is allocated a frequency band, a small range of frequencies, so that there is no interference between the different users.

Receiving signals

Microwaves and radio waves are absorbed by very thick or dense objects, like hills for example. However, long wave radio waves, especially those with wavelengths of about 1000 m, can be diffracted along valleys and around hills, as shown in Figure 1. If you live somewhere that does not have a clear straight path, or line of sight, to the transmitter, you can still receive radio waves, but microwaves are not diffracted by such large objects.

Microwaves

Satellites are used to transmit information quickly around the world, as shown in Figure 2. Some areas do not get good reception of radio signals but can receive signals from a satellite. A satellite can also provide a wide area with satellite TV. Many radio frequencies are reflected by the **ionosphere**, which is a high and electrically charged layer of our atmosphere. This means they cannot be used to communicate with satellites. Microwaves are used instead, as these can pass easily through the whole atmosphere.

Dangers of microwaves and radio waves

We cannot detect **microwaves** or radio waves, so we must be careful not to expose our bodies to dangerous levels of these radiations. People are not allowed near powerful transmitters, like the one in the photograph, when they are switched on. Microwaves are reflected by metal and radio waves are absorbed or reflected, so metal can be used to screen rooms from these radiations.

Microwaves with a frequency of about 2450 million Hz are particularly dangerous. They make water molecules vibrate strongly, so they have a big heating effect on anything containing water. This is the frequency used in microwave ovens to cook food.

Science in action

Microwave ovens can be used to cook any food that contains water. The microwaves penetrate deep inside the food and cook it all the way through. The metal walls of the oven reflect the microwaves, which are then absorbed by the food. The door contains a metal mesh to reflect microwaves too.

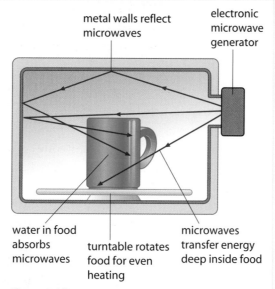

Figure 4 Microwave oven.

Transmitter towers.

Examiner feedback

It is important to remember when microwaves and radio waves are used and why they are used for different applications.

Practical

You can use a microwave transmitter and receiver to check whether microwaves obey the law of reflection, and see what materials absorb them.

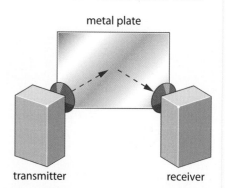

Figure 3 The angle of incidence equals the angle of reflection.

Questions

1 A radio station broadcasts on 2 million Hz, a TV station broadcasts on 2000 million Hz, and the emergency services use a radio frequency of 200 million Hz. Which uses the longest wavelength?

2 Why do microwave ovens have a safety lock to prevent them operating while the door is open?

3 A radio aerial receives a radio broadcast. Describe two things that happen to the metal aerial.

4 BBC 4 long wave radio broadcasts at 198 kHz. What is the wavelength?

5 Radio 1 is broadcast with a wavelength of 3.01 m. What frequency is this?

6 Describe the different ways that a television signal might reach your TV set.

7 Explain why radio waves can be received over a large area but microwaves need repeating transmitters on hills and buildings.

8 A student says that we should not use microwaves for communications because microwaves cook meat and so they will cook us. Explain to the student what is wrong with this conclusion.

Mobile phones

Learning objectives

- describe how microwaves are used in mobile phones
- explain how Bluetooth is used
- analyse data on safety of mobile phones
- evaluate the possible risks of using mobile phones.

Mobile phone networks

Mobile phones use microwaves and a cellular network system, as shown in Figure 1. The phone communicates with a local mast or base station. The mast sends another microwave signal to a central base, which sends the signal on to the base station or mast for the receiving phone. Mobile phones use powers of up to about 2 W. Whenever the phone is switched on it keeps in touch with the base station by sending messages and it uses more power if reception is bad, for example in a tunnel.

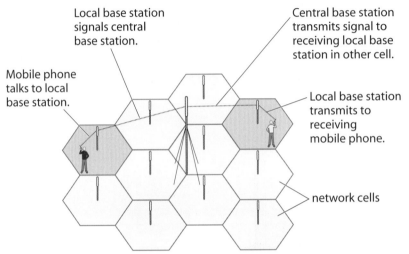

Local base station signals central base station.

Central base station transmits signal to receiving local base station in other cell.

Mobile phone talks to local base station.

Local base station transmits to receiving mobile phone.

network cells

Figure 1 A mobile phone network.

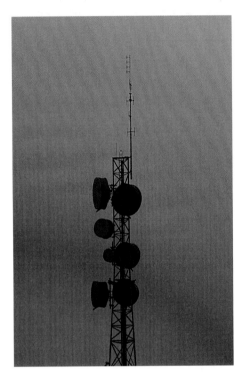

A microwave transmitter tower.

For longer distances, mobile phone microwave signals are sent via several masts because otherwise the curved shape of the Earth would block the signal. Microwaves need a line of sight, a straight line, between the masts as the wavelengths are too small to be diffracted around hills. For international calls, a satellite link is used.

A communication satellite.

Bluetooth

Bluetooth is a low power (about one milliwatt) system that uses microwaves over a range of up to 10 m to connect up to eight items like televisions, mobile phones and PCs. Bluetooth uses a frequency of 2450 million Hz, the same as microwave ovens, but at a much lower power.

Are mobile phones safe?

The Health Protection Agency (HPA) is a government group, made up of independent scientists, that is looking at the evidence about the effects of radiation on health. This was the advice on their website in 2010:

'There are thousands of published scientific papers covering research about the effects of various types of radio waves on cells, tissues, animals and people. The scientific consensus is that, apart from the increased risk of a road accident due

Using a Bluetooth headset.

to mobile phone use when driving, there is no clear evidence of adverse health effects from the use of mobile phones or from phone masts. However, there is now widespread use of this relatively new technology and more research is needed in case there are long-term effects.'

They also said:

'Given the uncertainties in the science, some precaution is warranted particularly regarding the use of handsets held against the head. This is especially relevant to the use of handsets by children and the Agency recommends that excessive use by children should be discouraged.'

So the research so far indicates that phones are safe, but we can't be sure that there are no long-term effects until we have studied lots of people that have used phones throughout their lives – and that is going to take many years. The reason for taking extra care with children is that they are still growing, their skulls are thinner, and they are going to be using mobiles for many years to come.

Route to A*

You may be given some information about an investigation and asked questions about whether the study was well designed and if the conclusions are reliable. Sometimes the marks will be for the explanation you give. For example, if you are asked if a sample is big enough, sometimes it may be difficult to decide. In this case there may be marks for saying 'yes, because there is enough data to see a pattern showing a link' or for saying 'no, because the sample size is too small and a pattern could be just coincidence.' There is no mark for saying 'yes' or 'no' without an explanation.

Science skills

In 2006 a scientific paper was published reporting a Danish study of mobile phone use and cancer. 420 095 adults from all over Denmark who first used a mobile phone between 1982 and 1995 were monitored for up to 21 years. The number of people in the group who got cancer was compared with the number that would be expected to get cancer – the number of people in a similar sample who did not use phones but who got cancer.

	Number in study	Number with cancer	Number expected to get cancer
men	357 553	12 627	11 802
women	62 542	2374	2447
men and women	420 095	15 001	14 249

a Taking the whole group, did more or fewer people get cancer than expected?

b Why were the scientists more confident about the result for men than for women?

c The complete study looked at different types of cancer. Why do you think this might be important?

Questions

1 Why are satellites used for international phone calls?

2 A company wants to put a mobile phone mast next to a school. Give reasons for and against the positioning of the mast next to the school with your evaluation as to whether it is a suitable site.

3 Why has there been no study of the effects of mobile phones on the health of children who use them?

4 A mobile phone has a SAR value, which is a measure of the energy per second absorbed by the head while the phone is used. The SAR value must be less than 2.0 W/kg. Explain whether it is completely safe to use a phone with a SAR value of: **(a)** 0.25 W/kg **(b)** 1.8 W/kg **(c)** 2.1 W/kg.

5 The SAR values are checked by independent consumer organisations. Why is this important?

6 Two Bluetooth devices can communicate until one is placed inside a microwave oven with the door shut. The oven is not switched on. Explain why the devices can no longer detect each other.

7 Describe how you could use two mobile phones to find out if microwaves are absorbed by water.

8 Describe how scientists could research whether there is a link between mobile phone use and brain tumours.

Making light work

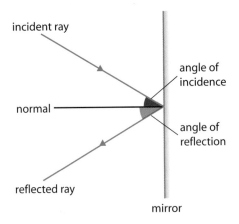

Figure 1 Reflection – the angles are equal.

The image is dim because not much light can get through the hole.

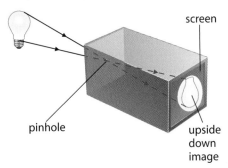

Figure 3 How a camera forms an image.

Mirrors

Lots of objects reflect light but in a mirror you see an **image**. The properties of the image in a mirror can be explained by constructing a ray diagram – we draw rays rather than waves when investigating images. To keep ray diagrams simple we draw only a few rays. When light is reflected the angle of incidence is always equal to the angle of reflection, as shown in Figure 1.

If you look at an image of yourself in a plane mirror, the image is upright (the same way up as you are) and the same size as you, but laterally inverted (i.e. left and right are swapped over). The image also appears to be behind the mirror and it is the same distance behind the mirror as you are in front. The rays of light do not pass through the image but only appear to come from it. This kind of image is called a **virtual image**. In Figure 2, two rays from an object are drawn to show how the image in a mirror is formed. The rays are reflected from the mirror surface and the dotted lines show that they appear to come from the image.

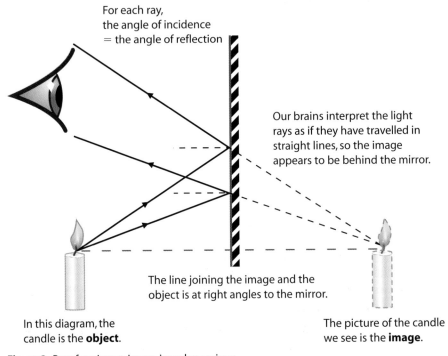

For each ray,
the angle of incidence
= the angle of reflection

Our brains interpret the light rays as if they have travelled in straight lines, so the image appears to be behind the mirror.

The line joining the image and the object is at right angles to the mirror.

In this diagram, the candle is the **object**.

The picture of the candle we see is the **image**.

Figure 2 Rays forming an image in a plane mirror.

Photography

Unlike a mirror, a camera produces a **real image**. It is called a real image because the rays of light do pass through it. To record the image, it must be formed on a light-sensitive surface. This could be photographic film or sensors that produce an electronic signal. Figure 3 shows the simplest basic camera, one without a lens. The light rays enter through a very small pinhole and produce an upside-down image on the screen. Images from cameras like this are quite dim. However, if you make the pinhole bigger to let in more light the image will be blurred. Replacing the pinhole with a lens allows more light in and focuses the image to give a sharp picture. The image is upside down and smaller than the object.

Questions

1 Which way up is the image in: **(a)** a plane mirror? **(b)** a camera?

2 Copy and complete Figure 4 to show how an object is reflected in a mirror.

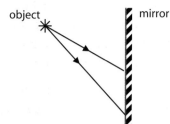

Figure 4

3 A mug is 8 cm tall, and you place it 10 cm from a mirror. **(a)** How tall does the mug appear to be in the mirror? **(b)** How far from the mirror does the image of the mug appear to be? **(c)** Is the image real or virtual?

4 Two mirrors are positioned so they are touching with an angle of 120° between them. Draw a ray of light incident on one mirror at an angle of 60° so that it reflects from both the mirrors.

5 Copy and complete Figure 5 to show how the periscope can be used to see over a high wall.

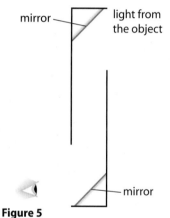

Figure 5

6 An optician's chart is on the wall 1 m behind the patient's head. The patient sees the chart in the mirror, which is 2.5 m away in front of the patient. How far away from: **(a)** the chart **(b)** the patient does the image of the chart appear to be?

7 The photograph shows a meter with a mirror behind the pointer. Explain how the mirror helps to read the meter accurately.

8 Write a Wiki page to describe how a digital camera produces an image of the object being photographed. **A***

Science skills

Some students use a pinhole camera, as shown in Figure 3, to obtain images of objects. They keep the camera the same distance from the objects and measure the object height and the image height.

a Which is the independent variable?

b What type of variable is the object height?

c Plot a graph to show these results.

d Are any of the results anomalous? If so, which one(s)?

e Describe the relationship between image height and object height, and explain how the graph shows this.

Object height/cm	Image height/cm
12.0	0.9
20.0	1.4
24.0	1.5
30.0	2.1
36.0	2.6
40.0	2.9

Taking it further

When drawing ray diagrams for mirrors you might wonder why the angle of incidence and reflection are measured to the normal and not to the surface. The reason is clearer when the surface is not a plane. When light is reflected from rough surfaces, or from curved mirrors, convex and concave, the law of reflection is still true.

Light and infrared

Science in action

In parts of the world where there is plenty of sunshine but not much fuel a solar cooker is very useful. This photograph shows one being used in the mountains of Nepal to boil water. The infrared radiation from the Sun is reflected from the metal onto the cooking pot.

Infrared radiation from the Sun boils water in this solar cooker.

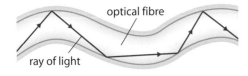

optical fibre

ray of light

Figure 1 A ray travelling through an optical fibre.

Infrared signals

Remote controls for TVs and other electronic equipment use infrared radiation. If you look at the output of a remote control with a digital camera you can see the flashing code that is being transmitted. This is because digital cameras are sensitive to some of the infrared wavelengths that we cannot see.

Infrared reflections

Infrared radiation behaves in a similar way to light. It is reflected from surfaces, especially shiny surfaces. Infrared rays travel in straight lines and are reflected from walls and ceilings. A remote control will not operate a TV if it is pointed too far to one side. However, if you aim it at the wall behind you the beam will reflect off the wall and it sometimes operates the TV.

Optical fibres

Optical fibres are fibres made of glass. The composition of the glass varies across the fibre so that light or infrared radiation passing down the fibre is refracted and reflected to keep it travelling along the centre, as shown in Figure 1.

Science skills

A student wanted to investigate the absorption of infrared radiation. He used a 20 cm block of jelly to model an optical fibre. He placed an infrared LED at one end and a detector at the other.

He measured the length of the jelly fibre and recorded the voltage signal reaching the detector, then cut off a piece of the jelly, and repeated the measurements with the smaller length. These are the results

Length of jelly fibre/mm	Reading on detector/V
200	0.12
180	0.14
150	0.20
100	0.36
80	0.46
40	0.70

a Which was the:

i independent variable?   **ii** dependent variable?

b What type of variable was:

i the length?   **ii** the voltage?

c Plot a graph of the student's results.

d Describe the relationship between the length of the fibre and the reading on the detector.

e The student realises that he has measured the length of the jelly but the path of the beam was at an angle through the jelly and not parallel to the sides. What type of error will this cause in his results?

Signals, especially telecommunications signals, can be sent along optical fibres instead of copper cables or by microwave and radio links. Many copper cables have been replaced by optical fibres. Advantages are:

- Much more information can be carried by the waves because light and infrared have higher frequencies than microwaves and radio waves. This means that thick, heavy, expensive copper cables can be replaced by a thin bundle of glass fibres.

- The information is more secure because, unlike with copper cables, it is not possible to pick up radiation from outside the glass fibres.

- Signals in fibres do not pick up noise, or unwanted signals, from outside the cables. This can be a problem with copper cables.

Compare these fibre optic cables…

…with these copper cables.

Science in action

These young people are only visible through an infrared or thermal camera, which picks up infrared radiation.

Objects emit radiation with a wavelength that depends on their temperature. Thermal cameras and night vision glasses allow us to see when there is no reflected light; see spread P1 1.1. They detect infrared radiation from warm objects like bodies and change the wavelengths to visible wavelengths that we can see. In the photograph, the faces are the objects with the highest surface temperature – higher than the clothes and surroundings.

Questions

1. What are the advantages of using fibre optic cables instead of copper cables for telephone wires?

2. Draw a diagram to show how an infrared remote control can switch off a TV by reflecting off the wall of a room.

3. Suggest why an infrared telescope would be placed in orbit around the Earth and not on the Earth?

4. A burglar alarm uses a beam of infrared radiation that falls on a sensor. If a burglar interrupts the beam an alarm sounds. Why is infrared radiation used and not light or ultraviolet radiation?

5. Infrared radiation is absorbed by gases like carbon dioxide and water vapour in the atmosphere. What effect does this have on the atmosphere?

6. An infrared remote control switches a TV on and off. Describe how you could use this in an experiment to see which materials transmit infrared radiation.

Route to A*

You may be asked a question about something you haven't studied, but which you can work out from what you *have* studied. It's important not to assume that you can't answer the question. For example, an infrared range finder works by sending out an infrared pulse and timing how long it takes for the reflection to return. You may not know this, but you know how infrared remote controls work, and how the echo of a sound wave can be used to measure a distance (see page 256), so you can apply this knowledge to explain how an infrared rangefinder works.

Sound

Learning objectives

- describe sound waves
- explain that sound is caused by vibrations in a medium
- explain that the pitch of a sound is determined by its frequency
- investigate the speed of sound
- evaluate experiments to measure the speed of sound.

Sound

Vibrations send longitudinal waves travelling to our ears. Inside our ears the waves cause vibrations that are sensed and interpreted by the brain as sounds. In air sound travels at about 330 m/s. It is faster in liquids and fastest in solids like wood or metal because the oscillations can be passed on more easily in these materials. Using a microphone, you can display the *graph* of the amplitude of the sound wave against *time* on an **oscilloscope** or computer screen. Remember that sound waves are longitudinal and the screen shows a graph, not what the sound wave looks like.

The guitar strings vibrate and start the air oscillating.

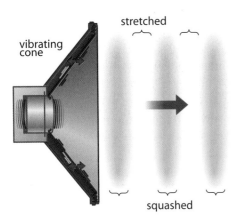

Figure 1 A loudspeaker vibrates, producing longitudinal sound waves in the air.

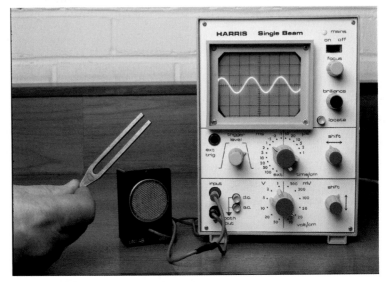

A graph of the vibrations of the tuning fork are shown on this oscilloscope.

Pitch and loudness

The **pitch** of a sound – how high or low it is – is determined by the frequency of the sound wave. The higher the pitch, the greater the frequency.
The loudness of a sound depends on the amplitude: the higher the amplitude, the louder the sound.

Human hearing

Humans hear sounds in the range from about 20 Hz to about 20 kHz. The highest frequency you can hear gets lower as you get older. Some animals, like whales, can hear lower frequencies, and some, like dogs, can hear higher frequencies.

Echoes

An **echo** is a reflection of sound from a hard surface. The further away the surface, the longer it takes for the sound to travel there and back. This delay can be used to work out the speed of sound, using speed = distance travelled ÷ time taken.

Route to A*

To calculate the wavelength of a sound, if you are given the speed and the pitch, remember that the pitch is the frequency of the sound.

So, from the wave equation $v = f\lambda$:

Wave speed = pitch × wavelength.

So $\lambda = \frac{v}{f}$

$$\text{wavelength} = \frac{\text{wave speed}}{\text{pitch}}$$

Examiner feedback

A common mistake is to think that we can't hear radio waves because the frequency is too high, but our ears only detect longitudinal waves; we can't hear any electromagnetic waves no matter what the frequency.

Refraction

Refraction occurs between layers of air at different temperatures. One example is when you hear a train in the distance only in certain weather conditions. When there is a cold layer of air next to the ground and a warmer layer above, the sound from a train can be refracted back down to Earth some distance away.

Diffraction

The photographer who took the photograph on the right would not have been able to see people on the other side of the doorway, but he would have been able to hear them. This is because sound has wavelengths of about 1 m so it is diffracted through gaps about the size of a doorway. Longer wavelengths are closer to the size of the door and are diffracted more, so the sound heard round a corner will have lost the higher frequencies.

Diffraction allows sound to travel round corners.

Science skills

Some students measure the speed of sound using a firework that ejects a flash with a loud bang. They are 500 m from the firework, measured with a tape measure. The observers use a stopwatch and start it when they see the flash. They stop it when they hear the bang. They repeat the experiment five times. Table 1 shows their results.

Table 1

Time taken for sound to arrive/s
1.31
0.94
1.45
1.67
1.52

a Why did they repeat the experiment five times?

b Are any of the results anomalous? If so, which ones?

c Calculate the mean value for the time.

d Calculate the speed of sound.

e Some students make the following statements about the experiment. Explain whether they are correct.

i The value will be much too big because the speed of light has not been taken into account.

ii The value would have been more accurate if a larger distance was used.

iii The value would have been more accurate if a more precise stopwatch, measuring to thousandths of a second, had been used.

iv We need to add the reaction time of the student starting the stopwatch.

f Explain whether the wind will affect the results.

Taking it further

Light has much smaller wavelengths than sound so the diffraction of light is much less.

Route to A*

The hum of a hummingbird is caused by the rapid beating of its wings setting the air vibrating. The wings of some hummingbirds beat 80 times per second. At this speed, the pitch of the hum is 80 Hz.

Questions

(Use speed of sound in air = 330 m/s)

1 The note middle C has a pitch of 256 Hz. What is the wavelength?

2 The speed of sound in water is 1500 m/s. What is the pitch of a sound with a wavelength in water of 0.03 m?

3 Draw a graph of a sound wave like Figure 2. On the same axes draw and label: **(a)** a sound wave that is louder; **(b)** a sound wave that has a higher pitch.

4 Describe how you would do an experiment to measure the speed of sound using the echo from a high brick wall at one side of a playing field. **A***

Assess yourself questions

1 Many electromagnetic waves can be used in communication. Which wave types link with which communication uses? *(3 marks)*

Wave type	Communication use
radio waves	an endoscope – a glass fibre with a camera used by doctors to see inside the body
microwaves	a satellite TV signal linking the transmitter to the satellite
infrared	a fibre optic telecommunications link
visible light	a terrestrial TV broadcast

2 Choose the correct answer.

(a) The shock waves from an earthquake are:

A all longitudinal
B all transverse
C both longitudinal and transverse *(1 mark)*

(b) Longitudinal waves travel through:

A gases only
B liquids only
C liquids and gases
D solids only
E solids, liquids and gases *(1 mark)*

(c) The wavelength of a longitudinal wave is the distance between:

A a compression and a rarefaction
B a crest and a trough
C two crests
D two rarefactions
E two troughs *(1 mark)*

3 (a) What is the difference between a transverse and a longitudinal wave? *(2 marks)*

(b) Water waves are passing a breakwater. Each complete wave takes 2.0 s to pass. The distance between two crests is 3 m and the distance between the top of a crest and the bottom of a trough is 90 cm. What is:

(i) the frequency of the waves? *(1 mark)*
(ii) the wavelength? *(1 mark)*
(iii) the amplitude? *(1 mark)*
(iv) the wave speed? *(1 mark)*

4 (a) When a train approaches, the noise of the rails vibrating can be heard before the train. Explain why this happens. *(2 marks)*

(b) In many science fiction films, missiles and explosions in outer space make loud noises. Explain why this is unrealistic. *(2 marks)*

5 (a) Copy these diagrams and complete them to show the waves after they have passed through the gap. *(3 marks)*

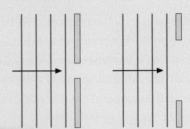

Figure 1

(b) What is the name of this effect? *(1 mark)*

(c) A time signal for setting radio controlled clocks is broadcast at a frequency of 60 kHz from Cumbria and can be received throughout the UK.

(i) What is the wavelength of the signal? (Radio waves travel at a speed of 300 000 000 m/s.) *(2 marks)*

(ii) Explain how the signal can be received all over the UK.

In this question you will be assessed on using good English, organising information clearly and using specialist terms where appropriate.

(6 marks)

6 A company sells coatings for optical instruments. These graphs show the percentage of the incident radiation reflected at different wavelengths for three coatings: Premier, Choice and Luxcoat.

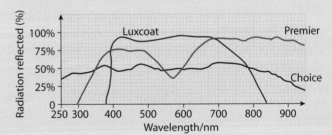

Figure 2 Graph of optical coating performance.

(a) Explain which coating(s) would be suitable for a beam splitter for visible light that transmits half of the beam and reflects the other half. *(3 marks)*

(b) Explain which material would be suitable for a mirror to reflect all visible light. *(3 marks)*

(c) Explain which material would be suitable as a mirror to reflect infrared radiation. *(3 marks)*

(d) What percentage of the incident light does Choice transmit at 750 nm? *(1 mark)*

(e) Explain whether the coating Luxcoat reflects ultraviolet light. *(2 marks)*

7 The data in Table 1 shows how heavy rainfall can affect the transmission of microwaves with a frequency 15 GHz (1 GHz = 10^9 Hz = 1 million kHz) and microwaves with a frequency of 39 GHz.

Table 1 How heavy rainfall affects microwave transmissions.

Rainfall rate mm/hour	Percentage energy loss per km travelled	
	Microwave frequency 15 GHz	Microwave frequency 39 GHz
0	60	64
10	82	78
20	80	96.8
30	88	98.5
40	97.5	100
50	99	100
60	100	100

(a) Explain which waves have the longest wavelength.
(1 mark)

(b) Are there any anomalous results? If so, which ones?
(1 mark)

(c) What percentage of the energy of the 15 GHz waves is left after 1 km when there is no rain? *(1 mark)*

(d) Which frequency is most affected by the rain?
(1 mark)

(e) A student says that the absorption of the 39 GHz microwaves is proportional to the amount of rain. Explain whether you agree. *(1 mark)*

(f) A microwave signal has to travel 1 km. It can be recovered if 10% of the original energy gets through. Estimate the maximum rainfall rate before the signal is lost if:
  (i) 15 GHz waves or
  (ii) 39 GHz waves are used. *(2 marks)*

8 Figure 3 shows waves entering a harbour.

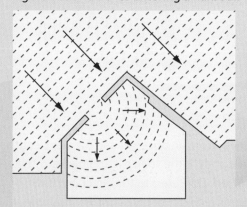

Figure 3 How waves change when they enter a harbour.

This effect is called:
A diffraction
B dispersion
C reflection
D refraction.

9 In 2010 the Cohort Study on Mobile Communications (COSMOS) was started. It is looking at the health and mobile phone use of people aged 18–69 in Britain, Finland, the Netherlands, Sweden and Denmark. It is one of the largest studies of this subject conducted. It will use data from volunteers' phone bills and health records as well as questionnaires.

Unlike previous studies, the study will look at long-term use, as people will be monitored for 10, 20 or 30 years. This will give time for diseases to develop. Findings will be reported during the study. Previous studies have depended on people remembering how much they used their phone in the past.

In Britain, COSMOS is inviting 2.4 million mobile phone users to take part, through the country's four top carriers: Vodafone, O2, T-Mobile and Orange. It hopes 90 000–100 000 will agree.

The study will examine all health developments and look for links to neurological diseases such as Alzheimer's and Parkinson's as well as cancer.

It will also take account of how users carry their phone, for example in a trouser or chest pocket or in a bag, and whether they use hands-free kits.

(a) Explain why the study uses such a large number of people. *(1 mark)*

(b) Why do you think phone bills and health records will be looked at, as well as questionnaires? *(1 mark)*

(c) Explain why the study will continue for such a long time. *(1 mark)*

(d) Explain an advantage of this study, which is looking at what happens over the next 30 years, rather than studies that look back over the last 30 years. Is there a disadvantage? If so, what is it? *(2 marks)*

(e) What do you think the organisers would do if they discovered a link between mobile phone use and a type of cancer after only eight years? *(1 mark)*

(f) Why is the study limited to:
  (i) people over 18?
  (ii) people under 69? *(2 marks)*

(g) Why do you think they will look at how users carry their phone? *(2 marks)*

10 Compare how a terrestrial TV signal from a transmitter reaches your TV set with how a satellite TV signal reaches it.

In this question you will be assessed on using good English, organising information clearly and using specialist terms where appropriate. *(6 marks)*

The Doppler effect

A moving source

Have you ever noticed that a vehicle, especially one with a siren like a police car or ambulance, sounds higher pitched (i.e. the frequency is higher) as it comes towards you and lower pitched as it moves away from you? This is called the **Doppler effect**. This happens to all waves, including electromagnetic waves.

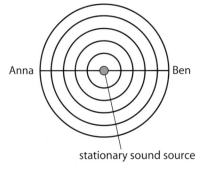

Figure 1(a) Waves from a stationary source.

Figure 1(b) Waves from a source moving towards Anna and away from Ben.

Figure 1(b) shows that the waves moving towards Anna are squashed together. The wavelength has decreased, and, as the speed of the waves has not changed, the frequency has increased. The waves moving towards Ben are stretched out, so he observes a longer wavelength and lower frequency. These small changes are called **Doppler shifts**.

Notice that it is not enough to say the source is moving. If the observer is moving at the same speed and in the same direction as the source there is no effect; the source must be moving *relative* to the observer. Some speed traffic cameras use the Doppler effect. A beam of microwaves is sent towards the car. The car reflects the beam back to the detector. Because the car is moving, the microwaves arriving at the detector will be Doppler shifted, and the faster the car is travelling the greater the Doppler shift. The Doppler shift is used to calculate the speed of the car.

Electromagnetic waves

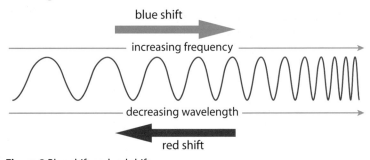

Figure 2 Blue shift and red shift.

When a visible light source moves away from an observer and the wavelength increases we say there has been a **red shift**. If the source is approaching, the wavelength decreases: it is **blue-shifted**. This refers to the direction shown by the arrows, which is not always towards red light or blue light. For example, if microwaves are red-shifted the new wavelength will be closer to radio waves.

A speed camera that uses the Doppler effect.

Starlight

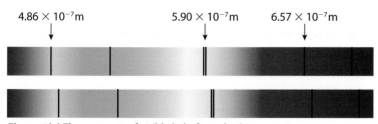

Figure 1(a) The spectrum of visible light from the Sun.
Figure 1(b) The spectrum of visible light from a distant star.

Safety note: do not look directly at the Sun with or without any optical instruments.

The spectrum of light formed by the Sun contains a number of dark lines. These are wavelengths of light that are missing because they have been absorbed by elements in the outer part of the Sun's atmosphere. Elements always absorb exactly the same wavelengths so when astronomers first looked at the spectra of other stars they expected to see the same black lines. They did see similar lines, but they found that the lines were often blue- or red-shifted. This indicated that the stars were moving relative to the Earth.

If a star is moving away from the Earth the lines seen are red-shifted; the pattern of black lines is closer to the red end of the spectrum. If the light is blue-shifted, the star is moving towards the Earth. The faster the star is moving the bigger the observed shift. Note that on a planet orbiting a distant star similar to our Sun, the spectrum of that star would look just like the Sun's spectrum. It is because of the relative movement of the distant star and Earth that we see the shift in the spectrum.

Taking it further

The red shift observed in starlight is not just due to the Doppler effect. Stars, including our Sun, are moving apart because the Universe itself is expanding – see lesson P1 6.2 for more details.

Questions

1 Describe the changes to the pitch of the sound heard by people on the platform as a train passes.

2 A light source is moving so that an observer sees the light 'red-shifted'. **(a)** What happens to the wavelength and the frequency of the observed light? **(b)** Draw a diagram to show how the light source is moving relative to the observer.

3 Two go-karts are being driven along a race track at the same speed. Explain whether the drivers notice any change in the sound of: **(a)** their own go-kart; **(b)** the other go-kart.

4 A satellite orbits the Earth transmitting a beam of microwaves. **(a)** Describe how the frequency of the microwaves received by a detector changes as the satellite passes overhead. **(b)** What is this effect called?

5 Explain how a driver of a moving car hears a siren but can **NOT** hear the pitch of the siren changing.

6 A laser beam is used to measure the speed of a car. The light is directed at the car and reflected back to a detector. **(a)** How does the wavelength change if the car is: **(i)** approaching the laser? **(ii)** travelling away from the laser? **(b)** The car is travelling towards the laser and it speeds up. What difference will this make to the wavelength of the light detected? **(c)** The laser and detector are now driven at the same speed behind the first car. Explain whether there are any changes to the wavelength of the light received.

7 Explain why the motion of a siren affects the pitch of the sound heard by a stationary observer. How can this effect be demonstrated in the science laboratory?

8 In Doppler ultrasound scans of the heart, computers use the Doppler effect to produce an image of the blood flow inside the heart. Ultrasound waves are sent towards the heart and are reflected back. Explain how the Doppler effect can be used to give information about the speed and direction of the moving blood flow in the heart.

Ⓐ*

The expanding Universe

Learning objectives

- explain that the red shift is evidence that all galaxies are moving apart
- explain that the red shift is evidence that the Universe is expanding.

What stars can tell us

All of the information we have about a star comes from analysing the electromagnetic radiation we detect from the star. The same is true for galaxies. The line spectrum from a galaxy tells us about the elements in the outer atmosphere of its stars. A red shift in the radiation tells us how fast the galaxy is moving and whether it is moving towards us or away from us. Astronomers also want to know how far away stars and galaxies are. They have several ways of working this out, for example, stars look dimmer the further away they are.

Red-shifted light from galaxies tells us they are moving away.

Distant galaxies

When astronomers look at the spectra from distant galaxies they find that almost all of them, in every direction, show a red shift. One explanation for this is that almost everything in the Universe is moving away from us in all directions. Astronomers also discovered that the further away a galaxy is, the more its spectrum is red-shifted, which means the faster it is moving away. To discover this they used a different method to measure the distance to some nearby galaxies. Once they had done this, scientists had a graph like Figure 2 that they could use to find out how far away other galaxies were.

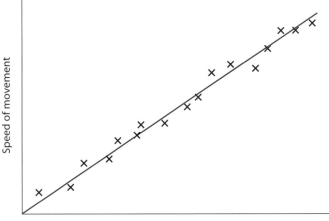

Figure 2 Astronomers' data showed that the further away a galaxy is the faster it is moving away from us.

Expansion

These observations led to the theory that the Universe is expanding. A balloon is a simple model of an expanding Universe. The rubber of the balloon expands when it is inflated, and everything on the surface expands. Galaxies A and C started off further apart than A and B, so when the balloon is inflated the distance between A and C increases more quickly than the distance between A and B. The balloon is just a simple model – the theory is that the Universe is expanding in three dimensions. Just as the rubber between the 'balloon galaxies' expanded, space is expanding in the Universe. It is difficult to understand that there is nothing outside the Universe for it to expand into; all the space is part of the existing Universe.

Figure 3 When the balloon expands, everything gets further apart.

Questions

1 If you see that light from a galaxy has a red shift, what does this tell you?

2 Two galaxies show different red shifts. How could you tell which one is moving away faster?

3 The Andromeda galaxy is unusual, as it has a blue shift. What does this tell us?

4 Distant galaxy A is further away than distant galaxy B. What can you predict about the electromagnetic radiation astronomers detect from these galaxies?

5 Spectrum X is part of the spectrum of the Sun. Spectrum Y is part of the spectrum from a distant galaxy.

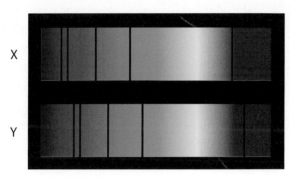

Figure 4 Spectrum X and spectrum Y.

Explain how the shift in position of the dark lines supports the idea that the Universe is expanding.

6 If the Universe is expanding at a constant rate, explain, with the aid of a diagram, why this means that a more distant galaxy is moving away faster than one that is not so far away.

7

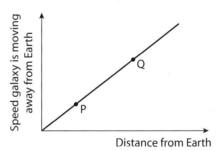

(a) What does this graph tell you about how the speed of a galaxy is related to its distance from Earth?

(b) Describe how the spectrum of galaxy P looks different from the spectrum of galaxy Q.

(c) A burst of radiation from a distant astronomical object was seen with the largest red shift ever recorded. What does this tell you about the object?

8 Explain what astronomers mean by red shift and how it provides evidence that the Universe is expanding.

Examiner feedback

Remember that red shift is not the same as 'getting redder'; the wavelengths get longer and the frequencies lower. For example, microwaves might become radio waves.

Taking it further

Scientists found that some stars vary in brightness with a frequency that depends on how bright the star really is. A star looks dimmer the further away it is, so by measuring the frequency they could work out the actual brightness of the star and compare it with how bright it looked from Earth. This allowed scientists to calculate the distance to the star, and so to the galaxy it was in.

Taking it further

The cosmological red shift is due to the whole 'fabric' of the Universe expanding. The space that the electromagnetic waves travel through is stretching, which causes the wavelength to increase and the frequency to decrease. Compare this to a Doppler shift, which is caused by the relative movement of the source and observer. The source and observer are moving away from the other through space, which is not stretching. The effect is the same, a red shift, but the reason for it is different.

The Big Bang theory

Going back in time

If the Universe is expanding, then last year it was smaller than it is now. When scientists realised this they suggested an explanation for how the Universe began. A suggested explanation is called a **hypothesis**. Their hypothesis was the idea that sometime in the past the Universe must have been very small and that it exploded and has been expanding ever since. If you were to make time go backwards, everything in the Universe would crunch back together into a single point about 13.7 billion years ago. Playing time forwards again from there, a tiny dot suddenly explodes and starts expanding to become the Universe we see today. The explosion is called 'the **Big Bang**'.

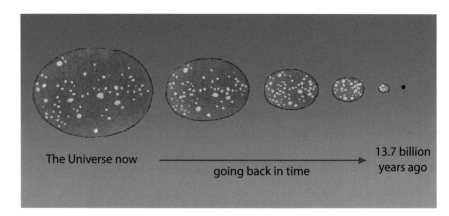

The Universe now   ⟶ going back in time   13.7 billion years ago

Figure 1 The Universe has been expanding for 13.7 billion years.

When the Big Bang hypothesis was first suggested some scientists disagreed with it. They already had a theory that the Universe had always existed. This theory is called the **Steady State theory**. It says that as the Universe expands new galaxies of stars are being formed in the spaces between the other galaxies. This would keep the density of the Universe constant; it would be a steady state.

Cosmic microwave background radiation (CMBR)

Scientists used the Big Bang hypothesis to make a prediction. They said that, if there had been a Big Bang, the small Universe would have been white hot. It has been expanding and cooling ever since, so they predicted that, by now, the radiation from the Big Bang would have been red-shifted as far as the microwave region of the electromagnetic spectrum. In 1964, at Princeton University in the USA, scientists started to search for this radiation.

At the same time, just 40 miles away, scientists Arno Penzias and Robert Wilson were experimenting with the horn-shaped radio wave detector shown in the photo. They wanted to get rid of all radio interference but, no matter how hard they tried, they could not get rid of a microwave radiation with wavelength 7.35 cm. They even cleared out some pigeons that had nested in the structure. The microwave radiation was evenly spread over the sky, 24 hours a day. They realised it came from outside our galaxy, but they could not explain it. When a friend told Arno Penzias about the work of the scientists at Princeton he contacted them and they all realised that the **cosmic microwave background radiation** (CMBR) had been found.

Penzias and Wilson with the horn-shaped receiver that detected CMBR.

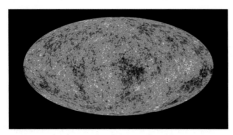

Cosmic microwave background radiation.

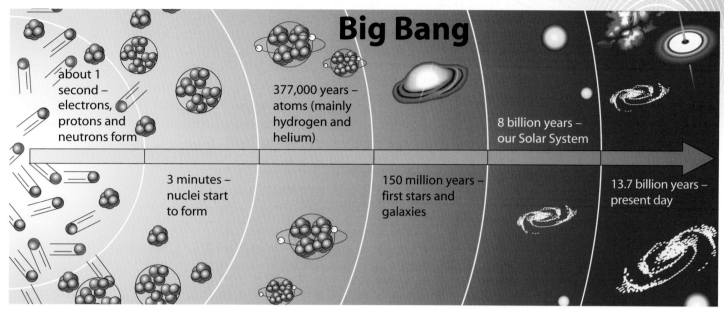

Big Bang

about 1 second – electrons, protons and neutrons form

377,000 years – atoms (mainly hydrogen and helium)

8 billion years – our Solar System

3 minutes – nuclei start to form

150 million years – first stars and galaxies

13.7 billion years – present day

Figure 2 Timeline of the Universe.

Evidence for the Big Bang theory

The **Big Bang theory** is now widely accepted. The red shifts we see in the light from galaxies are strong evidence to support it. More importantly the CMBR is very strong evidence to support it, as there is no other explanation for CMBR arriving at Earth from all directions. Most cosmologists accept the Big Bang theory as the explanation for the origin of the Universe.

Why was there a Big Bang?

This is a question that science will probably never be able to answer. Time started, mass and space were all created at the moment of the Big Bang so there is no way to collect evidence of anything that happened before it, if anything did. The question is one that scientists will almost certainly never have enough reliable and valid evidence to answer.

Questions

1 What does the Big Bang theory say?

2 Give two pieces of evidence for the Big Bang theory.

3 'Why was the Universe created?' Suggest one reason why scientists cannot answer this question.

4 If new data were collected that did not support the Big Bang theory, what should scientists do?

5 Explain why the discovery of the CMBR was so important.

6 Some theories of the Universe suggest that there was a previous Universe that collapsed to a Big Crunch before the Big Bang. Explain whether scientists have any proof of this theory.

7 **(a)** Describe cosmic microwave background radiation (CMBR). **(b)** Explain why it is important in the Big Bang theory.

8 The Steady State theory of the Universe says that the Universe has always existed and as it expands new galaxies of stars are formed in the spaces between the other galaxies.

   Explain the main differences between the Steady State theory and the Big Bang theory, and why the Big Bang theory is the one accepted by most cosmologists today.

ISA practice: modelling optical fibres

You have been asked to investigate how the strength of a signal transmitted by an optical fibre is affected by the length of the fibre. The optical fibre will be modelled using a long rectangular block of jelly.

Hypothesis

The longer the optical fibre, the lower the light intensity reading will be in millivolts.

Section 1

1 In this investigation you will need to control some of the variables.

   (a) Name one variable you will need to control in this investigation. *(1 mark)*

   (b) Describe briefly how you would carry out a preliminary investigation to find a suitable value to use for this variable. Explain how the results will help you decide on the best value for this variable. *(2 marks)*

2 Describe how you would carry out the investigation. You should include:

- the equipment that you would use
- how you would use the equipment
- the measurements that you would make
- a risk assessment
- how you would make it a fair test.

You may include a labelled diagram to help you to explain your method.

In this question you will be assessed on using good English, organising information clearly and using specialist terms where appropriate. *(9 marks)*

3 Design a table that will contain all the data that you would record during the investigation. *(2 marks)*

Total for Section 1: 14 marks

Section 2

Two students, Study Group 1, carried out an investigation to test the hypothesis. They used a block of jelly to model an optical fibre. They measured the length of the jelly block. They sent light through different lengths of jelly fibre and used a detector in an electric circuit to convert the light intensity to a reading in millivolts.

Figure 1 shows their results.

   20 cm jelly: 100 mV
   16 cm jelly: 155 mV
   12 cm jelly: 241 mV
   8 cm jelly: 374 mV
   4 cm jelly: 580 mV
   2 cm jelly: 722 mV

Figure 1 The results of Study Group 1's investigation.

4 (a) (i) What is the independent variable in this investigation?

     (ii) What is the dependent variable in this investigation?

     (iii) Name one control variable in this investigation. *(3 marks)*

   (b) Plot a graph to show the link between the length of the jelly and the light intensity reading in millivolts. *(4 marks)*

   (c) Do the results support the hypothesis? Explain your answer. *(3 marks)*

The results of three other study groups are shown below. Figure 2 shows the results of another two students, Study Group 2.

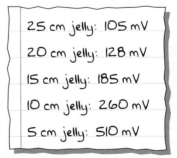

   25 cm jelly: 105 mV
   20 cm jelly: 128 mV
   15 cm jelly: 185 mV
   10 cm jelly: 260 mV
   5 cm jelly: 510 mV

Figure 2 Results from Study Group 2.

Table 1 shows the results of Study Group 3, a group of students who used a brighter lamp with the same jelly.

Table 1 Results from Study Group 3.

Length of jelly/cm	Light intensity/mV			
	Test 1	Test 2	Test 3	Mean
3	764	771	769	768
6	378	380	385	381
9	270	268	356	298
12	182	187	186	185

Table 2 shows the results from Study Group 4, a company that produces fibres for transmitting infrared (IR) signals. It tested two fibre materials: one is a type of glass and one is a crystal. For this test, the company used an IR source with a wavelength of 0.002 mm and an IR detector in an electric circuit that converted the IR intensity to a reading in millivolts. It used different lengths of fibres and measured the voltage.

Table 2 Results from Study Group 4 testing two kinds of optical fibre.

Length of fibre/m	Percentage of signal transmitted (%)							
	HMF glass fibre				Crystal fibre			
	1	2	3	Mean	1	2	3	Mean
1.0	193	196	196	195	183	182	181	182
2.0	191	193	189	191	163	167	168	166
3.0	188	186	168	181	153	150	153	152
4.0	184	181	181	182	138	138	139	138

Study Group 4 then investigated how different wavelengths of IR radiation affected the transmission of the signal. Figure 3 shows their results as a graph.

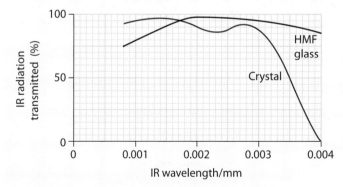

Figure 2 This graph shows how the transmission depends on the wavelength of the infrared radiation for a 1 m length of crystal and a 1 m length of glass fibre.

5 Describe one way in which the results of Study Group 2 are similar to or different from the results of Study Group 1, and give one reason why the results are similar or different
(3 marks)

6 (a) Draw a sketch graph or chart of the results from Study Group 2.
(3 marks)
   (b) Does the data support the hypothesis being investigated? To gain full marks you should use all of the relevant data from Study Groups 1, 2 and 3 to explain whether or not the data supports the hypothesis.
(3 marks)
   (c) The data from the other groups only gives a limited amount of information. What other information or data would you need in order to be more certain as to whether or not the hypothesis is correct? Explain the reason for your answer.
(3 marks)
   (d) Use Studies 2, 3 and 4 to answer this question. What is the relationship between the length of the fibre and the intensity of the light transmitted? How well does the data support your answer?
(3 marks)

7 Look back at the investigation method of Study Group 1. If you could repeat the investigation, suggest one change that you would make to the method, and explain the reason for the change.
(3 marks)

8 The fibre optic company is not convinced that the jelly is a suitable model for the fibre optic cable. Use the results of the investigation to help them decide whether or not the jelly is a suitable model for the cable.
(3 marks)

Total for Section 2: 31 marks
Total for the ISA: 45 marks

Assess yourself questions

1

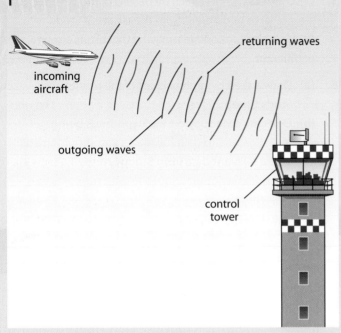

Figure 1 Aircraft being tracked by radar.

Figure 1 shows an aeroplane being tracked by radar.

(a) Which of these is used for radar?

gamma rays   infrared   visible light
microwaves   radio waves   *(1 mark)*

(b) The radar operators use the Doppler effect to tell whether the plane is flying towards or away from the tower.

Explain how the observers in the tower can tell if the aeroplane is flying towards the tower.   *(2 marks)*

2

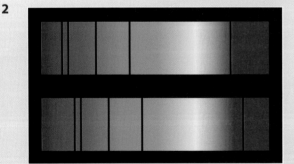

Figure 2 Spectra from two distant galaxies.

Figure 2 shows the spectrum of light from two distant galaxies. Decide whether each of these statements is **TRUE** or **FALSE**.

(a) The red end of the spectrum is the higher energy end of the spectrum.

(b) The dark lines are missing wavelengths of light.

(c) The red end of the spectrum is the longer wavelength end of the spectrum.

(d) The top spectrum is for the galaxy that is furthest away.

(e) The bottom spectrum is for the galaxy that is moving fastest.   *(5 marks)*

3   Table 1 shows the distance from Earth of different galaxies and the speed at which the galaxies are moving away from Earth.

Table 1 Distance to galaxies A to E.

Galaxy	Distance (light years)	Speed/km/s
A	77 000 000	1100
B	1 000 000 000	15 000
C	1 500 000 000	23 000
D	2 500 000 000	4000
E	4 000 000 000	60 000

(a) Are there any anomalous values in this table? If so, which value(s)?   *(1 mark)*

(b) What does the data tell you about the distance to a galaxy and the speed it is moving away from Earth?   *(1 mark)*

(c) Explain what data scientists collected and what they measured to produce this table.   *(2 marks)*

4   The cosmic microwave background radiation (CMBR) is important evidence for the Big Bang theory. Explain what it is and why it is important.

In this question you will be assessed on using good English, organising information clearly and using specialist terms where appropriate.   *(6 marks)*

5   Some students investigate the Doppler effect. They use a loudspeaker emitting a sound with a frequency of 256 Hz and put this in a car that is driven along a straight racetrack at speeds of 10 mph, 20 mph and up to 70 mph. The frequency is picked up by a microphone and a computer displays the frequency received. The students record the results in a table, and work out the speed in m/s and the increase in frequency. They plot a graph of frequency increase against the speed of the car.

Figure 3 shows their graph.

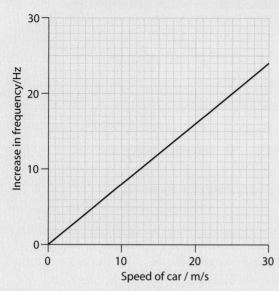

Figure 3 Graph of increase of frequency against speed of car.

(a) How can you tell that the car was driven towards the students and not away from them? *(1 mark)*

(b) Which is the independent variable in this investigation? *(1 mark)*

(c) Describe the relationship between the frequency increase and the speed of the car. *(2 marks)*

(d) Explain how the graph tells you this. *(1 mark)*

(e) Use the graph to find the frequency increase at 29 m/s. *(1 mark)*

(f) From your answer to (e) work out the frequency heard by the observers when the car was travelling at 28 m/s and explain whether the observers could hear the sound. *(2 marks)*

6 The Steady State theory is an alternative to the Big Bang theory. In the Steady State theory, the Universe expands and has always existed. As it expands, matter is created in parts of the Universe to keep the density of matter, like stars and galaxies, looking the same.

(a) What is the difference in the way that the Steady State theory and the Big Bang theory consider the origin of the Universe? *(2 marks)*

Radiation detected from distant galaxies has a red shift.

(b) Explain what is meant by 'red shift'. *(2 marks)*

(c) Explain whether the red shift evidence:

  (i) supports the Big Bang theory' *(2 marks)*

  (ii) supports the Steady State theory. *(2 marks)*

(d) Suggest a reason why scientists cannot answer the question, 'Why was the Universe created?' *(1 mark)*

7

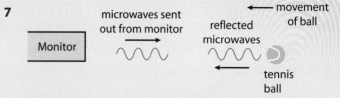

Figure 4 Equipment for measuring speed.

A monitor to measure the performance of a tennis player's serve sends out microwaves towards the ball, and displays the speed of the ball. The microwaves have a wavelength of 12.5 cm.

(a) What is the frequency of the microwaves? (speed of microwaves in air = 300 000 000 m/s) *(2 marks)*

Some microwaves are reflected from the ball, and detected by the monitor.

(b) Describe how this can be used to calculate the speed of the ball. *(3 marks)*

GradeStudio Route to A*

Here are three students' answers to the following question:

Dark lines in the spectra from most distant galaxies shows a 'red shift'. Explain what is meant by a 'red shift' and how this supports the theory that the Universe began as a very small point.

In this question you will be assessed on using good English, organising information clearly and using specialist terms where appropriate. (6 marks)

Read the answers together with the examiner comments. Then check what you have learnt and try putting it into practice in any further questions you answer.

B Grade answer

Student 1

> This is incorrect – a red shift is a shift towards longer wavelengths, for example, blue might become green, or red might become infrared.

> It would be better to say 'the Earth'.

> This sentence is not needed, the fact that they are moving away suggests they started from a point.

A red shift is when the dark lines move into the red part of the spectrum. When there is a red shift it is because galaxies are moving away from us. This means the Universe is expanding. So a long time ago it must have all started from a small point.

Examiner comment

This candidate has understood that red shift shows the galaxies are moving away from the Earth, and that this implies that at some time in the past they were all at the same point.

The explanation of red shift is incorrect and they have not mentioned the change in the frequency or wavelength.

A Grade answer

Student 2

> The important point to note is that we know what the wavelengths should be (so we know they are red shifted).

The dark lines are missing wavelengths in the spectrum. They are shifted towards the red end of the spectrum when the galaxies are moving away from Earth because the galaxies and the Earth are getting further apart. If most are red shifted, most galaxies are moving away, so 14 billion years ago they were all at the same point, implying the Universe started from a very small point.

> This is true, but is not needed. If they had, by mistake, written 14 *million* years it would have lost a mark. It would be best left out.

Examiner comment

Like student 1, this candidate has explained how the red shift leads to the idea that the Universe started from a point. They did not point out that the dark lines were known wavelengths,

or the effect of red shift on the size of the wavelength, or of the frequency.

A* Grade answer

Student 3

Refers to 'known' wavelengths

Clear explanation of red shift, and reference to change in wavelength.

Use of correct terminology.

> The dark lines are where certain, known wavelengths are missing from the spectra. When these are compared with our Sun, the lines from distant galaxies are all at longer wavelengths; this is called a red shift. This shift in wavelength happens because the source is moving away. This tells us that the galaxies are all moving away from Earth, and if all the galaxies in the Universe are moving away then some time in the past they must all have started from the same small point.

Examiner comment

This candidate has covered all the main points in the process:

- Dark lines occur at particular wavelengths.
- In the spectra from the distant galaxies the lines are shifted towards the longer wavelength, or red, end of the spectrum.
- The wavelength appears to have increased (or frequency decreased).
- This occurs because the galaxies are all moving away from the Earth.
- This suggests that a long time in the past they all started from the same point.

MOVING UP THE GRADES

- Read the question carefully.
- These questions carry a maximum of either five or six marks.
- Plan your answer by noting at least five/six relevant points you are going to make.
- Put these points into a logical sequence.

Examination-style questions

1 The following is an extract from an advertisement.

> ### Experience a new level of comfort
> #### with warm-water under-floor heating
>
> Central heating radiators warm a room by moving cold air across
> our feet, warming the air and convecting it round the room. Most
> of the heat from under-floor heating is transferred by radiation. We
> are most comfortable when the heat we feel is radiated, making our
> heads slightly cooler than our feet.

(a) Explain why the air heated by a central heating radiator moves round the room. *(4 marks)*

(b) The diagram shows a section of the floor of a room. The room is heated by under-floor heating.

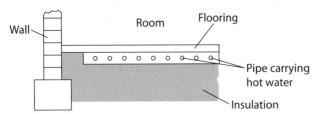

(b) **(i)** How is energy transferred by heating from the hot water pipes through the flooring into the room?
(1 mark)

(ii) The table gives information about different flooring materials.

Flooring material	U value in arbitrary units	Nature of the flooring surface
Ceramic tiles	23.0	Dark-coloured, matt
Concrete	12.5	Light-coloured, matt
Vinyl	20.0	Light-coloured, shiny
Wood	1.5	Dark-coloured, shiny

Which flooring material would be most suitable for use with under-floor heating?
Give reasons for your answer. *(4 marks)*

(c) A room has a concrete floor of mass 480 kg.

The specific heat capacity of concrete is 2400 J/kg/°C.

The under-floor heating system during one day transfers 9 MJ of energy.

(i) Calculate the maximum temperature rise of the concrete floor.

Write down the equation you use. Show clearly how you work out your answer. *(3 marks)*

(ii) Give a reason why the temperature rise of the floor is likely to be less than the value you have
calculated. *(1 mark)*

2 **(a)** The diagram shows two syringes, **A** and **B**.

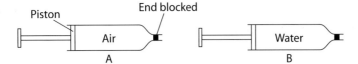

Syringe **A** contains air. Syringe **B** contains water.

One end of each syringe is blocked.

A force is applied to the piston of one of the syringes as shown in the diagram.

Does the syringe above contain air or water? Give a reason for your answer. *(1 mark)*

(b) A woman spills some liquid nail varnish remover on her hand. She notices that the liquid soon disappears and that her hand feels cold. Explain why her hand feels cold. *(2 marks)*

(c) When someone runs water for a bath, they notice that one of the taps becomes coated in a film of moisture.

Is it the hot-water tap or the cold-water tap that becomes coated in moisture? Explain your answer. *(2 marks)*

(d) Use the kinetic theory to explain why a liquid cools down when it evaporates.

In this question you will be assessed on using good English, organising information clearly and using specialist terms where appropriate. *(6 marks)*

3 The bar chart gives the cost of generating electricity in the UK using different types of power stations.

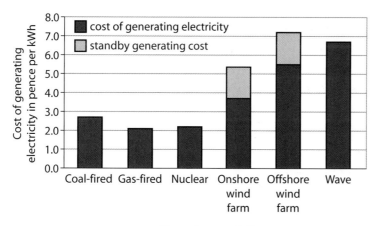

(a) Choose the correct ending **A**, **B**, **C** or **D** to complete the sentence.

The information is displayed as a bar chart because …

A both variables are categoric.

B one variable is categoric, the other variable is controlled.

C one variable is categoric, the other variable is continuous.

D both variables are continuous. *(1 mark)*

(b) The cost of generating electricity at a wind farm has a *standby generation cost* added. This is to cover the cost of generating electricity when the wind farm is not working.

(i) When is a wind farm not likely to be working? *(2 marks)*

(ii) Why do the other types of power station on the bar chart not have a standby generation cost added? *(2 marks)*

(iii) Why is a gas-fired power station most likely to be used for standby generation? *(1 mark)*

(c) The costs of generating electricity given in the bar chart include:

- the capital cost of building and equipping the power station
- the cost of the fuel burned (where applicable)
- the cost of operating and maintaining the power station
- the cost of decommissioning the power station.

The costs do not include the cost of removing carbon dioxide emissions.

    (i) Why do nuclear power stations have high decommissioning costs? *(2 marks)*

    (ii) All new fossil-fuel power stations will, by law, have to remove carbon dioxide emissions. Explain why. *(2 marks)*

    (iii) If the cost of removing carbon dioxide emissions is added to the values given on the bar chart, which type of power station will produce the cheapest electricity? *(1 mark)*

4 Describe, as fully as you can, the similarities and differences between the ways that sound and light travel from one place to another.

In this question you will be assessed on using good English, organising information clearly and using specialist terms where appropriate. *(6 marks)*

5 The diagram compares the spectrum of light from the Sun with the spectra of light from three galaxies, **L, M** and **N**.

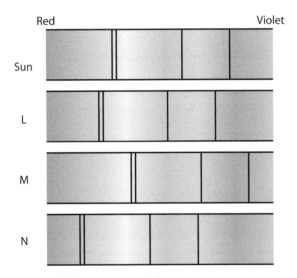

(a) Describe the differences between the spectra and use these differences to deduce what you can about the galaxies **L, M** and **N**.

In this question you will be assessed on using good English, organising information clearly and using specialist terms where appropriate. *(6 marks)*

(b) The spectra of light from distant galaxies provide evidence that the Universe is expanding and support the 'Big Bang' theory for the origin of the Universe.

What is the 'Big Bang' theory? *(2 marks)*

(c) In 1948, George Gamow predicted that there should be microwave radiation left over from the 'Big Bang'. This radiation was discovered in the 1960s and was confirmed by the Cosmic Background Explorer (COBE) satellite in the early 1990s.

Which of the following statements best describes the discovery?

A It disproves the involvement of a god in the origin of the Universe.

B It gives information that helps us know what happened before the 'Big Bang'.

C It provides evidence that eliminates all other theories of the origin of the Universe.

D It provides evidence in support of the 'Big Bang' theory.   *(1 mark)*

6 (a) Some students investigated the diffraction of microwaves using the apparatus below.

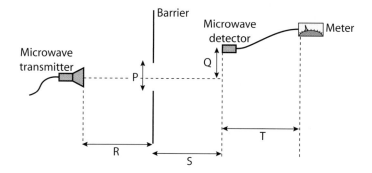

The students wanted to find out how the reading on the meter changed with the distance **Q**.

(i) Which was the dependent variable and which was the independent variable?   *(2 marks)*

(ii) To make it a fair test, which distances had to be controlled?

A   P, Q and R

B   R, S and T

C   P, R and S

D   P, Q and T   *(2 marks)*

(b) The teacher told the students to make the gap width, **P**, the same value as the wavelength of the microwaves.

The frequency of the microwaves was 1×10^{10} Hz.

The speed of microwaves is 3×10^8 m/s.

What should the gap width be, in centimetres? Write down the equation you use. Show clearly how you work out your answer.   *(3 marks)*

(c) Television and radio programmes are often transmitted from the same transmitting mast. The carrier wave for television programmes has a higher frequency than the frequency of the carrier wave for radio programmes.

There is a high hill between one particular house and the transmitting mast. The householder receives signals from the mast by diffraction round the hill. He finds that he can receive radio programmes but not television programmes.

What can be deduced about the diffraction of waves round an obstacle and the wavelength of the waves?

Explain your answer.   *(3 marks)*

Glossary

2,4-D (short for 2,4-dichlorophenoxyacetic acid) A common selective weedkiller, used against broadleaf plants.

A

absorb Take in, or soak up; for example when energy of radiation is absorbed by matter.

accurate A measurement that is close to the true value.

acid Substances with a pH of less than 7, which turn litmus paper red and release hydrogen ions in solution.

acid rain Rain that has a pH of less than 5.6 because of dissolved pollutants, usually sulfur dioxide.

adaptations A characteristic that helps an organism to survive in its environment.

adult cell cloning Process in which the nucleus of an adult cell is inserted into an unfertilised egg cell from which the nucleus has been removed, and the cell divides and develops into a new individual.

aerobic respiration Respiration that requires the presence of oxygen to release energy from glucose, producing carbon dioxide and water.

agar A nutrient-rich jelly obtained from seaweed used for growing microbes.

aggregate A material such as gravel, crushed rock or ash, made up of coarse particles. It is used in building, in particular for making concrete.

air A mixture of gases, mainly nitrogen and oxygen, that covers the Earth's surface.

alcohol In drinks, ethanol, obtained by fomenting sugars in fruit or grain.

alkanes Hydrocarbons that have only C–H and single C–C bonds, with the general formula CnH2n+2.

alkenes Hydrocarbons with one (or more) C=C double bonds

alloys Mixtures of metals blended to have specific properties.

amplitude The maximum displacement of a particle as a wave passes; half the height of a wave.

anaerobic digestion The breakdown of dead plant or animal material by anaerobic respiration.

anaerobic respiration Respiration which doesn't need oxygen – the release of energy from glucose without oxygen. In muscle cells this produces lactic acid as a waste product.

angle of incidence The angle between the normal and the incident ray.

angle of reflection The angle between the normal and the reflected ray, or wave direction.

anomalous An anomalous result is a result that is too far away from the rest of the results to be reliable.

antibiotics Chemicals produced by microbes, used to destroy bacteria.

antibodies Chemicals to attack infections produced in the body by white blood cells when the immune system detects the presence of a particular pathogen.

antiseptics Chemicals that are used to stop the growth of microorganisms on the skin, wounds or other living tissue.

antitoxins Substances produced in the body by white blood cells to neutralise poisons produced by microbes.

antiviral (drug) A drug used to treat infections caused by viruses, such as flu or measles.

aquatic Living in water.

aseptic Conditions that are free from disease-causing micro-organisms.

asexual reproduction Reproduction from one cell of a parent organism, without fertilisation of gametes, that is, fusion of male and female sex cells.

atmosphere The layer of gases surrounding the Earth.

atomic number The number of protons in the nucleus of atoms of a particular element.

atoms Particles with no overall electric charge, containing protons, neutrons and electrons. The smallest pieces of an element that still have the properties of that element.

autism A disorder in which a person finds it difficult to communicate with others and to interact socially.

autoclave A device used for sterilising laboratory equipment with superheated steam.

auxins Plant hormones, produced in the buds, that help rooting and bud formation.

B

bacteria Single-celled microorganisms without a nucleus. Bacteria can reproduce very quickly and some cause disease.

balanced diet A diet made up of a variety of different foods to provide the energy and all the nutrients needed to stay healthy.

balanced equations Chemical equations with the same numbers and types of atoms on both sides of the arrow.

barrage A barrier across a river or estuary used to control water flow and prevent floods. Turbines can be placed in a barrage to generate electricity.

Big Bang theory The theory that the entire Universe originated that in an explosion from a single point about 14 billion years ago.

biodegradable Can be broken down easily into simpler chemicals by natural, biological processes.

biodiesel A renewable fuel made from vegetable oil that can be used in place of diesel from crude oil.

biofuels Fuels made from living sources such as plant matter.

biogas Fuel made by the anaerobic fermentation of waste food or sewage by microbes, or when waste wood is heated in a limited supply of air. A mixture of mostly methane and carbon dioxide.

bioleaching The process of extracting metals from their ores using bacteria or other microorganisms.

biomass Biological material; in particular, the total mass of living material at a specified level in a food chain or a specified area.

blast furnace Furnace in which ore containing iron oxide is heated with limestone and coke to produce iron.

blue shift The decrease in wavelength (increase in frequency) of electromagnetic radiation from approaching stars or galaxies due to the Doppler effect.

Bluetooth A low-power system that uses microwaves to exchange information over short distances between devices such as mobile phones, TVs and laptops.

brain The centre of the nervous system, responsible for interpreting sensory signals, co-ordinating motor responses and higher activities such as thought and memory.

brittle Easily cracked or broken.

C

caffeine Drug found especially in coffee and tea that is a mild stimulant to the central nervous system.

calibration Checking that the points on a measuring scale are set correctly, so that accurate readings can be taken.

callus Cluster of cells grown by tissue culture.

camouflage Body colouring and/or shape that helps conceal an organism in its environment.

cannabis (also called marijuana) An illegal drug that can produce a sense of euphoria (well-being), but also anxiety and loss of short-term memory.

carbohydrates Food type, including sugars and starch, that is the main energy source in the diet. Carbohydrates contain only the elements carbon, hydrogen and oxygen.

carbon capture and storage Techniques for removing carbon dioxide from exhaust gases and preventing it reaching the atmosphere; intended to reduce global warming.

carbon cycle The way in which carbon atoms circulate between living organisms and the physical environment.

carbon-neutral Having no overall carbon dioxide emissions; usually refers to a fuel that releases as much carbon dioxide when it is produced and burned as was absorbed by the plants from which it is made as they grew.

catalysts Chemicals that speed up a reaction but are not themselves used up.

categoric variable A variable that can only take particular values, for example days of the week or different types of food.

cell membrane The thin outer layer of a cell that controls what goes into and comes out of a cell.

cement A powder used in construction that sets hard when mixed with water. It is made by heating limestone with clay.

central nervous system The brain and spinal cord.

cerebral palsy A medical condition in which the brain does not co-ordinate movement properly. It is caused by damage to the brain before birth or in early childhood.

characteristics The features of an organism, such as its size, colour or behaviour; many characteristics are coded for by genes.

chemical bonds The strong links that form between atoms during chemical reactions and hold compounds together.

chemical energy Energy stored in the chemical bonds of compounds, such as those in the cells of living organisms.

chemical formula A way of using letters and numbers to describe the types of atoms and their numbers in an element or compound.

chemosynthesis The construction of molecules, such as glucose, using smaller molecules as building blocks and energy from other chemicals.

chlorinated With chlorine added to kill bacteria and other microorganisms.

cholesterol A fatty substance made in the liver and used in cell membranes.

chromosomes Immensely long molecules of DNA containing many regions called genes, each of which carries the genetic information that influences a characteristic of the organism. Chromosomes are found in the nuclei of cells.

classification A system for grouping organisms according to their characteristics.

clinical trials Set of tests on people that provide data on the effectiveness of a drug.

clomiphine A fertility drug that works by blocking the effect of oestrogen on the pituitary gland.

clones Individuals that are genetically identical to the parent because they were produced by mitosis.

cocaine An illegal, highly addictive drug produced from the leaves of the coca plant (Erythroxylum coca) It produces feelings of euphoria (well-being) and high energy.

combustion Burning. The reaction that occurs when a fuel combines with oxygen in a heat-producing oxidation reaction.

common ancestor An organism or species that is an ancestor (in evolutionary terms) of two or more later organisms or species.

competition The struggle between individual organisms for a share of a limited resource, such as water or food; for example, competition between two predators hunting the same prey.

complete combustion Combustion continued until no further reaction with oxygen is possible, for example the complete combustion of alkanes in oxygen to give water and carbon dioxide.

compost Remains of plants and other organic waste broken down by microorganisms; it can be mixed with soil for use as a garden fertiliser.

compost heap A pile of mainly garden and kitchen waste that decays to produce compost.

compound Substance that contains two or more different elements chemically joined together to form a new substance with new properties.

compression Squashing of a substance, for example a medium through which longitudinal waves are passing.

concrete A building material made by mixing cement, sand and gravel with water; it sets to become a very hard 'artificial rock'.

condense Turn from a gas or vapour to a liquid.

conduction Transfer of energy through a material (usually a solid) by transfer of vibration from particles to their neighbours.

conductor A material that allows electricity to flow through it easily, or that readily transfers energy by heating. Metals are good conductors.

conservation of energy The principle stating that energy cannot be created or destroyed; it can only be transferred usefully, stored or dissipated (wasted). The total amount of energy does not change.

conservation of mass In chemistry, the law that mass is neither created nor destroyed in chemical reactions. The mass of reactants in a chemical reaction must equal the mass of the products.

continental drift The extremely slow movement of the continents across the surface of the Earth.

continuous variable A variable that can take any value, such as the time taken for a chemical reaction to happen.

continuous variation Variation within a population of animals or plants that is strongly affected by the environment, for example height.

control measures Actions that reduce a hazard to an acceptable level of risk.

control variables Variables that need to be kept constant throughout an experiment to ensure that they do not affect the dependent variable.

convection The movement of particles in a gas or liquid depending on their temperature. Hotter, less dense regions float and cooler, denser regions sink.

core The central part of the Earth.

corrosion Damage or destruction of a metal or other substance by chemical action.

cosmic microwave background radiation (CMBR) Radiation from an early stage of the Universe.

cost-effective A measure is cost-effective if it saves more money than it costs.

covalent bonds Pairs of electrons shared between two atoms, which hold the atoms together within a molecule.

cracking The process by which long-chain hydrocarbons, usually alkanes, are broken up into shorter and more useful hydrocarbons, usually alkanes and alkenes.

crests The points at the maximum positive amplitude of a transverse wave.

crude oil Oil as it is found naturally, consisting mainly of hydrocarbons.

crust The thin, hard and brittle outer layer of the Earth.

culture medium A solution or jelly containing nutrients for the growth of microorganisms.

culture plates Plates coated with a jelly containing nutrients for the growth of microorganisms.

cuttings Small pieces of a plant, such as leaf or stem, used to grow new plants.

cycle A series of processes that occur in the same order and repeat.

cytoplasm The substance outside the nuclei in cells, in which many of the chemical reactions take place. These reactions are catalysed by enzymes.

D

decay The breakdown of dead plant and animal material by fungi, bacteria and other organisms.

decolourise Remove colour from.

decommission Take out of use.

decompose Break down into simpler substances.

deficiency diseases Diseases caused by a lack of an essential nutrient in the diet.

dense Having a high mass in a small volume. Density is mass per unit volume.

dependent variables In experiments, dependent variables are the variables that are measured for each change in the independent variable.

detritus feeders Organisms that feeds on detritus, that is, organic waste.

diabetes Disease of the body in which blood glucose concentration is not controlled because the pancreas fails to produce enough insulin.

diffraction The spreading out of waves after they pass through a narrow gap; this effect is most noticeable when the gap is the same size as the wavelength of the wave.

digest Break down into smaller particles, as when food is digested in the gut.

digesters Large vessel in which dead plant or animal material is broken down by microorganisms, for example in in-vessel composting.

disinfectants Substances used to kill microorganisms on non-living surfaces.

displacement reaction A type of chemical reaction in which one element reacts with a compound of a second element and the result is the second element and a compound of the first element.

displayed formula A diagram showing the atoms in a molecule and the bonds between them.

distillation A method for separation of a mixture of liquids with different boiling points.

distribution The area of the environment in which a species lives.

DNA (deoxyribonucleic acid) The genetic material, found in the nucleus of living cells. Chromosomes are made up of DNA, and a gene is a section of a chromosome.

Doppler effect A change in the wavelength (and frequency) of a wave caused by relative movement of the source and the observer.

double-blind trials Trials in which neither the subjects nor the experimenters know which substance is the test substance and which is the control.

driptips Leaf tips that have evolved into a shape that enables water to drip off the leaf.

drought A period of time when there is a lack of water for organisms.

drugs Any substance that, when absorbed into the body, alters normal body function. Medical drugs such as antibiotics are used to fight illness or disease. Recreational drugs such as alcohol and caffeine are stimulating or give a sense of well-being.

E

earthquake Shaking and distortion of the ground due to the sudden movement of tectonic plates.

echo Repetition of a sound produced when the sound is reflected back from a surface.

ecological relationship A relationship between organisms that have developed similar characteristics because of their similar lifestyles.

ecstasy The illegal synthetic drug MDMA (3,4-methylenedioxymethamphetamine).

ectothermic Animals that use external methods such as basking to maintain their body temperature.

effector An organ or cell that brings about a response to a stimulus.

efficiency The proportion of the energy supplied to a device that is transformed usefully rather than wasted.

egest Expel waste material that was not digested from the gut.

elastic potential energy Also called strain energy; the energy stored in an elastic object because of its shape when it is stretched or squashed.

electrolysis Decomposition of a molten (or dissolved) ionic compound produced by passing an electric current through it.

electromagnetic waves A form of energy that is transferred as fast-moving waves. Electromagnetic waves include X-rays, radio waves, light and infrared radiation. They can travel through a vacuum.

electron shells The positions that electrons can occupy around an atom, also known as energy levels.

electronic structure The number and arrangement of electrons in the electron shells around an atom.

electrons Tiny particles with a single negative charge each that occupy energy levels around an atom's nucleus. Electrons are responsible for the chemical bonds between atoms, and move through metals when a current flows.

elements Substances containing only one type of atom.

embryo transplanting Splitting early embryos into separate cells and placing them into the wombs of other, surrogate, mothers to develop.

emit Give out, for example when light is emitted by a light bulb.

emulsifier Substance added to an emulsion of two liquids that do not mix to stabilise it, that is, stop it from separating.

emulsion Mixture of two immiscible liquids, such as an oil and water, in which tiny droplets of one liquid are distributed evenly through the other liquid.

enzymes Protein molecules that act as biological catalysts to speed up the rate of reactions taking place in and around cells.

epidemic The widespread outbreak of an infectious disease within a country.

ethene (ethylene) The smallest alkene, C_2H_4. Contains a double bond between the carbon atoms and is often used as a chemical feedstock.

evaporate Turn from a liquid to a vapour or gas.

evolution Changes in the characteristics of species over time.

evolutionary relationship The existence of similar characteristics in different organisms because they evolved from a common ancestor.

excrete Discard waste products from cell reactions within the body, such as urine from kidneys.

extremophiles Organisms that are adapted to an extreme condition of the environment.

F

faeces Waste matter remaining in the gut after food has been digested, which is egested from the body.

fats Organic compounds, not miscible with water, that form the main part of cell membranes and are important for energy storage.

fermentation One kind of anaerobic respiration by microorganisms.

fertilised (egg) An egg cell in which male gametes have joined with the cell nucleus to form a zygote (an egg cell that can develop into a new animal or plant).

fertilisation The process by which male and female gametes fuse (join) to form a zygote (an egg cell that can develop into a new animal or plant).

filtration Method used to separate an insoluble solid from a liquid.

fixing Absorbing carbon dioxide from the air and converting it into complex carbon compounds. Plants fix carbon dioxide during photosynthesis.

flagella (sing. flagellum) Tiny 'tails' on cells that enable the cell to move.

flammable Easily ignited and burned.

fluids Any substances that can flow: liquids and gases are fluids.

food chain A diagram that shows who eats what in a single set of feeding relationships.

food web A diagram that shows all the feeding relationships between organisms living in the same area.

fossil fuels Fuels such as coal, crude oil and natural gas, formed over millions of years from the remains of ancient animals and/or plants.

fossils Remains of organisms that lived in the past found preserved in rock, or evidence of organisms having been there (such as footprints).

fractional distillation A method used to separate two or more miscible liquids with different boiling points, involving boiling the mixture, then condensing the vapour at different temperatures.

fractionating column Tower in which fractional distillation takes place.

fractions Mixtures of compounds with similar boiling points, produced by fractional distillation.

free electrons Electrons in a metal that are free to move and thus to carry current or transfer energy.

frequency The number of times per second that something happens, usually the number of waves per second; measured in hertz (Hz).

FSH The hormone that, in women, stimulates follicles in the ovaries to release an egg.

fuel cells Devices in which a fuel such as hydrogen is oxidised continuously and directly, rather than by burning, to generate electricity.

G

gametes Specialised sex cells, such as sperm or eggs, involved in sexual reproduction in plants and animals.

gamma rays The range of the electromagnetic spectrum of waves that has the shortest wavelength and highest energy; given off by radioactive nuclei.

gas The state of matter in which a substance has a fairly low density, expands to fill any container it is put in, and can be compressed when put under pressure.

gas turbine A type of engine in which fuel is burnt in air to produce expanding gases, which are used to turn a turbine or turbines.

gateway drug An illegal drug that does not have especially harmful effects, but can lead users on to consumption of more harmful drugs.

gel A jelly-like material with a grid structure that can trap water.

genes Small sections of DNA in chromosomes. Each gene contains the code for a particular inherited characteristic, that is, to make a particular protein.

genetic engineering The process of taking genes from one organism and putting them into the cells of another so that the cells include the characteristic of the new gene.

genetically modified (GM) An organism that has been genetically engineered.

geothermal energy Energy for electricity generation by means of steam heated by hot underground rocks.

glands Small organs responsible for the production and release of a particular substance for the control of bodily functions by chemical means.

global dimming The decrease in energy from the Sun reaching the Earth caused by the presence of particles in the atmosphere.

global warming The rise in mean surface temperatures on the Earth, thought to be due to increasing amounts of greenhouse gases such as carbon dioxide.

glucose A simple sugar (carbohydrate) produced in plants by photosynthesis and from starch by digestion, broken down in respiration to release energy.

gravitational potential energy The energy stored in an object because of its height above the ground.

gravitropism Growth (of a plant root) downwards.

greenhouse effect The trapping of warmth by greenhouse gases such as carbon dioxide in the Earth's atmosphere that keeps the surface of the Earth warm enough for life.

greenhouse gases Gases in the atmosphere that contribute to the greenhouse effect, such as carbon dioxide.

group Vertical column in the periodic table.

H

hardening Changing an unsaturated oil into a saturated fat by reaction with hydrogen.

hazards Things that can go wrong with an experiment and cause injury to people or objects.

heat exchanger A device that transfers energy through heating from a fluid flowing on one side of a barrier to a fluid flowing on the other side, without the two fluids coming into contact.

heat sink A device with a high heat capacity that can absorb energy from a small object at high temperature. Heat sinks are used, for example, to cool electronic components.

herbicide Chemical that kills plants, used to treat weeds in crops.

heroin A highly addictive, illegal narcotic drug (a drug that causes numbness and drowsiness).

hertz A unit of frequency, the number of cycles per second.

high-carbon steels Hard, strong steel alloys containing between 0.6 and 1 per cent carbon.

homeostasis The processes that keep variations of some factors, such as temperature, water, mineral ions and blood sugar concentration, within limits in the body.

homeothermic Animals that keep their body temperature roughly constant, regardless of the surrounding temperature.

homologous series A group of similar compounds which just differ by a CH_2 group.

hormones Chemicals produced by one part of an organism, that control a process in another part of the organism.

host mothers Female organisms that have had an embryo from another female implanted in their womb.

hydration A chemical reaction involving the addition of water to a compound, for example the hydration of ethene to form ethanol.

hydrocarbons Compounds containing hydrogen and carbon only.

hydroelectricity Using water flowing down a hill to make electricity.

hydrogel Polymers that contain a lot of water in their structure. They are used as dressings for some wounds, and for making soft contact lenses.

hydrogenation A chemical reaction in which hydrogen is added to a compound, e.g. the hydrogenation of unsaturated oil to make saturated fat.

hydrophilic 'Water loving' part of a molecule able to dissolve in water.

hydrophobic 'Water hating' part of a molecule able to dissolve in oil or fat.

hydrothermal vents Cracks in the ocean floor where heat and chemicals escape from the rocks below into the water.

hydrotropism Growth (of a plant root) towards water.

hygiene Hand-washing, cleaning floors and surfaces, and other procedures designed to reduce the chances of infection from bacteria and other microorganisms.

hypothesis A scientific explanation that is thought up and suggested to explain something. It is used to make predictions that can be tested scientifically.

I

image A picture of an object formed by light rays, for example by a mirror or lens.

immiscible Liquids that cannot dissolve into one another, for example oil and water.

immune Protected against disease by the production of antibodies.

immunisation Injecting or swallowing a vaccine to provide immunity against a disease or diseases.

impulses Form in which information is transmitted by nerve cells.

in vitro fertilisation (IVF) Fertilisation of an egg outside the body of a female by the addition of sperm, as a means of producing an embryo.

incident The ray of light hitting a mirror or an interface between two transparent materials.

incinerator A furnace for burning waste under controlled conditions.

incomplete combustion (partial combustion) Burning of carbon-based fuels to form carbon monoxide, rather than carbon dioxide.

incubation Growing microbes or hatching eggs in an incubator.

incubator A container in which the temperature and humidity are controlled, used to hatch eggs or grow microorganisms.

independent variable A variable that is changed or selected by the investigator.

infrared radiation (IR) Electromagnetic radiation that we can feel as heat. IR has a longer wavelength than visible light, but a shorter wavelength than microwaves.

ingest Take food into the body.

inherit In biology, to receive a genetic characteristic from a parent.

inoculating loop A small loop of wire with a handle, used to spread a microbial culture on an agar plate.

inoculation Injection with microbes (living or dead).

insulate Prevent electricity from flowing, or transfer of energy through heating or cooling.

insulator A material that does not easily conduct electricity, or readily transfer energy by heating. Gases are good insulators.

intensity (radiation) The amount of energy arriving on a unit area of surface each second.

in-vessel composting Forming compost from waste plant material within a large vessel in which conditions of temperature and moisture can be controlled. (Not needed for the exam.)

ionic bond A chemical bond in which oppositely charged ions are held together by mutual attraction.

ionising radiation High-energy radiation that ionises atoms by removing electrons. Ionising radiation includes some ultraviolet radiation, X-rays and gamma rays.

ionosphere The outer layer of the Earth's atmosphere. It is called the ionosphere because the air is ionised by the Sun's radiation.

ions Electrically charged particles containing a different number of protons and electrons. Charged particles.

K

kidneys Organs that control the content of blood by filtering out waste substances such as urea, and regulating ion and water content.

kilowatt-hours (kWh) A unit of measurement for electrical energy. 1 kWh = 3.6 megajoules (3,600,000 J). Also sometimes called a Unit of electricity.

kilowatts (kW) A measure of power often used for electrical devices. 1 kW = 1000 W.

kinetic energy The energy an object has because it is moving.

L

landfill site A place where rubbish is dumped and buried in pre-prepared areas.

lattice A regular, continuous structure of atoms or ions, for example in a crystal.

leachate A liquid produced when water or some other solvent percolates through a permeable material.

leaching Injecting liquid into rock or other permeable material in order to produce a leachate.

leprosy (Hansen's disease) A serious infectious disease of the skin and nerves caused by Mycobacterium bacteria.

lichen Organism formed from a fungus and lichen that can live in extreme conditions; used as an indicator of air pollution.

limestone A type of sedimentary rock consisting mainly of calcium carbonate, formed from the remains of marine animals.

lithosphere The Earth's crust and the upper part of the mantle.

longitudinal waves Waves in which the oscillations are parallel to the direction of energy transfer.

low-carbon steels The most common form of steel, containing approximately 0.05 to 0.15% carbon.

M

malnutrition The result of eating an unbalanced diet. Malnutrition can cause illness or make people prone to catch diseases.

mantle A thick layer of hot, almost molten rock inside the Earth between the crust and the core.

mass number The number of protons and neutrons in the nucleus of an atom.

maturation The process of becoming an adult.

mean The numerical average of a set of data.

mechanical waves A wave in matter such as a water wave. Any waves other than sound or electromagnetic waves.

medicine The science of preventing, alleviating or curing disease, illness or injury.

medium The material that a wave travels through.

menstrual cycle The monthly cycle of changes in a woman's reproductive system, controlled by hormones.

metabolic rate A measure of the energy used by an animal in a given time period.

methanogens Microorganisms that produce methane.

mica A type of transparent mineral that can be split into thin sheets.

microorganisms Organisms so small they can only be seen through a microscope.

microwaves Electromagnetic radiation that has wavelengths from about 10 cm to 0.1 mm – longer than infrared but shorter than radio waves.

minerals Simple chemicals found in the soil and rocks.

miscible Liquids that can dissolve into one another.

mixture Two or more substances mixed in any proportion which are not chemically combined.

MMR A vaccination for measles, mumps and rubella (German measles).

molecular formula The chemical formula showing the different elements and the number of atoms of each element in a molecule, for example CH_4 (methane).

molecules Particles made of atoms joined to each other by covalent bonds.

molten Melted; liquid.

monomers The small molecules that are the subunits of polymers.

mortar A paste made from slaked lime and water that was once used to stick bricks together.

motor neurones Nerve cells that carry information to an effector organ, such as a skeletal muscle.

moult Shed fur, feathers, skin or scales. For example, cold-adapted mammals lose some of their thick fur in summer.

MRSA A type of bacteria resistant to antibiotics (methicillin-resistant Staphylococcus aureus).

mutation A change in a gene that may result in different characteristics.

N

National Grid The system of power stations, cables and transformers that transfer electricity all over the country.

natural selection When the environment selects individuals so that only the best adapted survive and breed.

negative ion An atom that has acquired a negative charge by gaining one or more electrons.

negatively gravitropic Growth (of a plant stem) away from the pull of gravity.

nervous system The body system that transmits sensory information and muscle signals, co-ordinates body action and is responsible for thinking and memory. [It consists of the brain, spinal cord and neurones or nerves.]

neurones (nerve cells) Cells specialised to transmit electrical nerve impulses and so carry information from one part of the body to another.

neutralise Make a solution neither acid nor alkaline. In a neutralisation reaction an acid and a base combine to make a salt.

neutrons Sub-atomic particles found within the atomic nucleus that have no electric charge and a relative mass of 1.

nicotine The active component of the recreational drug tobacco; a stimulant that causes dependence.

non-renewable A resource that cannot be replaced once it has been used up. Fossil fuels are all non-renewable.

normal A line perpendicular (at right angles) to a surface.

nuclear energy Energy released by reactions that take place within the nuclei of atoms.

nuclear fission A reaction in which a large, unstable atomic nucleus splits into smaller nuclei, releasing neutrons and much energy.

nucleus (biology) The large organelle inside a cell that contains genetic material.

nucleus (chemistry, physics) The central part of an atom, containing most of the mass. It is made up of protons and neutrons.

nutrients Substances that a living thing needs so that it can grow healthily.

O

observations Measurements or collections of data.

oestrogen A sex hormone produced in the ovary that is responsible for egg release and for female secondary sexual characteristics.

optical fibres Thin glass or plastic strands that can transmit light or infrared radiation over long distances.

ores Rocks containing a high concentration of a particular metal or metal compound.

organic Relating to or derived from living organisms.

oscillation Vibration or repetitive pattern of movement, for example, up and down or side to side.

oscilloscope An electronic device used to show how voltage changes with time.

ovum An egg cell.

oxidation A type of chemical reaction. When a substance is oxidised it gains oxygen, loses hydrogen or loses electrons.

oxidised Gained oxygen in a chemical reaction.

P

pandemic A disease that is spread rapidly across many countries.

partial combustion See incomplete combustion.

particulates Very small solid particles produced when fuels burn

passive infra-red devices (PIRs) Burglar alarms that detect infrared radiation emitted by the human body.

pathogens Microorganisms that cause illness or disease.

payback time The time it takes to get back in savings the money spent on reducing energy consumption.

penicillin A group of antibiotics produced from Penicillium fungi.

periodic table A table of all the elements arranged in order of increasing atomic number, and set out to show patterns in their properties.

permeable Allows the passage of water or a particular material.

Petri dishes Shallow, round glass or plastic dishes with lids that are used for growing microorganisms.

photosynthesis The process by which green plant cells produce sugars and oxygen from carbon dioxide and water using light energy.

phototropism Growing towards or away from the light.

physical conditions Conditions of the environment caused by physical processes, such as temperature and amount of water.

phytomining Growing plants as a way of concentrating metals or other minerals from the soil.

pitch How high or low a note sounds. This is related to the frequency of the sound wave.

placebo A dummy medicine.

placebo effect An improvement in a patient's medical condition produced by taking a placebo.

plasmid A loop of genetic material outside the main chromosome in a bacterium

plutonium A heavy element, one form of which can be used as a fuel in nuclear power stations.

pollination The transfer of pollen from one flower to another so that fertilisation is possible.

pollution Damage to the environment or to living things caused by harmful chemicals.

pollution indicators Organisms whose presence or absence indicates that there is pollution.

poly(ethene) Polymer (plastic) made from ethene.

polymers Long-chain molecules made by joining many short molecules (monomers) together.

polymerisation Reaction in which many short molecules (monomers) are joined together to make a polymer.

positive ion An atom that has acquired a positive charge by losing one or more electrons.

positively gravitropic Plants that grow downwards with the pull of gravity.

positively hydrotropic Plants that grow towards a source of water.

positively phototropic Plants that grow towards the light.

potential difference See voltage.

power The amount of energy transferred per second.

precision The closer the measurements are to each other and the mean of the results, the greater the precision of the results. This does not mean that your results are accurate

prediction Predictions provide a way to test a hypothesis

pressing Method used to separate vegetable oil from crushed plant material using pressure.

producers Organisms that make their own food, e.g. plants and green algae by photosynthesis, or some bacteria by chemosynthesis.

proteins Large molecules that play an important role in all living things and are an important part of the human diet.

protons Sub-atomic particles found within the atomic nucleus that have a single positive charge and a relative mass of 1.

pure culture A culture containing only one type of microorganism.

pyramid of biomass A diagram that shows the mass of living organisms at each stage in a food chain.

R

radio waves Electromagnetic radiation with the longest wavelength and lowest frequency.

radioactive Having some atoms with unstable nuclei, which may spontaneously break down and give out radiation.

random error An unpredictable variation around the true value, causing each reading to be slightly different.

randomised controlled trial A way of making the test of a new drug or treatment fair. Patients are randomly put into either a treatment group or a control group, and neither the doctor nor the patient knows which group any patient is in until the trial is over.

range The spread between maximum and minimum values in a set of experimental results.

rarefaction Spreading out of material as a longitudinal waves passes through it

reactive Easily taking part in chemical reactions.

real image An image that light rays pass through, so that it can be seen on a screen placed at that point.

receptors Organs or cells that are sensitive to external stimuli.

rechargeable batteries Batteries that can be recharged.

recreational drugs Drugs that are taken voluntarily for personal pleasure or satisfaction rather than for medicinal purposes.

recycling Processing used materials so that they can be made into new products.

red shift The increase in wavelength (decrease in frequency) of electromagnetic radiation from distant, receding galaxies due to the Doppler effect and the expansion of the Universe.

reduction A type of chemical reaction. When a substance is reduced it loses oxygen, gains hydrogen or gains electrons.

reflected Waves are reflected when they bounce off an object, for example light bouncing off a mirror.

refracted Waves are refracted when they change direction as they go through an interface into a different material, where the wave's speed is different.

relay neurones Neurones that carry information from a sensory nerve cell to a motor nerve cell.

reliable (measurement) A measurement is reliable if you get almost the same value every time it is repeated.

reliable (energy) An energy source is reliable if it can supply energy at all times, or at clearly defined times.

renewable A resource that can be replaced once it has been used, for example timber is renewable because new trees can be grown.

repeatable Results are repeatable if is possible to get the same or similar results if the investigation is repeated.

reproducible Results are reproducible if they are still similar when the method is changed, different equipment is used, or if someone else does the investigation.

resistant A pathogen is resistant if it cannot be destroyed by the action of antibiotics.

respiration The breakdown of sugar in cells to release energy, carbon dioxide and water.

ripple tank A shallow tank of water for investigating the behaviour of water waves.

rooting powder A powder containing the plant hormone auxin, which encourages a cutting from a plant to grow roots.

rotting The breakdown of biological material.

runners Underground stems that some plants have, which produces new plants by asexual reproduction.

S

Sankey diagram A type of flow diagram showing energy transfers in a process, where the width of the arrows is proportional to the amount of energy transferred in each process.

saturated (chemistry) A carbon-chain molecule that only has single bonds between the carbon atoms.

saturated (air) Air that is full of water vapour and cannot hold any more.

sea-floor spreading The widening of the Atlantic Ocean due to the movement of rock away from the mid-Atlantic ridge as new rock is formed at the ridge.

selective weedkillers Chemicals that kill broad-leaved weeds but not wheat or other grasses.

sensory neurones A nerve cell that carries information to the brain or spinal cord.

sexual reproduction Producing offspring by the fusion of male and female sex cells (gametes).

shape-memory polymers Polymers that revert back to their original shape when the temperature is hot enough.

shock waves Fast-moving waves produced after an explosion or an earthquake.

side effects Unwanted reactions to a drug or other medicine. For example, some people are allergic to penicillin.

simvastatin A type of statin, designed to reduce levels of cholesterol in the blood.

sludge digester A tank in which sludge (biological waste) is fermented with bacterial to produce a gas rich in methane.

solar cells Cells that convert light into electrical energy.

smart materials Materials whose properties change if their environment changes.

solute Substance that is dissolved to make a solution.

solvent Substance into which a solute dissolves to make a solution.

specialise When cells specialise, they change to be more suited to do a specific task. For example retina cells become specialised to sense light .

species A group of organisms that have many characteristics in common and are able to breed together.

specific heat capacity The energy to raise the temperature of 1 kg of a material by 1 °C.

spectrum A series of waves arranged in order according to their wavelengths and frequencies.

spinal cord An important part of the central nervous system, which carries sensory and motor nerve impulses to and from the brain.

spoil Mining waste.

stable Staying the same, not changing.

statins Drugs that act to reduce levels of cholesterol in the blood.

Steady State theory A theory that says the Universe has always existed as it does now and that as it expands, matter is created to keep it the same.

step-down transformer A device that changes a high voltage into a lower one.

step-up transformer A device that changes a low voltage into a higher one.

sterilised Containing no microbes.

steroids A group of chemicals that includes hormones such as oestrogen and medical drugs.

stomata (sing. stoma) Tiny holes in the surface of leaves for the exchange of gases between the air spaces inside the leaf and the air outside.

storage organs Special underground organs, such as a potatoes, that plants have to store food over winter.

symptoms Indicators of illness.

synapse A junction of two nerve cells.

systematic errors Errors that produce a spread of readings around a value other than the true value. Systematic errors can be caused by the measuring instrument, the recording method or something about the environment.

T

tariff The amount that customers pay for electricity or another commodity.

tectonic plates Massive sections of the Earth's surface that gradually move around, transporting the continents.

territory Area defended by an animal against other animals.

testes The male reproductive organs in humans and other animals.

testosterone The main male sex hormone, produced in the testes. It is responsible for the development of the male reproductive organs and other male characteristics.

test-tube baby A baby produced by in vitro fertilisation (IVF).

thalidomide A sedative drug used in the 1960s. It was withdrawn when it was found to cause serious deformities in children when taken by pregnant mothers.

theory When data from testing predictions supports a hypothesis it becomes a theory that is accepted by most, but not necessarily all, scientists.

theory of evolution The theory that explains how species change as a result of natural selection.

thermal decomposition Breakdown of a chemical compound by heating.

thermal imaging camera A camera that takes pictures based on the infrared radiation that objects emit rather than on the light they reflect.

tidal power Electricity generated from the movement of the tides.

tidal stream turbines Water turbines anchored in an estuary or other tidal area, which generate electricity from tidal movements.

tissue culture Growth of cells and/or tissues outside the animal or plant. Whole plants can be grown from plant cells using tissue culture.

toxicity How poisonous a drug or other substance is.

toxins Poisons produced by microbes.

transformers Device consisting of two coils on an iron core, which can change the voltage of an alternating electricity supply.

transgenic organism An organism that contains genes from another organism.

transition metals Everyday' metals such as iron and copper, found in the block of the periodic table between Groups 2 and 3.

transmission lines Electrical cables that carry high-voltage electricity from a power station to an electricity substation.

transmit Allow to pass through. When waves are able to pass through a material they are transmitted.

transverse waves Waves in which the oscillations are perpendicular to the direction of energy transfer.

trophic level Level of a food chain, such as producer, primary consumer or secondary consumer.

troughs The lowest points in a trans+H333verse wave.

true value The result you would get if there were no errors at all in your measurements.

TV pick up A sudden surge in electricity usage, often correlated with a break in a popular TV programme.

U

U values A measure of the insulating properties of a material. The lower the U value, the better the insulating properties of the material.

ultrasound Sound frequencies above 20 kHz, the upper threshold of human hearing.

ultraviolet Electromagnetic radiation that has a shorter wavelength than visible light but longer than X-rays.

uncertainty Not knowing a measurement with complete accuracy.

unidirectional From a particular direction.

Unit (electrical) One kilowatt-hour is sometimes called a Unit of electricity.

Universe Everything that exists. It includes all matter and space.

unreactive Does not become involved in chemical reactions.

unsaturated Organic compounds that contain C=C double bonds.

uranium A heavy element, one form of which can be used as a fuel in nuclear power stations.

urine Liquid that is left in kidney tubules after all the substances that the body needs have been reabsorbed.

uterus The part of the female reproductive system where an egg cell develops into a fetus

V

vaccination (immunisation) Injecting or swallowing vaccines, in order to stimulate the body to develop immunity.

vaccine Preparation made from dead or inactive pathogens, which can be injected so that white blood cells make antibodies to destroy live pathogens of that type.

vacuum A place where there is no matter at all – empty space.

validity Whether or not an experiment has actually investigated the hypothesis and the prediction it set out to investigate.

virtual image An image that light rays do not pass through; they only appear to come from the image.

viruses Extremely small microbes that cause certain types of disease, for example measles, flu and the common cold.

viscous Thick and slow-flowing: opposite of runny.

vitamins A group of organic substances needed in the diet in small quantities for good health.

volcanoes Openings in the Earth's crust where magma (molten rock from deep underground) can escape to the surface.

voltage The difference in the energy carried by electrons before and after they have flowed through an electrical component.

W

watts (W) The unit for measuring power.
1 watt = 1 joule per second.

wave power Generation of electricity using the movement of water in ocean waves.

wavelength The length of a single wave, measured from one wave crest to the next.

waves Oscillations that travel and transfer energy.

weeds Plants that are growing where they are not wanted.

white blood cells Cells circulating in the blood that are an important part of the immune system. They are the body's main line of defence against disease.

wind turbines Turbines that rotate in the wind, driving electric generators.

windrow composting Outdoor composting on a large scale. (Not needed for the exam.)

X

X-rays Electromagnetic radiation that has a shorter wavelength than UV but longer than gamma rays.

Y

yield Amount of a crop that a given area of land produces.

Z

zero error A systematic error that arises when a measuring instrument does not read exactly zero when there is no input.

Index

2,4-D (2,4-dichlorophenoxyacetic acid) 30

A

absorbing radiation 190
absorption of waves 242
acid rain 60, 110, 137
adaptations of animals 52–53
adaptations of plants 50–51
aerobic respiration 57
agar gel 18
Agent Orange 30
aggregate 114
air, composition of 173
alcohol 36
alkanes 130–131, 148
alkanes, boiling points 132
alkenes 149
alloys 126
aluminium 119, 125
amplitude 240
anaerobic digestion 67
anaerobic respiration 57
angle of incidence 242
angle of reflection 242
animal adaptations 52–53
antibiotics 12
antibiotics, resistance to 14
antibodies 10
antiseptics 9
antitoxins 10
antiviral drugs 15
aquatic organisms 61
asexual reproduction 74–75
athletics, steroids in 40–41
atmosphere 168, 172–173, 243
atmosphere, changing over time 174–175
atomic numbers 105
atomic particles 101
atoms 100
autism 17
autoclave 18
auxins (plant hormones) 28
auxins (plant hormones), uses 30–31

B

bacteria 9
bacteria, chemosynthetic 56
bacteria, killing 12
balanced diet 4
balanced equations 102–103
barrage power extraction 222

bees, effect of changing environments 59
Big Bang theory 262–263
biodegradable materials 154
biodiesel 158–159
biofuels 219, 220
biomass 219
biomass and energy 62–63
biomass pyramid 62
birds, effect of changing environments 59
blast furnace 120
blood, cholesterol level 5
blood, white cells 10–11
blue-shift light 258
bluetooth 248
body temperature 22–23
brain 20
brass 127
brittle substances 126
bromine water 162
bronze 127

C

caffeine 37
calcium oxide 113
callus 76
camouflage 54
cannabis 37
cannabis, mental illness 38–39
carbohydrates 4, 64
carbon, reduction and oxidation 118
carbon compounds in animals 68
carbon cycle 68–69
carbon dioxide, capture 68
carbon dioxide, effect on marine life 177
carbon dioxide, global warming 176–177
carbon dioxide, testing for 113
carbon footprint of cement 114
carbon monoxide 134
carbonates 110–111
carbon-neutral fuels 159
catalysts 148
categoric variation 72
cell membrane 20
cement 108, 114
central nervous system (CNS) 36
cerebral palsy 27
changing state of matter 192
characteristics of organisms 72
cheating in sport 40–41
chemical bonds 102
chemical energy 62, 158, 204
chemical formula 100
chemical symbols 100
chemosynthetic bacteria 56

chlorinated handwash 9
cholesterol 5, 164
chromosomes 72
classification of living things 82
clinical trials 34
clomiphine 27
clones and cloning 74, 76–77
coal, burning of 134
cocaine 37
cold, animal adaptations to 52, 195, 199
cold, plant adaptations to 50
combustion of fuels 68, 134–135
common ancestors 83
competing for resources 54
complete combustion 134
compost heaps 67
compounds 100–101
compression 238
concrete 114
concrete, suitability of 115
condensation 132, 193
conduction of heat 194–195
conductors 124
conservation of atoms 102
conservation of energy 205
conservation of mass 103
continental drift 170–171
continuous variation 72
contraceptive pill 25
contraction of muscles 20
convection 196–197
convection currents 168, 196
cooking with oil 164
cooling by evaporation 192–193
copper 120, 124
core of the Earth 168
cosmic microwave background radiation
    (CMBR) 262
cost effective insulation 202
covalent bonds 102, 130
cracking of oil 148–149
crest of a wave 238
crude oil 130
crude oil, cracking 148–149
crude oil, separation of 132–133
crust of the Earth 168
culture medium 18
culture plates 19
cupronickel 127
cuttings of plants 75
cycle of a wave 239
cytoplasm 20

D

decay of dead waste 64–65

The periodic table of elements

Period

Key

1	relative atomic mass — 235
H	**U**
1	atomic (proton) number — 92
hydrogen	uranium

	1	**2**								
1										
2	7 **Li** 3 lithium	9 **Be** 4 beryllium								
3	23 **Na** 11 sodium	24 **Mg** 12 magnesium								
4	39 **K** 19 potassium	40 **Ca** 20 calcium	45 **Sc** 21 scandium	48 **Ti** 22 titanium	51 **V** 23 vanadium	52 **Cr** 24 chromium	55 **Mn** 25 manganese	56 **Fe** 26 iron	59 **Co** 27 cobalt
5	85.5 **Rb** 37 rubidium	88 **Sr** 38 strontium	89 **Y** 39 yttrium	91 **Zr** 40 zirconium	93 **Nb** 41 niobium	96 **Mo** 42 molybdenum	**Tc** 43 technetium	101 **Ru** 44 ruthenium	103 **Rh** 45 rhodium
6	133 **Cs** 55 caesium	137 **Ba** 56 barium	139 **Lu** 57 lanthanum	178 **Hf** 72 hafnium	181 **Ta** 73 tantalum	184 **W** 74 tungsten	186 **Re** 75 rhenium	190 **Os** 76 osmium	192 **Ir** 77 iridium
7	**Fr** 87 francium	**Ra** 88 radium	**Ac** 89 actinium						

A block of rare elements called the lanthanides wedges in after element 57. They are all very similar and are of no particular interest at this level.

A second block of rare elements appears after element 89. Many, such as uranium (element 92) are unstable and radioactive. From element 93 onwards, the elements do not occur naturally on Earth.

Group

0

3	4	5	6	7	
					36 **He** 36 helium
11 **B** 5 boron	12 **C** 6 carbon	14 **N** 7 nitrogen	16 **O** 8 oxygen	19 **F** 9 fluorine	20 **Ne** 10 neon
27 **Al** 13 aluminium	28 **Si** 14 silicon	31 **P** 15 phosphorus	32 **S** 16 sulfur	35.5 **Cl** 17 chlorine	40 **Ar** 18 argon

			3	4	5	6	7	0
59 **Ni** 28 nickel	63.5 **Cu** 29 copper	65 **Zn** 30 zinc	70 **Ga** 31 gallium	73 **Ge** 32 germanium	75 **As** 36 arsenic	79 **Se** 36 selenium	80 **Br** 36 bromine	84 **Kr** 36 krypton
106 **Pd** 46 palladium	108 **Ag** 47 silver	112 **Cd** 48 cadmium	115 **In** 49 indium	119 **Sn** 50 tin	36 **Sb** 51 antimony	36 **Te** 52 tellurium	36 **I** 53 iodine	131 **Xe** 54 xenon
195 **Pt** 78 platinum	197 **Au** 79 gold	201 **Hg** 80 mercury	204 **Tl** 81 thallium	207 **Pb** 82 lead	209 **Bi** 83 bismuth	**Po** 84 polonium	**At** 85 astatine	**Rn** 86 radon

Course Structure

	Print	Digital	Both
Biology	Student Book 978 1 408253 74 8 *Spring 2011*	ActiveTeach 978 1 408262 25 2 *Spring 2011*	Teacher and Technician Planning Pack with CD-ROM, also online and via your VLE 978 1 408253 76 2 *Spring 2011*
	Teacher Book 978 1 408253 75 5 *Spring 2011*	ActiveLearn Online Student Package *Autumn 2011* Single user 978 1 408280 20 1 10 user pack 978 1 408280 28 7 50 user pack 978 1 408280 27 0	Activity Pack with CD-ROM, also online and via your VLE 978 1 408253 73 1 *Spring 2011*
Chemistry	Student Book 978 1 408253 79 3 *Spring 2011*	ActiveTeach 978 1 408262 26 9 *Spring 2011*	Teacher and Technician Planning Pack with CD-ROM, also online and via your VLE 978 1 408253 78 6 *Spring 2011*
	Teacher Book 978 1 408253 80 9 *Spring 2011*	ActiveLearn Online Student Package *Autumn 2011* Single user 978 1 408280 26 3 10 user pack 978 1 408280 25 6 50 user pack 978 1 408280 24 9	Activity Pack with CD-ROM, also online and via your VLE 978 1 408253 77 9 *Spring 2011*
Physics	Student Book 978 1 408253 83 0 *Spring 2011*	ActiveTeach 978 1 408262 27 6 *Spring 2011*	Teacher and Technician Planning Pack with CD-ROM, also online and via your VLE 978 1 408253 82 3 *Spring 2011*
	Teacher Book 978 1 408253 84 7 *Summer 2011*	ActiveLearn Online Student Package *Autumn 2011* Single user 978 1 408280 30 0 10 user pack 978 1 408280 31 7 50 user pack 978 1 408280 29 4	Activity Pack with CD-ROM, also online and via your VLE 978 1 408253 81 6 *Spring 2011*
Science	Student Book 978 1 408253 85 4 *Spring 2011*		
	Teacher Book 978 1 408253 86 1 *Spring 2011*		
Additional Science	Student Book 978 1 408253 71 7 *Spring 2011*		
	Teacher Book 978 1 408253 72 4 *Spring 2011*		

Visit
www.pearsonschools.co.uk/aqagcsescience
to download sample material